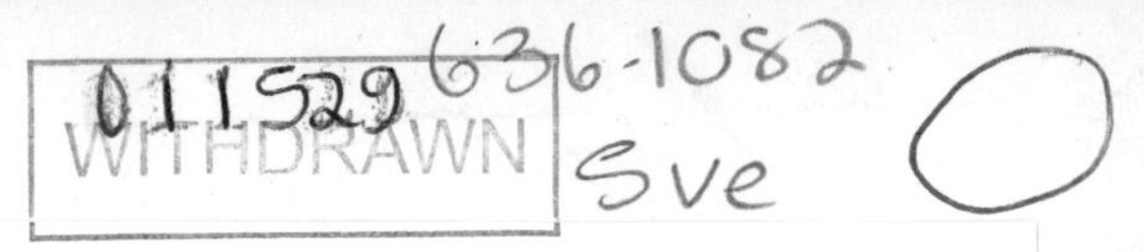

THE PROFESSIONAL HANDBOOK OF THE DONKEY

compiled for
The Donkey Sanctuary by

Dr Elisabeth D. Svendsen, M.B.E.

Foreword by Lord Soulsby

Whittet Books

First published 1997

Whittet Books Limited, 18 Anley Road, London W14 OBY

Cataloguing in publication data
A catalogue record for this book is available from the British Library

ISBN 1 873580 37 1

The Donkey Sanctuary is at Sidmouth Devon EX10 ONU
Tel: (01395) 578222
Fax: (01395) 579266
Registered Charity No. 264818

Dr Svendsen would like to give special thanks to Mal Squance, for organising the production of this book; to Marie Long for proof-reading it; and to Sarah Bagwell for collating all the material.

The compiler, contributors and publisher are grateful to the following for permission to reproduce illustrations that appear on the pages indicated in brackets: K. Allen-Melvin (326), Association des eleveurs d'ânes Pyreneens (142, 143), Association Française de l'Ane Grand Noir du Berry (140), M. Audiot (160, 161), Sarah Bagwell (287), Danny Bryan (36, 42, 70, 77, 90, 114, 116, 120, 154, 237, 290(4)), Maxine Carter (115), Comune di Ortueri (152), Hilary Cotter (17), Julie Courtney (304, 306, 307, 310, 311, 313, 318), M. Durrant (250), Pippa Edney (144, 145), Evening Courier, Halifax (328), June Evers (61, 127, 164, 172, 178, 209, 228, 232, 233(2), 284), Dr Jane French (131, 133, 135), Feseha Gebreab (213), Mr & Mrs Groen (16), Dr Colin P. Groves (10, 12), Roy Harrington (168), Lise Kragh (257(2), 259(2), 260 (2), 261, 262), Dorothy Morris (117, 264), Tom Morse-Brown (267, 268, 269, 270, 271, 278(2), 279; also drawings on pp. 33, 72, 74, 79, 80, 81, 274, 285, 286, 303), Julie Mutter (298), M. Philippe (156), Queen Elizabeth Hospital for Children, Hackney (14/15), Anthony Reynolds (265), M. Richard (159), Pascual Rovira, ADEBO (146, 148, 149), Ken Searle (38), Mrs Leslie Sims (333), Mike Stamp (139), Paul Starkey (185, 186, 187, 188, 189, 190, 191, 192, 193, 194(2), 195, 196, 197 (2), 200, 201, 204, 206), Mal Squance (176, 177), Paul Svendsen, (173, 182, 293), Bill Tetlow (281, 323, 325), Rosalind de Wesselow (88, 89), Zoological Society of London (11)

Printed by Midas

CONTENTS

FOREWORD

Lord Soulsby of Swaffham Prior, M.A., Ph.D., D.Sc., D.V.M.&S., D.V.M., D.V.S.M., F.R.C.V.S.
Emeritus Professor of Animal Pathology, University of Cambridge

THE DONKEY OR ASS, *Equus asinus,* in the wild is an example of unrestrained liberty, but in bondage often an object of abject slavery, overladen, underfed, beaten and generally ill used. 'To the smallest ass shall go the biggest stick.' Undeserving of these treatments, the donkey in fact plays an important role in the provision of energy for agricultural production by way of traction for cultivation and transport of produce. The Western World may not fully appreciate the role of the donkey, along with other draught animals, in the provision of food with a burgeoning world population likely to reach 8 billion before the middle of the next century and when we will need to produce as much food in the next 25 years as has been produced in the last 10,000 years. Hence the health and welfare of the donkey will be of crucial importance to those who will depend on it for their livelihoods. Should a donkey fall ill or die, the family it supports may suffer great hardship and even disaster from which it may not recover. The World Health Organisation's Alma Ata declaration of 1978 recognised the role of agriculture and animal husbandry in the target of 'Health for all by the year 2000' and it is certain that the donkey will play an important, but probably unsung role in reaching this goal.

In the Western World the heyday of the donkey was in the 19th century when, for example, in the United Kingdom the 'poor man's horse' was used for all manner of draught purposes. Now its role has changed to one of provision of recreation and companionship, at the seaside providing rides for children, harnessed to children's carts or decked out for the show-ring.

And yet there is much ignorance and misunderstanding of the needs of the donkey with respect to its health and welfare, perhaps epitomised in the lines of G.K. Chesterton:

With monstrous head and sickening cry
And ears like errant wings
The devil's walking parody
Of all four-footed things

But now we have a very welcome volume to set aright the oft unfair and libellous comments and treatment of the donkey. This *Professional Handbook* is a rich and much needed source of important information about the care and attention due to the donkey, as well as to its origins, management and nutrition.

I anticipate great use will be made of this book internationally as it is an authoritative guide to the donkey on health and disease founded on fact. Much of the information is unique and seldom appears in textbooks dealing with the horse.

I commend the Donkey Sanctuary for its initiative in producing this new and up-to-date edition. Not only will it produce a better deal for the donkey but will also promote the health and welfare of those who so much depend on the donkey.

PREFACE

Dr Elisabeth D. Svendsen, M.B.E.

THERE IS LITTLE doubt that the donkey and mule have been not only the most used, but the most abused, animals in history. The donkey has spent hundreds of years being used by man but, despite this, in the past little attempt has been made to study any aspect of this equine. Vast sums of money have been spent on the horse by its wealthy owner, but overseas the donkey owner has represented the poor populations, often hardly able to afford medical care for his children, let alone veterinary care for the donkey.

Even today, the stoic, hard-working donkey is often misunderstood by its owner and, unfortunately, often by veterinarians worldwide. In Third World countries, because of the poverty of the owners, vets are rarely called, and in more prosperous countries where veterinary attention is given there is a tendency for vets to treat the donkey as a small horse.

In an attempt to rectify the situation our charity, The Donkey Sanctuary, first produced *The Professional Handbook of the Donkey* in 1986, with contributions from experts in various fields, and there is no doubt that their shared knowledge has had an impact on donkey welfare worldwide. This book was distributed free by us to almost every veterinary university in the world and to date it has been the only teaching material on donkeys available to students. *The Professional Handbook of the Donkey* passes on information gleaned at the Sanctuary from the Veterinary Department and from farriers, giving professional and practical advice with regard to nutrition, land management, handling, showing, breeding, etc. It deals also with the laws passed to help donkeys in this country, the problems faced by donkeys working abroad and the immense rewards in terms of love and loyalty to be gained from this delightful equine.

This third edition contains many new chapters, as a result of increased knowledge and experience. It is aimed at the professional, with medical chapters and technical advice on many donkey health problems, and includes chapters for the layman.

My aim in producing this book is to ensure that as much information as possible on this species is passed on, making the donkey more respected and enabling it to be treated in its own right.

My thanks to all the contributors and to the staff of our four charities, whose never-failing care, love and respect for the donkey is an inspiration to all.

1

INTRODUCTION AND ORIGINS OF THE DONKEY

Robert Camac

LOOK CLOSELY AT A GROUP OF DONKEYS. You will notice how they differ in size, shape, colour, markings, and even in the texture of their coats. So it would be surprising if they shared one common ancestor or originated in one region of the world. A short history of the donkey can only be general, but before finding out who these ancestors were, where they lived and what they looked like, you need to know something about the features of the donkey in Great Britain today.

Grey in various shades is the predominant colour. Brown donkeys are fairly plentiful. Other colours are black, roan (which is a mixture of white hairs and another colour, usually brown) and piebald or skewbald or broken coloured, that is a combination of brown-and-white or black-and-white markings, which were very popular in the late 1960s but are less so now. Finally there are the rarer colours of pure white and chestnut. The 'cross' which is immediately associated with the donkey is most clearly marked on greys and browns, less distinct on lighter colours, invisible on blacks and missing on white and broken coloured donkeys. But, as with most things connected with the donkey, there are always exceptions!

Because size is important, it will be useful to have some idea of the height of the donkey. This is measured in 'hands', which is the average breadth of a person's hand, four inches. The measurement is taken at the withers. These are the highest point of the donkey's shoulder, where the neck joins the back, and most of the donkeys you see will be between 9½ and 11 hands (38 and 44 inches or to be right up-to-date 96.5 and 111.8 centimetres).

Now for the donkey's pedigree. Its ancestors were wild asses from Africa and Asia. In Africa there were two separate species: the Nubian,

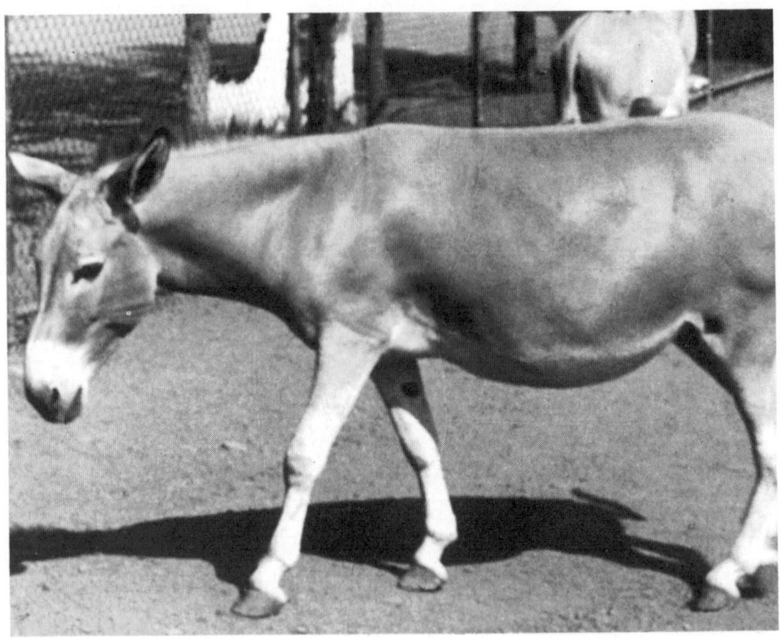

Nubian wild ass, Equus africanus africanus. *Photographed in Catshill Game Park, New York State: bred in Munich Zoo from a stock imported from northern Eritrea by Heck in 1937.*

standing 12 hands, from the north between the Mediterranean coast and the Sahara Desert; and the Somali, standing 14 hands, from further east to the south of the Red Sea. The Nubian wild ass had a shoulder cross which was not very marked, being either rather short or very thin, but it had no stripes on its legs; in contrast the Somali wild ass had no shoulder cross, but very prominent leg-stripes, reminiscent of the zebra. The regions where they lived were hot and dry, so that there was little difference between their winter and summer coats. In winter both were grey. The summer coat of the Nubian was reddish and that of the Somali was yellowish.

The Asiatic branch of the breed came from a much larger area stretching from the Red Sea to Northern India and Tibet, in which it had to adapt to differences of climate, terrain and altitude. Consequently there is no single type of Asiatic wild ass. The further east the ass was found, the larger, heavier and stronger the animal. The Syrian wild ass measured under 10 hands. Its neighbour to the east was the light-coloured swift-footed Onager, which measured 12 hands. East again was the Kulan, standing half a hand higher, darker in colour, with a very marked broad stripe along its back and growing a thick winter coat. Like all Asiatic wild asses, it did not have a shoulder stripe. Then came the largest and heaviest of all the Asiatic wild asses, the Kiang, standing 14 hands, living on the Tibetan plateau to the north of the Himalayas and adapting to extremes of

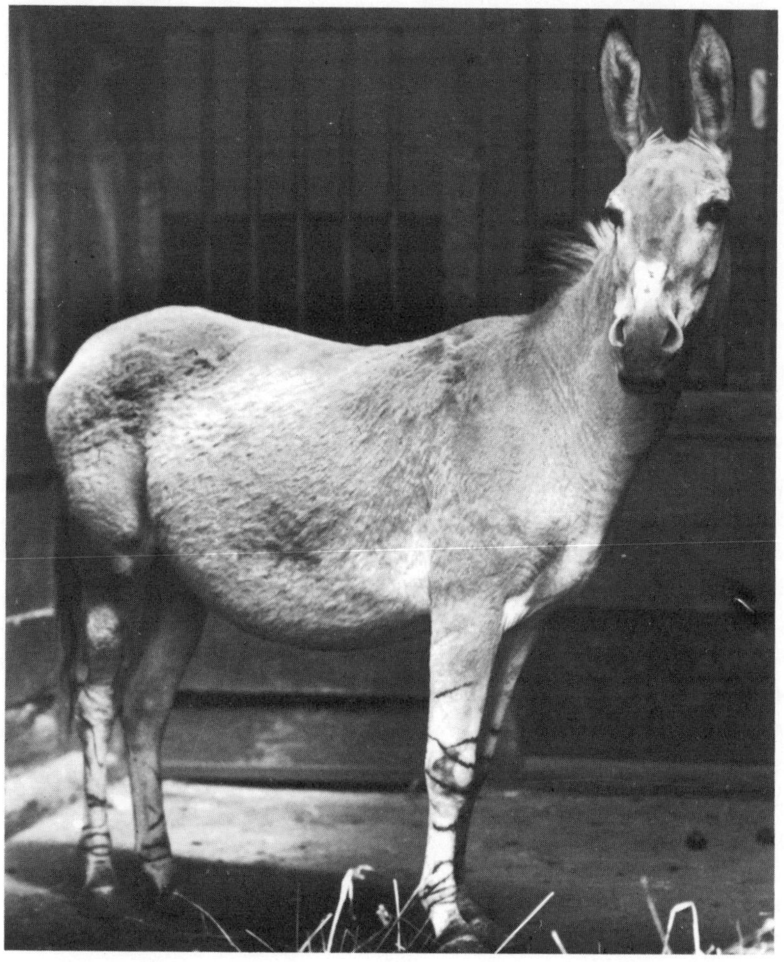

Somali wild ass, Equus africanus africanus somaliensis.

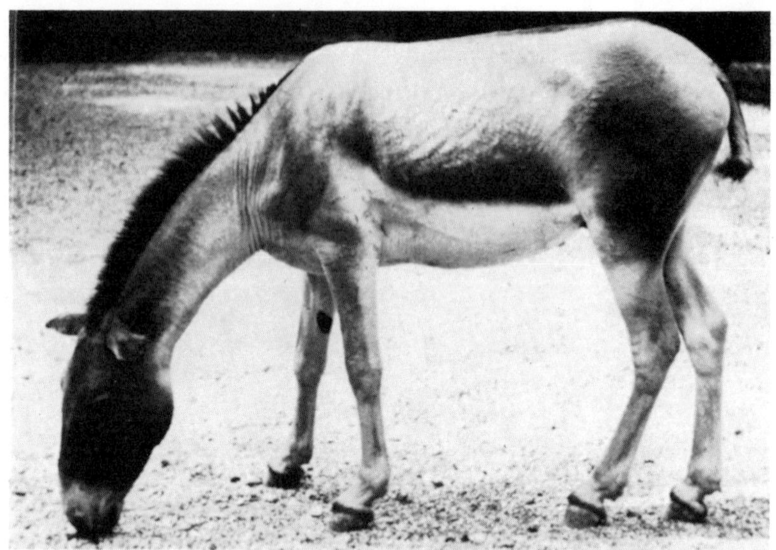

Western kiang, Equus kiang kiang, *in Munich Zoo, 1933.*

climate. It has certain features more like a horse than our domesticated donkey, such as shorter ears and a rounder foot.

Through all these countries lay the trade route from the Pacific Ocean to the Mediterranean given the romantic name of the 'Silk Road'. The journey lasted several years and no single animal can have completed the entire journey. Donkeys were among the draught animals used and with unplanned matings, while passing through the territories of the various Asiatic wild asses, there is no doubt that some mixing of the breeds occurred over the years by the time the journey ended. Carrying the valuable bales of silk, the donkeys arrived in Alexandria. Through Asia Minor donkeys came to Greece, where they proved to be ideal animals to work on the narrow paths between the vines. Their use in the cultivation of the grapes spread through the Mediterranean countries to Spain, whose coast at the Southern tip is separated by only a few miles from North Africa.

One such Mediterranean country was Italy, and with the Roman army the donkey travelled throughout the Roman Empire as a pack animal, and later was used in agriculture and in the new vineyards which the Romans planted as far north as France and Germany. With the Roman invasion of Britain, donkeys came to England. For 1,500 years no one bothered about them, a situation which was repeated though for a shorter period, in the twentieth century.

So why did the donkey begin to attract attention, and why was he suddenly needed? The answer is, 'war'. For hundreds of years the demand for horses as cannon fodder had been difficult to meet. They were either requisitioned by the army or taken in payment of taxes. By the sixteenth century horses had become scarce and expensive. The desperate farmer needed a replacement, and the replacement in England and Wales was the neglected donkey. Years later, at the end of the nineteenth century, Welsh bred donkeys were to be much sought after and commanded a high price.

So far there has been no mention of Ireland, which many people think of as the home of the donkey. Once again it was England's wars - this time with the Irish - which brought the donkey to Ireland with the army of occupation. In this country, too, the army began to buy cheap horses required for England's other wars, and the Irish farmers were more than happy to take cash, replace their horses with cheaper donkeys and put the surplus cash under the bed!

In Scotland the donkey has never been so commonly used. Two reasons for this are probably the cold winters of the country, unlike the mild though damp climate of Ireland, and Scotland's extensive area of forests, very different from the donkey's original habitat.

Whilst the donkey, particularly the white ass, had some aristocratic and even royal owners, nevertheless in England and Wales it remained the 'poor man's horse'. It was cheap to keep, at least until the end of the eighteenth century, when the Enclosure Acts abolished certain commons rights and deprived commoners of their free grazing. The farmers complained that 'There was no money in breeding donkeys' - a cry to be heard from donkey breeders again in the 1970s!

The breeding of mules by crossing a donkey stallion with a horse or pony mare showed more profit. The New Forest in Hampshire was a centre for this activity, since it was near the port of Southampton from which the young mules were shipped to the United States of America. However, they were small and not of good quality, and to produce bigger animals, better able to work in that country, the New Forest Jack-ass was replaced as a stallion by the larger Spanish or Maltese ass.

The hey-day of the donkey in Britain was during the last century when it was used on farms, and increasingly in towns as a pack animal. In Ireland

the donkey carried the peat from the bogs and drew the carts loaded with potatoes or with flax to be woven into Irish linen. In fashionable spas, donkeys transported corpulent ladies to take the waters. On the sands, the donkeys gave rides to young visitors. In the mining areas, it was the coal miners who rode their donkeys to work at the collieries. Donkeys pulled lawn mowers on the lawns of prosperous houses and the rubbish carts of the local councils. They carried the laundry and delivered the milk. In fact, donkeys also supplied the milk! In London a herd of milch-asses made a daily milk round of some smart residential districts where the donkeys were milked in the street to produce asses' milk for the children of well-to-do families. For the successful tradesman and the London costermonger the donkey barrow came to replace the baskets and the hand carts. Hundreds of donkeys were drawn up at the markets for the carts to be filled with fresh fruit, vegetables and fish, and on Bank Holidays, the donkey would be used to take the family for an outing. With all this activity there was a thriving trade in donkeys. At the Islington cattle market, thousands of them found new owners each year, and a steady demand for donkeys for a few weeks or even a few days ensured that hiring was a flourishing business. Donkeys were shown at the International Horse Show and at the Royal Show and special donkey shows were held at Islington. But changes were on the way.

In war there were no more cavalry charges, so the slaughter ceased. Horses became more plentiful, and donkeys were no longer needed to replace them. But it was the invention of the internal combustion engine that was the danger to them both, and signalled the end of the donkey's role as a working animal, with the result that about sixty years ago it was estimated that the donkey population was about one hundred. This was surely nonsense, if only because of the number of seaside towns where beach donkeys were still a popular attraction. The significance of this casual estimate was the indifference it showed. To obtain a more accurate figure was too much trouble. The donkey had once more become a neglected animal.

Queen Elizabeth Hospital for Children, Hackney.

This state of affairs continued until about 1963 when something unexpected happened. Hundreds of Irish donkeys were imported to meet the demands of a new market, people eager to own a donkey. To work? No. For the first time in the thousands of years since it had become domesticated, the donkey was no longer required as a working animal. It had become a popular pet.

Generally speaking the donkey was the first equine that these purchasers had owned. But their enthusiasm to learn soon overcame their lack of knowledge of how to look after the donkey. They bought books. They attended lectures. They joined the recently formed Donkey Breed Society (then called the Donkey Show Society). They learned about feeding and grooming, and the care of the donkey's foot. They were entranced by

Weston-Super-Mare: donkeys on the sands.

donkey foals, so they looked around for a suitable stallion for their mare and found out what special care she would need when in foal, and later how to look after the foal. All this newly acquired knowledge was responsible for an impressive improvement in the fitness and condition of the donkey. Owners showed their animals at Horse and Agricultural shows, which had now begun to hold classes for donkeys, and they had them inspected to be registered in the new Stud Book to acquire a pedigree. Children rode them. Adults drove them, sometimes in 'Elegant Carriages' far grander than the donkey had ever known before. The donkeys were proving hugely popular and giving untold pleasure to their owners, their families and friends and to the public.

However, when times are hard and families are forced to make economies, the future of an animal which is a pet is more at risk than an animal that works and earns its keep. Unemployment and redundancies caused by the recession brought a drop in the number of donkey owners, and a reduction in breeding has corrected the over-breeding of earlier years. This new situation, which has already lasted several years, is not unsatisfactory. Although fewer in number, today's donkey-owners have shown themselves to be responsible, committed, dedicated animal lovers. This care is reflected in an increase in the value of sound, healthy animals.

Some people will argue that whatever improvement in the breed has taken place, nevertheless this new status is not natural for one of the oldest breeds of working animal in the world. What is the aim of this improvement? Might it not be better achieved by the introduction of a larger breed of donkey from abroad? Or is the object solely to produce a friendly pet?

Nowhere is the friendliness of the donkey more evident than in one group of donkeys which has never lost its appeal, especially to children. The beach donkey has been a feature of the British seaside since before the First World War. Some of the 'stands' have been in the same family for up to four generations. Many seaside towns have made regulations, setting out the donkey's daily working hours and its right to have one day off work each week. They also stipulate the maximum age and weight of the riders.

More people now drive a donkey and this calls for a fit, active animal. Initially, however, few owners showed an interest in this pursuit. Since then, the popularity of driving, including competitive events, continues to

Bonnie, Clipper and Neddy driving as unicorn team at the 20th century Four in Hand Club, August 17th, 1996, at Fordingbridge, Hampshire.

increase. The expertise of whips is now of such a high standard that at the inaugural meet in the New Forest of the recently formed Four in Hand Club in 1996, out of the thirty-three entries, two were donkey turnouts.

For many people their main object is just to enjoy owning a donkey, looking after it and for the family to have fun with it. Now that donkeys are no longer required for their earlier trades, what can be wrong with that, provided that the families appreciate the responsibility that they are taking on? It is a novel situation, but it has prevented the donkey from becoming once again the poor neglected creature that no one bothered about. Yet - and here is the donkey's latest surprise for us - it has attracted attention in a second new role in this mechanised world. Because of its temperament, it is admirably suited to the modern medical approaches in working with the physically and mentally disabled, whether being driven or ridden or just being on hand to be petted and patted. In a small but increasingly important role, the donkey has found fresh work in the twentieth century to help casualties of this century's so-called progress.

All this is very different from anything in the donkey's long history. But today what is the alternative? And, provided that future over-breeding is avoided, need there be an alternative?

MR ROBERT CAMAC'S family comes from Ireland. After leaving Epsom College he joined the Royal Navy and saw service in 1944 first in a destroyer escorting convoys in the English Channel and on the D-Day Landings, and later with a minesweeper flotilla in the Far East. After the war he qualified as a solicitor and practised in London until his retirement.

A founder member of the Donkey Breed Society, he was legal adviser on the Society's registration as a charity. He was also Treasurer before being elected Chairman in 1973. He was the first joint director of the Society's highly successful Annual British Championship Show, and was on the Society's panel of judges. He is one of the Society's two Honorary Life Vice Presidents.

Mr Camac is a former trustee of the International Donkey Protection Trust and the Slade Centre.

2a
MEDICAL
Michael Crane

IN MANY WAYS the equine practitioner can safely treat a donkey as any small equine. There are however important differences of physiology, behaviour and management which influence the common diseases encountered. Successful diagnosis and treatment often depend on an appreciation of these differences. This chapter will attempt to discuss the common donkey conditions encountered in the UK, highlighting areas where donkey and mainstream equine medicine may diverge.

The donkey in its natural habitat will wander and browse on sparse fibrous vegetation over long distances in an arid semi-desert environment. In the UK most donkeys are kept as pets, enjoying a surfeit of good grazing and taking little exercise. The implications of this are significant both in terms of longevity and the common problems encountered.

Relatively little research has been diverted towards the understanding of disease processes in either environment, consequently much of the following information is based on the clinical data kept at the Donkey Sanctuary and personal observation.

Many donkeys are unaccustomed to routine handling and examination. They are by nature stoical and undramatic in their display of clinical signs and a minor change in normal behaviour or feeding may be significant. Therefore time taken in observation, offering a bucket of feed, and thorough history taking is time well spent.

It is frequently impossible to successfully examine or treat a donkey if it is separated from its companion - be it equine, bovine, caprine or ovine. Much aggravation and distress to both patient and attending vet will be avoided if 'bonded' animals are kept in contact.

When assessing the significance of clinical signs it is necessary to be aware of certain idiosyncrasies. The lame donkey will often spend increasing periods of time laid down whilst lameness examination is often hindered by a refusal to 'trot in hand'. Coughing with respiratory disease is rarely heard yet dyspnoea and pyrexia often accompany advanced hyperlipaemia. Colic and general pain are usually accompanied by depression and anorexia rather than the classic equine colic symptoms of sweating, rolling, flank watching, etc.

Similarly certain recognised and well practised equine examination techniques need to be amended and reconsidered for application to the donkey. Rectal examination can be resented and may be dangerous in the small or fractious individual. However an examination of rectal faeces is a useful indicator of gastro-intestinal function, particularly with regard to hyperlipaemia. Paracentesis abdomenis is complicated by thick ventral abdominal fat even in apparently non obese patients - a 10cm paravertebral needle inserted carefully after dermal local anaesthesia is often necessary to reach the peritoneal cavity. Gastric intubation and endoscopy are only tolerated with great care, and prior sedation is recommended. Paradoxically, given the apparent rarity of a cough response to respiratory disease, the larynx and caudal pharynx appear particularly sensitive and the use of diluted local anaesthetic is advisable before distal endoscopy is attempted.

A full routine clinical examination is to be commended for any ailment, particularly in view of the predispositon to develop hyperlipaemia.

Reference values for physiological, haematological and biochemical parameters are given in Table 1.

Most major problems encountered by donkeys in developed countries are the consequence of ignorance and management by neglect. Many are fed in excess of their needs, often having access to unnecessary supplementary feeding as well as excess grazing. However, despite such problems, many pet donkeys survive well beyond the expected lifespan in their 'natural environment'. Consequently, care and management of chronic geriatric problems is commonplace in donkey medicine.

Hyperlipaemia

Hyperlipaemia is a life-threatening condition. It is the most common serious medical condition of donkeys and should be considered whenever a sick donkey is presented.

The condition occurs when food intake is compromised and

Table 1 Physiological, haematological and biochemical values for donkeys (and young donkeys and ponies where they differ significantly)

	median	5%	95%
Temperature (°F)	98.8	97.2	100
pony	100-101		
young donkey	99.6	97.8	102.1
Temperature (°C)	37.1	36.2	37.8
pony	37.8-38.3		
young donkey	37.6	36.6	38.9
Pulse (beats/min)	44	36	68
pony	36-40		
young donkey	60	44	80
Respiration (breaths/min)	20	12	44
pony	10-14		
young donkey	28	16	48
Packed cell volume (l/l)	0.33	0.25	0.38
pony	0.40±0.055		
young donkey	0.34	0.27	0.43
Haemoglobin (g/100 ml)	11.6	9	15.3
pony	13.6±1.6		
young donkey	11.6	9.3	15
Neutrophils (%)	50.5	28	78
young donkey	45	25	71
Neutrophils (10^9/l)	5.0	2.2	13.3
young donkey	6.3	3.3	14
Lymphocytes (%)	43	17	65
young donkey	50	16	67.5
Lymphocytes (x 10^9/l)	4.2	1.8	7.8
young donkey	6.2	2.5	14.0
Eosinophils (%)	4	1	10
young donkey	2	0	10

	median	5%	95%
Eosinophils ($x10^9/l$)	0.38	0.09	1.15
young donkey	0.30	0	1.63
Basophils (%)	0	0	0.08
young donkey	0	0	0
Basophils ($x10^9/l$)	0	0	0.5
young donkey	0	0	0
Monocytes (%)	1	0	5
young donkey	1	0	6
Monocytes ($10^9/l$)	0.13	0	0.80
young donkey	0.16	0	0.81
WBC (x $10^9/l$)	10.2	6.1	16.1
young donkey	13.5	7.8	21.9
RBC ($x10^{12}/l$)	5.5	4	7.3
pony	8-12		
young donkey	6.3	5.0	8.1
Mean corpuscle volume (fl)	64	57	79
pony	36±5		
young donkey	54	49	70.5
young horse	35.5±7.2		
Mean corpuscular haemoglobin (pg)	21.9	18.9	28.6
pony	12.1±2.2		
young donkey	18.5	16.4	25
Mean corpuscular haemoglobin concentration (g/100 ml)	34.8	31.4	39.1
young donkey	35	25.3	54.0
Creatinine (µmol/l)	75	53	141
pony	134		
young donkey	83	61	107
Creatine phosphokinase (iu/l)	40	15	149

	median	5%	95%
young donkey	41	21	180
Total bilirubin (μmol/l)	2.7	1.4	7.7
pony	10.3±3.4		
young donkey	2.7	1.4	6.1
Urea (mmol/l)	3.9	1.9	7.6
young donkey	3.7	1.5	6.1
Triglyceride (mmol/l)	1	0.2	4.3
young donkey	0.7	0.2	2.0
Total protein (g/l)	70	58	82
young donkey	64	53	78
Albumin (g/l)	28	20	34
young donkey	28	21	32
Total globulins (g/l)	40	29	53
young donkey	34	23	50
γ-Glutamyl transferase (iu/l)	17	8	49
young donkey	16	8	39
Glutamate dehydrogenase (iu/l)	1.6	0.4	8
young donkey	1.2	0.4	3.9
Immunogamma globulin T(iu/l)	1	1	4
young donkey	1	1	6
Aspartate aminotransferase (iu/l)	109	59	199
young donkey	103	63	172
Glutathione peroxidase (iu/l)	12.1	4.5	51
Alkaline phosphatase (iu/l)	265	150	563
pony	70±18		
young donkey	305	212	576
Sorbitol dehydrogenase (iu/l)	0.3	0	1.5
young donkey	0.4	0.1	1

(Jane M. French and Valerie H. Patrick)

consequent fat mobilisation becomes unregulated. Insensitivity to insulin may be a predisposing factor in the donkey in this process. Lipid accumulates in the liver and blood and impairs the function of other organs, notably kidneys, pancreas and heart. The resulting toxaemia is frequently fatal.

Epidemiological studies indicate that female animals appear more likely to become hyperlipaemic, as are obese individuals. Donkeys in the latter group are more likely to die than underweight animals, with animals of ideal weight showing the highest survival rate. Nevertheless it is recommended that hyperlipaemia be considered as a primary or complicating factor in any sick donkey.

Hyperlipaemia may occur secondary to inappetance induced by concurrent disease (e.g. respiratory disease, gastro-intestinal impaction, severe parasitism or severe lameness) or primary in the absence of other disease processes. Donkeys seem to be more susceptible to developing hyperlipaemia at times of environmental or social stress (e.g. transportation, inclement weather, diet change, loss or separation from companion animals). Donkeys with this primary condition are more likely to survive than those with concurrent disease.

The clinical characteristics of hyperlipaemia are frequently non specific. Typical signs include vague changes in characteristic behaviour patterns, depression, inappetance, reluctance to move and often degrees of ataxia on forced movement. Temperature may be raised (to 102°F, 38.9°C) along with pulse and respiration dependent on the severity of the accompanying toxaemia. Intestinal mobility and faecal output are reduced, with faeces often hard, dry and covered with foetid mucous. Episodes of abdominal pain may be evident and thorough rectal examination can be impaired by the dry, tacky nature of the rectal mucosa.

Terminally total anorexia is accompanied by severely congested mucous membranes, halitosis, dependent oedema, weight loss and neurological signs (head pressing, ataxia, circling, convulsions, etc.).

Blood samples for routine haematological and biochemical profiles are essential for diagnosis, monitoring of treatment and assessment of prognosis.

Such is the incidence of hyperlipaemia in sick, obese donkeys that one can recommend the taking of blood samples at the start of a clinical examination. An initial assessment by eye of the relative turbidity of the serum after clotting is a very useful guide to treatment and nursing care.

The mortality rate for hyperlipaemia in donkeys is high, with rates of 60% to 95% being reported. Successful treatment would appear to demand early recognition and diagnosis, correction of the underlying disease or cause, intensive treatment and careful attention to nursing care. A critical assessment of each of these factors will not only improve the chances of recovery but also ensure that terminal cases do not suffer unduly.

It is our experience at the Donkey Sanctuary that cases with a plasma triglyceride concentration in excess of 30μmol/l or with severe hepatic or renal dysfunction carry a very poor prognosis.

Therapy of hyperlipaemia is aimed at treating any underlying disease, correcting fluid and energy balance, and maintaining gastro-intestinal function.

Close attention is given to the need for fluid therapy. Oral glucose-electrolyte solutions are useful in the field (up to 3L per treatment) but repeated intravenous therapy is often necessary.

Flunixin meglumine (1.1mg /kg Finadyne; Schering-Plough) is useful as an analgesic and for its potential benefit against endotoxaemia.

Despite evidence of its questionable therapeutic value Protamine Zinc Insulin can be administered at 30iu I/M bid.

Patients are kept at grass whenever possible and nursing staff are encouraged to hand feed biscuits, mints, carrots, etc, and to exercise donkeys to browse in hedgerows and wild non-toxic vegetation. The maintenance of some gastro-intestinal function through the course of the illness would appear to be particularly crucial for a successful outcome.

Unfortunately a significant proportion of cases will necessitate euthanasia. It is our experience that recovery is marked by a return of appetite and a significant fall in plasma triglyceride levels within 2 to 3 days of the start of the disease process. The perseverance with intensive therapy much beyond this point is frequently of little benefit, particularly if early diagnosis has not been possible. Counselling at this stage can hopefully prevent the need for the patient's terminal deterioration before euthanasia is discussed.

On post mortem an enlarged friable pale fatty liver is characteristic. Fatty change may also be seen in other organs, notably the kidneys and myocardium. Non-specific change relating to toxaemia and microinfarction may also be identified. Significant inflammation of the pancreas with oedema and adhesions to surrounding organs is observed, and release of pancreatic enzymes is often responsible for rapid post mortem autolytic changes.

As high mortality rates are to be expected, even with intensive treatment, emphasis must be placed on owner education and prevention.

Careful dieting of obese individuals and the provision of appropriate supplementary feed for ill, elderly or malnourished individuals is to be recommended.

An awareness of high risk situations, with close attention to feed intake at these times, is warranted. The provision of small frequent supplementary feeds at times of transportation, mixing with new arrivals or introduction to a new environment may be prophylactic. A particular 'risk' situation is at the time of a companion's death. The stress of this event would appear to be reduced if the surviving individual is allowed an hour or so with the body of its dead companion.

The treatment of any sick donkey should include monitoring for the early correctable signs of hyperlipaemia and the provision of adequate nutritional support.

Donkeys at pasture should have adequate access to shelter, additional feed and water when there is a risk of inclement weather.

Dieting the obese donkey

Ideally adult donkeys of 10 to 11hh should not weigh in excess of 180kg and be without any appreciable fat deposits which characteristically form over the ribs, rump and crest. A number of donkeys develop broad pendulous abdomens through lack of exercise and the weight of intra abdominal fat. One should aim for a gradual weight loss over a period of months rather than any drastic action which might on its own precipitate a hyperlipaemic crisis. The use of a heart girth tape is a useful monitor in the absence of weighing facilities. The loss of 2-4kg per month, equating to approximately 1-2cm of heart girth is advisable.

The fatty crest, characteristic of many obese individuals, would appear to be particularly resistant to diet and should be tolerated as a cosmetic blemish once the overall body condition is satisfactory.

The partial replacement of hay by barley straw, the use of shavings beds, restriction of grazing with electric fencing and the gradual elimination of supplementary feeding and excess 'tit-bits' should all be considered.

Laminitis

Laminitis is a common yet often unrecognised problem in the donkey. The causes and consequences would appear to be similar to other equids. Access to succulent pasture and obesity are the usual precipitating factors. The consequences are serious yet owners are often unaware that their static or recumbent donkey is in pain. On closer inspection stance, weight shifting and increased digital pulses are all indicative of laminitis. Donkeys may hold a forefoot forward and off the ground suggesting a unilateral problem. When the suspect foot is lowered after examination, the contra-lateral foot is raised in a similar fashion.

Clinical and radiographic examination frequently suggest that repeated episodes of laminitis are often unrecognised. Many such donkeys are clinically foundered with marked rotation and remodelling of the distal phalanx. A convex sole, a stretched white line and a predisposition to abscessation and seedy toe follow.

Our recommended treatment protocol for acute cases is:

1) Remove or treat initiating cause.
2) Blood sample for routine haematology and biochemistry.
3) ACP 10mg/ml, 0.25ml per 50kg bodyweight I/V followed by 1x25mg ACP tablet orally per 50kg bodyweight BID.
4) Analgesics, Phenylbutazone 1/2g BID until metabolic profile known.
5) Padded foot bandages.
6) Attention to diet e.g. meadow hay, straw, Dengi Hi Fi, and specific supplementation e.g. Farriers Formula.
7) Deep shavings bed if unable to stand.
8) Corrective foot trimming as necessary.

In chronic cases particular care is given to diet, routine farriery and good foot hygiene. In some instances long term analgesia with phenylbutazone is necessary.

Gastro-intestinal disease

Donkeys differ somewhat from other equids in two broad areas of gastro-intestinal disease problems: colic and geriatric dental disease.

Abdominal pain rarely causes the classic symptoms of rolling or sweating, flank watching or kicking at the abdomen. In fact these symptoms are generally only seen once the condition is severe and well advanced.

Colic is first evidenced by slight behavioural changes, deteriorating appetite and a general dullness. In consequence, there is often a significant delay before veterinary advice is sought. A brief survey of the last 100 cases of colic at the Donkey Sanctuary indicates a predominance of impactive conditions (table 2), often of elderly donkeys.

These individuals frequently have poor dentition and are unable to masticate winter forage or long grass effectively.

Table 2 Last 100 colics at the Donkey Sanctuary

Torsions	15
Impactive	37
Spasmodic	2
Tumour obstruction/ enteroliths/intussusceptions	6
Ulcerative colon	1
Enteritis	8
Undiagnosed	12

All of the routine diagnostic techniques and treatments applicable to other equids may be employed with the reservations mentioned in the introductory paragraphs.

The progressive anorexia of many colic cases is responsible for the high accompanying incidence of secondary hyperlipaemia. This, added to the age of many of the patients, often precludes surgical intervention.

The importance of parasites in alimentary diseases is discussed in Chapter 4. However, it should be emphasised that any differential list of the causes of donkey colic should include larval cyathostomiasis, particularly in late winter and spring, even if worming history appears adequate.

Many donkeys live well beyond thirty years of age, with molar teeth frequently loose, lost or displaced. Periodontal disease of varying degrees is almost inevitably present. Many of these animals keep surprisingly good condition despite losing many molar teeth. However, evidence of quidding or unthriftiness, difficulty in mastication or drooling saliva necessitates thorough dental examination. The use of a Haussman gag, light sedation and a pen torch are recommended. Hooks and steps are common where opposing teeth are lost, broken or misplaced. Extensive periodontal disease results in loose teeth that are easily extracted per os. Few problems

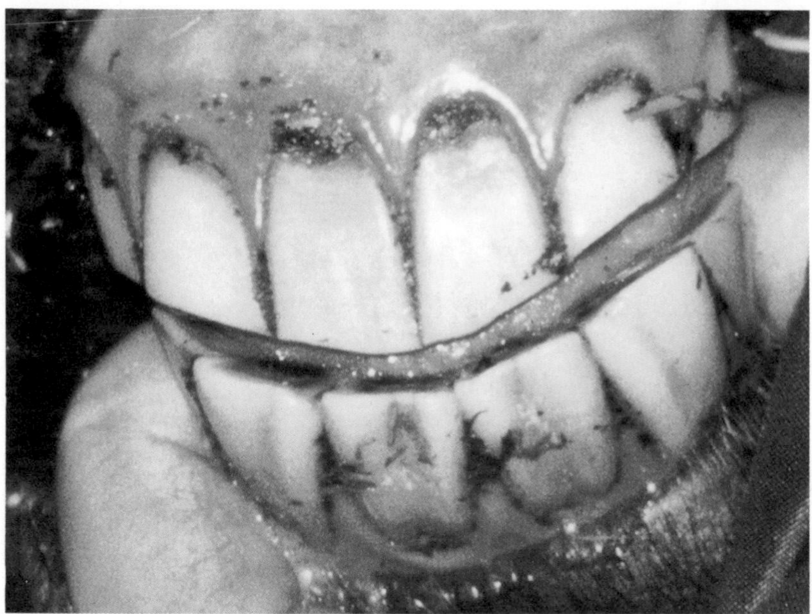

In early teens a marked 'seagull shape' develops between upper and lower incisors and may be retained beyond age 20 years.

are encountered if their residual sockets are left unpacked. Post operative analgesics and antibiotics are usually administered.

Periapical osteitis and subsequent clinical disease would appear to be surprisingly uncommon. Diagnostic lateral and oblique radiographs can be taken and treatment is undertaken by standard techniques.

Annual or twice yearly rasping of teeth, concentrating particularly on those individuals over 15 years of age or with a history of dental disease is recommended. Chopped forage and supplementary feeding are advisable when individuals are unable to masticate effectively (e.g. Dengi Hi Fi, Mollichaff, coarse mix, etc.).

Ageing by dentition is similar to the horse/pony with regard to eruption times, however later age-related changes differ.

The corner incisors may not be fully 'in wear' until age 9 or 10 years. In early teens a marked 'seagull' shape develops between upper and lower incisors, this can be retained beyond 20 years in some cases.

The infundibulum may be retained in the lower incisors until around 20 years of age and finally disappears from the corners in the mid 20s. In

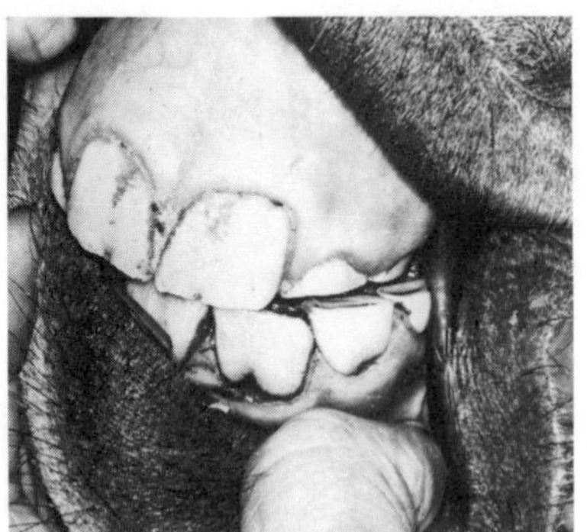

$2^1/_2$ years: permanent central incisors erupt.

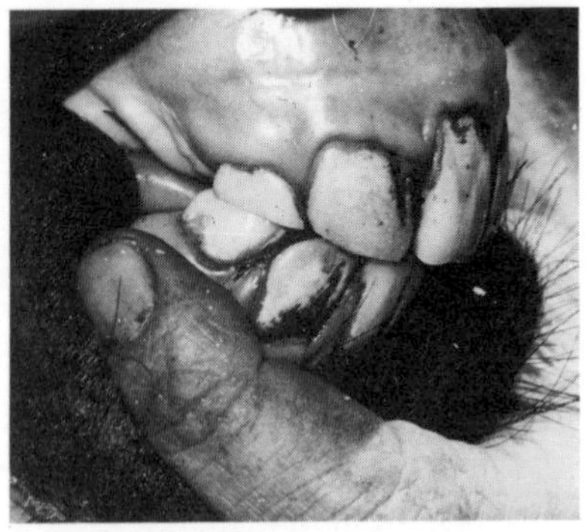

$3^1/2$ years: permanent lateral incisors erupt.

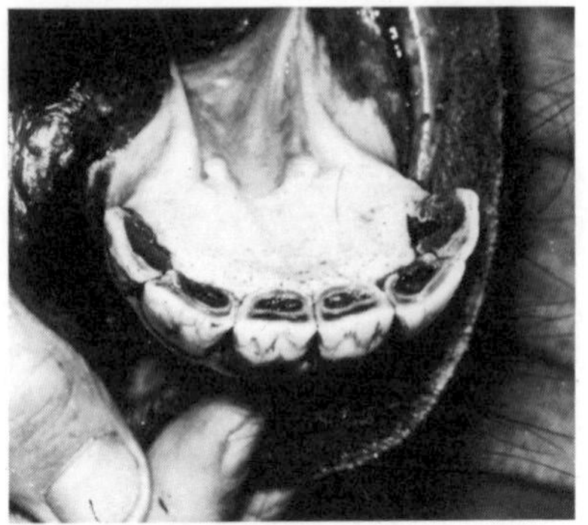

5 years: permanent corner incisors just in wear. They erupt at $4^1/2$ years.

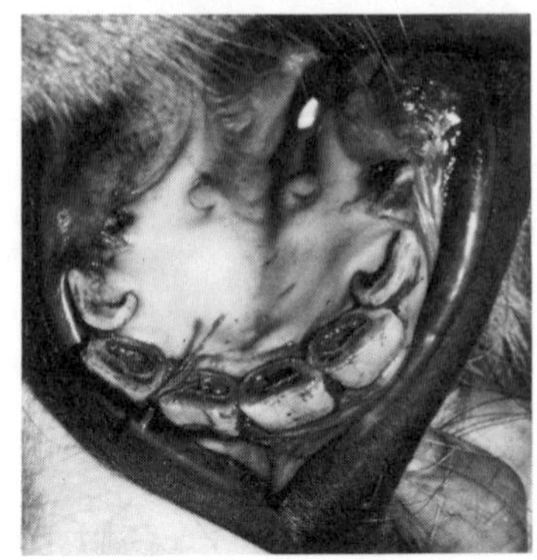

6 years: teeth oval infundibulum.

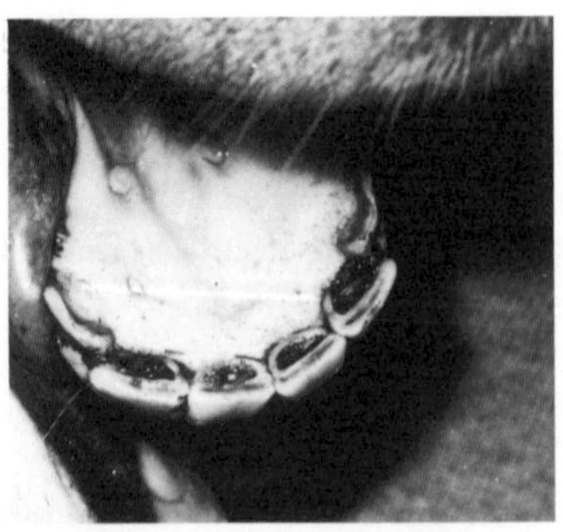

8 years: dental star now appearing in central incisors.

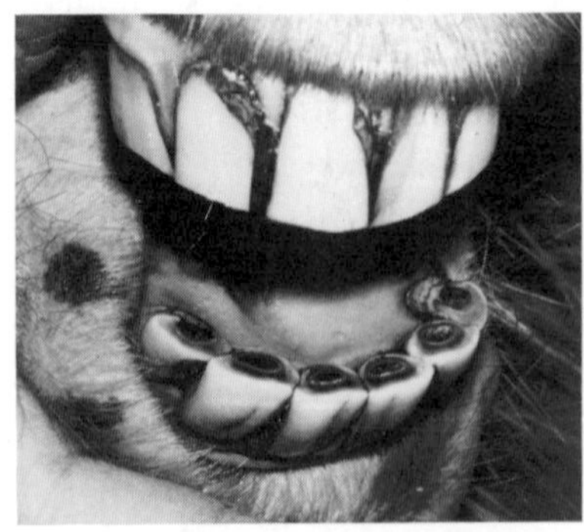

11 years: infundibula of central and middle incisor becoming shallow. Incisors quite long and dental star apparent in all teeth.

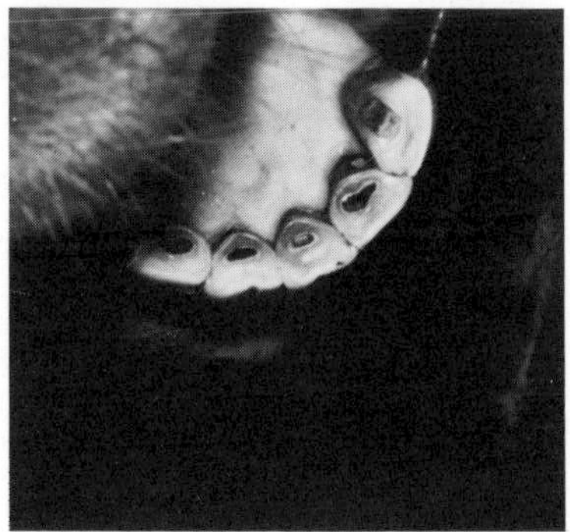

14 years: pronounced triangular shape. Infundibula further back on the tooth and wearing out.

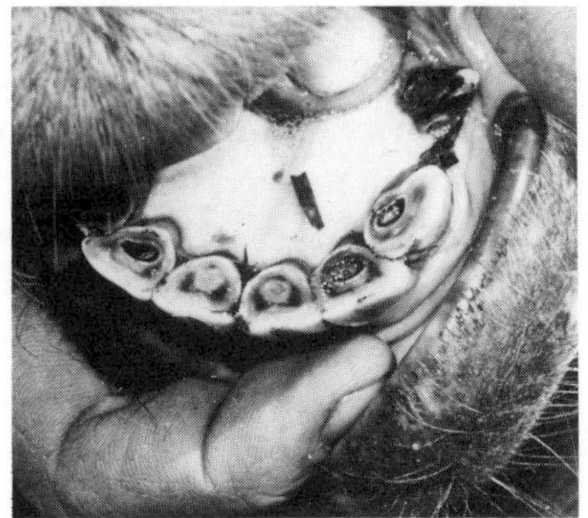

15-20 years: infundibulum disappeared from central incisors. Note triangular shape teeth.

later life, the upper incisors recede to gum level while the lower incisors become long and loose.

Galvayne's groove is absent and no predictable hook appears on the caudal edge of the upper corner incisor.

Stringhalt

A stringhalt-like condition is seen in a significant number of elderly donkeys (over 20 years of age). This involuntary flexion of one or both hind limbs can be quite severe and result in some individuals having a most bizarre gait.

Surgical treatment has not been attempted at the Donkey Sanctuary and there is little response to anti-inflammatory medication.

Respiratory disease

Serological and bacteriological investigation suggest that donkeys are susceptible to the same spectrum of respiratory viral and bacterial pathogens as other equids. All donkeys at the Donkey Sanctuary are vaccinated against equine influenza using the standard equine protocol and no cases have been recorded in recent years. Anecdotal accounts of influenza in donkeys suggest that the clinical reaction may range from the almost asymptomatic to a severe and life-threatening form. The latter reaction may be the result of secondary bacterial broncho-pneumonia with concomitant hyperlipaemia. The pyrexia and anorexia associated with respiratory disease have been responsible for hyperlipaemia episodes. Consequently supportive therapy and thoughtful nursing should accompany the treatment of any respiratory infection.

Strangles - Streptococcus equi infection - is seen with pyrexia and oculo-nasal discharge but without the obvious lymph node enlargement so typical in other equines.

Purpura haemorrhagica has not been recorded at the Donkey Sanctuary.

Few donkeys take part in athletic competition and many are managed along the lines of benign neglect. Subjective assessment of donkeys with respiratory disease suggests that coughing is less characteristic. Consequently we encounter a high incidence of chronic, untreated, advanced respiratory disease, for which the underlying aetiology is often unclear.

Post mortem examination consistently reveals extensive areas of fibrosis and consolidation, emphysema and chronic abscessation.

The marked respiratory effort frequently results in degrees of tracheal collapse and pronounced respiratory noise. Intermittant pyrexia and nasal discharge, often mucopurulent, are associated with this condition. The nasal discharge may well be unilateral despite its origin in the lower respiratory tract. Affected animals are often in poor bodily condition and are slow to gain weight on supplementary feed.

Medical therapy with clenbuterol hydrochloride (max dose 0.32mg/kg bid), antibiotics and prednisolone (0.5mg/kg reducing to 0.1mg/kg on alternate days) is helpful in some cases. Iatrogenic laminitis has not been a noticeable risk of prednisolone administration.

However management of air quality is of prime importance and marked improvement of even severely dyspnoeic cases is reported, particularly when allowed access to open grazing away from dung heaps and barns.

The role of parasites, particularly lungworm, in respiratory disease is included in Chapter 4.

Urogenital

Renal failure occurs commonly in elderly cachexic animals or as a common consequence of hyperlipaemia.

Sizeable cystic calculi have been identified in geldings requiring surgical

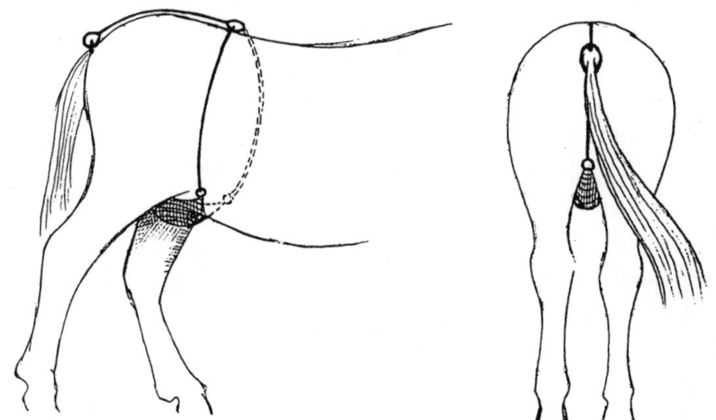

Fig. 1 Treatment of penile prolapse by support (after Cox).

excision by laparotomy thorough a parapreputial approach.

Coital exanthema (Equine herpes virus - 3) is not uncommon and healing is assisted by cleansing and antiseptic emollient cream applied daily.

Penile prolapse can progress to balanoposthitis and paraphimosis of sizeable proportion. Massage, waterproof ointment and the use of a support is essential. This may be provided by a net e.g. mutton cloth supported by a surcingle and crupper. If unavailable these can be manufactured from rubber tubing (Fig 1). Given time and careful nursing, most such problems eventually resolve satisfactorily with this conservative approach.

Skin diseases

Pruritus leading to restlessness, a dishevelled coat, alopecia and excoriation is characteristic of parasite dermatoses. These are by far the commonest cause of dermatitis in the donkey and are specifically covered in Chapter 4. Treatment of the underlying cause as well as secondary lesions is mandatory. Consideration of future prophylactic measures may be advisable.

One rarely encounters cases of pruritic dermatitis in which parasites are not implicated.

A number of cases of eosinophic pustular/granulomatous dermatitis have been recorded, most probably due to an insect bite induced hypersensitivity. These lesions may cover extensive areas of the body with the head, neck, ventral thorax and lower limbs being predilection sites.

Severe cases have required treatment with systemic and topical antibiotics, oral prednisolone and local cleansing in addition to ectoparasiticides.

Urticaria is not recorded although a non-specific subcutaneous oedema below the ventral abdomen/thorax is not uncommon. The aetiology of these lesions is often obscure and they resolve without treatment over a period of weeks if exercise is encouraged. It is, however, advisable to eliminate potential systemic causes (e.g. hyperlipaemia, hypoproteinaemia, cardiovascular).

We encounter a similar spectrum of infectious dermatoses to those found in other equines and treat these accordingly.

Dermatophilus congolensis infection, particularly of the lower limbs of heavily coated individuals, may be extensive. Poor winter management is often implicated. Thorough clipping and debriding of lesions is required followed by dry housing. Topical and parenteral antibiotics may be indicated.

Both primary and secondary photosensitisation are recorded, the latter carrying a poor prognosis. Primary photosensitisation may necessitate corticosteroid/antihistamine creams initially and shade confinement until lesions have healed. The use of modern sun block creams has helped in allowing susceptible individuals to enjoy summer grazing.

Sarcoids must always be considered in the differential diagnosis of any dermal neoplasia. Melanoma, neurofibroma and squamous cell carcinoma are recorded infrequently as dermal neoplasms.

Therapeutics

It is generally assumed that pharmacological treatment regimes for the donkey can be extrapolated from data derived from the horse and pony. However, significant differences in distribution, clearance or half life between horses and donkeys have been shown for all drugs which have been investigated. Therefore, drug doses and dose intervals appropriate for the horse are probably not appropriate for donkeys.

This difference is most evident in the clearance of phenylbutazone which is approximately 10 times higher in the donkey compared to the horse (Matthews et al.1994).

Since inappropriate doses may lead to toxicity or ineffective treatment further investigation of pharmacokinetics in the donkey appears warranted.

References

Bathe, A.P., 'The Complete Lameness Work-up', The Fourth International Farriery and Lameness Seminar, Cambridge, 5-9 (1994)

Forhead, A.J., 'Equine Hyperlipaemia: Endocrine and Metabolic Basis of Risk Factors' (Ph.D. thesis) (1992)

Horspool, L.J.I., and McKeller, Q.A., 'Disposition of oxytetracycline in horses, ponies and donkeys after intravenous administration', *Equine Vet Journal* 22, 4, 284-285 (1990)

Horspool, L.J.I., Sarasola, P., and McKeller, Q.A., 'Disposition of ampicillin sodium in horses, ponies and donkeys after intravenous administration', *Equine Vet Journal Suppl.* 11, 59-61(1992)

Kinabo, L.D.B., and Bogan, J.A., 'Disposition of triclabendazole in horses, ponies and donkeys', *Equine Vet Journal* 21, 4, 305-307 (1989)

McConaghy, F.F., Davis, R.E., and Hodgson, D.R., 'Equine Sarcoid: A Persistent Therapeutic Challenge', Continuing Education Article #5 16, 8), Equine 1022-1031 (1994)

Matthews, N.S., Taylor, T.S., Mealey, K.L., Ray, A.C., Welfare, R.E., and Foster, E.L., 'Pharmacokinetics of Gentamycin, Ketamine and Phenylbutazone in Donkeys, Mules and Mammoth Asses', *Working Equines*, 2nd International Colloquium, Morocco 83-88 (1994)

Reid, S.W.J., Gettinby, G., Fowler, J.N., and Ikin, P. 'Epidemiological observations on sarcoids in a population of donkeys (*Equus asinus*)', *The Veterinary Record* (1994) 134, 207-211 (1994)

Trawford, A.F., and Tremlett, J.G., 'Efficacy of triclabendazole against *Fasciola hepatica* in the donkey (*Equus asinus*)', *The Veterinary Record* 139, 142-143 (1996)

Watson, T., ' Hyperlipaemia in ponies', *In Practice*, Sept (1994)

Various, *Equine Veterinary Education* (1995) Vol 7, 1

MICHAEL CRANE B.V.M.&S., M.R.C.V.S. graduated with distinction from the Royal (Dick) School of Veterinary Studies in 1983. After three years in mixed practice in Sussex he travelled to the Sultanate of Oman as Veterinary Surgeon and Livestock Manager to H.E. Said bin Salem al Wahaibi.

In the following three years he established a veterinary clinic and oversaw the development of livestock farms throughout Oman. On his return to the UK he established his own companion and equine practice in Gloucestershire.

Since July 1993 he has been associated with the Donkey Sanctuary hospital primarily in a clinical capacity and was appointed Senior Veterinary Surgeon in April 1997.

He is married with two daughters and has interests outside his veterinary work in golf, amateur dramatics, gardening and foreign travel.

2b
OCULAR DISEASE IN THE DONKEY

Bobbi Inglis

THE DONKEY'S EYES are very like those of the horse and there is very little information available specific to the donkey. While it is useful to extrapolate from the horse where there is a wealth of good information available, I find it is always helpful to keep the unique characteristics of the donkey in mind. The purpose of this addendum is to highlight some of these characteristics and to relate them to the veterinary management of ocular disease in the donkey.

Companion donkeys are generally easily managed patients, which helps when examining and treating them. Their typically small stature can also aid treatment, which is useful as informed owners can often manage treatment when required. The donkey's tractability means that chemical restraint/sedation is only occasionally needed. The donkey, like the horse, has very strong palpebral muscles which means to fully examine some painful eyes an auriculopalpebral nerve block is useful. We have found the technique to be the same as that for the horse. Donkeys are also generally quite tolerant of nasolacrimal or subpalpebral lavage devices when they are needed.

Donkeys are frequently very stoic, showing a muted pain response as compared to horses, which can mean that some ophthalmic problems are much worse or more chronic when first examined. The donkey's potential longevity can also contribute to differences in occurrence and management of some eye problems. Donkeys often feed with much of their head deep into hay or straw, this can contribute to organic foreign bodies lodging in the eyes, especially in winter when long tufts of hair on the face are common.

Anatomically, the nasal ostium is usually found on the dorsal surface of the false nostril about 1.5cm from the nasal mucocutaneous junction, quite easily located if you are aware of this difference from the horse. For the average donkey, a standard equine nasolacrimal cannula is used to cannulate it for flushing or to deliver medication to the eye, following a third eyelid flap or a temporary tarsorrhaphy. For third eye lid flaps and temporary tarsorrhaphies we use techniques similar to those used for horses.

Conjunctivitis is a fairly common occurrence in the donkey, probably related in some degree to their feeding habits. We find that most of our cases resolve quickly using cloxacillin or chloramphenicol based eye ointments. Resistant cases are cultured and isolates have been typical of those found in other equines. Parasitic or fungal conjunctivitis has not been identified in the population of donkeys here at the Sanctuary. Flies may, however, contribute to the spread of conjunctivitis, both as vectors and as irritants. Maintaining a good insect control programme benefits a donkey's eyes as well as skin.

Sarcoids do unfortunately occur in the periorbital area quite frequently. Treatment is as described in the surgery chapter of this book but sadly the prognosis is often more guarded because the aggressiveness of the treatment must be tempered by the need to avoid ocular damage and minimize cicatrization.

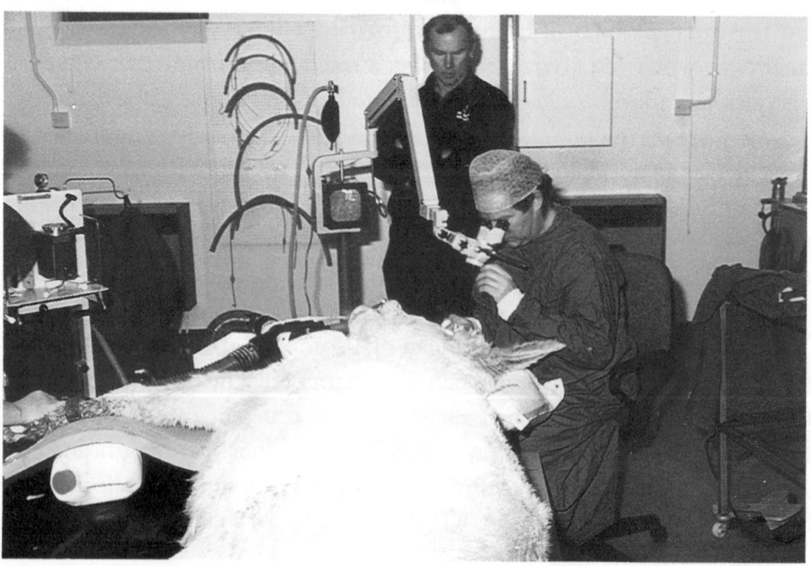

Paul Evans performing cataract surgery on Sam.

Corneal ulcers are an area where the more stoic attitude of the donkey can both help and hinder. The ulcer may result from an organic foreign body or from traumatic injuries. The browsing nature of the donkey may contribute to this form of insult. Where a horse may act differently and present with extreme photophobia and epiphora, a donkey may just squint slightly. Consequently, the initial insult may not be noticed until there is considerable damage and secondary infection. Fortunately, most donkeys are easy to medicate and in the case of deep ulcers, will tolerate nasolacrimal or subpalpebral means of delivering the medication.

Cataracts in donkeys follow the same general pattern as horses. Congenital cataracts do occur but fortunately complete bilateral cataracts are rare. It appears that senile cataracts are more common in Sanctuary donkeys than in the general equine population. This may be a combination of the greater age that donkeys can attain and the fact that the Sanctuary's reputation for providing a good home for blind and aged donkeys. Cataracts secondary to ocular disease and trauma do occur in the donkey as in the horse. Cataract surgery is much less common in equines than in canines partially because of the low occurrence of juvenile cataracts and also because managing the equine post-surgery can be difficult with resultant failure of the operation. Few donkeys would fall into the category where surgical removal of the lens would be beneficial and advisable. One Sanctuary donkey completed successful cataract surgery.

Sam arrived at the Sanctuary when he was 9 years old and was diagnosed as having bilateral juvenile cataracts which progressed to total bilateral cataracts by the time he was 11 years old. As a healthy, relatively young, docile, completely blind donkey with no other signs of ocular disease, it was felt that he was a good candidate to benefit from a unilateral cataract removal. Regaining some sight would enable him to join other partially sighted donkeys close to his own age. Also in his favour was that the operation and aftercare could be done on site, in our donkey hospital, which reduced the stress of transportation and change for him.

Consulting veterinary ophthalmologist, Paul Evans, performed the operation with the assistance of our veterinary and nursing staff. The cataract was removed under general anaesthetic using phacoemulsification and small incision surgery. It was necessary to perform anterior and posterior capsulectomies due to the opaqueness of the capsules. Partial anterior vitrification was also performed to limit the risk of subsequent retinal detachment. Post-operative recovery was uneventful probably due to Sam being such a co-operative calm patient. The return of useful vision was obvious within days. At his 6 month recheck, an excellent settled eye with a clear visual axis was recorded. Now more than two years on from the operation, Sam enjoys a life with other young partially sighted donkeys and their friends.

Lenticular sclerosis is a common finding in older donkeys and should probably be considered normal in any donkey over 20 years old. There is no obvious reduction in vision when maze tested.

Uveitis occurs in the donkey fairly commonly. In the population at the Sanctuary primary single episodes are seen rather than the periodic ophthalmia or recurrent uveitis often reported in the horse. This may relate to the relatively low incidence of periodic ophthalmia seen in the UK rather than a lower incidence in the donkey. Systemic non-steroidal anti-inflammatory drugs are very useful when combined with a cycloplegic drug and topical corticosteroid. Avoid systemic corticosteroid because of the possible link with laminitis in horses. Flunixin meglumate is used in severe acute cases for up to 48 hours, then phenylbutazone if prolonged use of a systemic anti-inflammatory is indicated.

Blind donkeys

There are many causes of full and partial blindness in donkeys. In many cases the blindness comes on slowly but the owner may not be aware of the loss of sight until it is severe or even complete. There are several reasons for this. One is that most donkeys are not used in an athletic fashion where more subtle changes in vision would show up. Another is the donkey's tremendous ability to cope with reduced vision. It is often a change of environment or circumstances that reveals the blindness. Careful questioning of the owners may reveal some clues as to the duration of the sight loss. Donkeys are intelligent, generally calm and careful animals. This is a great advantage when it comes to coping with blindness. Additionally, donkeys frequently form a strong bond with another donkey. In our experience their donkey friend often acts as the eyes of the blind donkey and the pair will almost always be found very near each other, even in a large field.

Gradual onset and ability to cope well if the paddock isn't changed means that a blind donkey can have a good quality of life. The real key is having a paddock, housing, etc., that is kept the same as much as possible, and sensitive owners who minimise the stress of necessary changes. For example, introducing the donkey to any new obstacle or new field helps him adjust. Movements around a blind donkey need to be unhurried and the donkey should be talked to as you move around him. It is fascinating to watch the ears of a blind donkey; they work like a radar to let the donkey know what is happening around him. It is often worth giving the owners of blind donkeys some advice about stabling, fields and general management. Also, discussing the degree to which a blind donkey may be relying on its donkey friend, or even other field companions, can be useful so that owners can be forewarned of the possible effects of a loss of the companion.

Ocular disease outside the United Kingdom

Discussion of ocular disease in donkeys outside the UK is beyond the scope of this addendum. However, lacrimal histoplasmosis as seen in donkeys in Egypt warrants discussion because it is an example of a causal agent creating a different syndrome in donkeys from that in horses. In horses, the fungus Histoplasmosis farciminosum causes epizootic lymphangitis, a suppurative disease of the lymphatic system, and rarely effects the horse's eyes. In donkeys, the same organism primarily causes a disease of the lacrimal system and surrounding ocular tissues.

A granulomatous reaction in the lacrimal sac occurs which can, in time, extrude through the lacrimal puncta to create a granulomatous nodule in the medial canthus. The clinical signs can progress through dacryocystitis, epiphora, blepharospasm, tear eczema, thickening of the lower eyelid and eventual protrusion into the medial canthus of a friable granulomatous mass.

Presumptive diagnosis is generally based on clinical signs and regional occurrence. This can often be confirmed by cytological examination of a direct smear from granulomatous tissue.

Treatments have included manual expression of the lacrimal sac combined with flushing of the nasal lacrimal duct and surgical removal of affected tissue in chronic cases. A more detailed description of this disease was presented by M. Saleh in the second edition of this book.

References

Barnett, K.C., Crispen, S.M., Lavach, J.D., Mathews, A.G., *Color Atlas and Text of Equine Ophthalmology*, Mosby-Wolfe (1995)

Evans, P.J., Personal communication and case notes

Misk, N.A., 'Ocular Diseases in Donkeys', *Equine Practice* 12 (4): 20-27 (1990)

Saleh, M., 'Lacrimal Histoplasmosis in Donkeys', in Svendsen, E.D. (ed) *The Professional Handbook of the Donkey*, 2nd Edition, The Donkey Sanctuary 123-129 (1989)

ROBERTA INGLIS D.V.M., M.R.C.V.S. obtained a degree in Veterinary Medicine from Purdue University, Indiana, in 1983. She worked in a small animal practice in Virginia for three years before moving to Cambridge where she became a Member of the Royal College of Veterinary Surgeons. After working for two years in a practice in Cambridge, she joined Ikin and Oxenham, a mixed animal practice in Sidmouth, Devon. This position gave her the opportunity to work as part of the veterinary team at the Donkey Sanctuary for seven years. Throughout her career she has maintained a special interest in ophthalmology. She is currently living in Devon with her husband, Philip, and daughter, Emily.

3a
SURGERY
Michael Crane

A THOUGHTFUL AND CONSIDERATE APPROACH will often enable simple examination and treatment procedures to be undertaken without the need to resort to sedatives. An appreciation of good practice in donkey handling will not only benefit veterinary surgeons but also farriers and owners attempting to socialise fractious individuals.

Patience, a quiet voice and a calm demeanour are essential. An arm around the neck and a hand over the dorsal nose will usually bring an errant donkey to a halt, enabling a standard adjustable headcollar to be fitted. When the donkey is tied up or held by an assistant the fitting of a headcollar has an appreciable composing influence. The assistant can then usefully distract the patient's attention with the odd mint, biscuit, treat, etc. The lifting of a leg is somewhat unreliable, many donkeys are adept at standing on two legs and accurately directing kicks. The firmly but carefully held ear maybe needed in a minority of instances, however the application of a twitch or twisting of the ear is never warranted. Applying a twitch to the lip would appear to have little effect in marked contrast to other equines.

One golden rule of donkey handling is to keep companions together at all times irrespective of the species of the companion. At the Donkey Sanctuary it is standard practice to maintain this contact at all times, even to the point of anaesthetic induction. Failure to appreciate the significance of these bonds can induce significant stress and a variable reaction to any sedative administered.

The standard local anaesthetic and regional nerve blocking techniques used in other areas of veterinary surgery can be usefully employed in the donkey; alone or combined with sedation they often avoid the need for general anaesthesia. The abaxial sesamoid nerve block is especially helpful in exploring and treating cases of pedal sepsis.

Once the donkey is restrained in a headcollar intravenous sedation can be reliably achieved by jugular venipuncture. Experience suggests that acetylpromazine at standard doses is ineffective in fractious individuals and may cause penile complications in both geldings and jacks.

Xylazine (Rompun Dry Substance - max. dose 1ml 5% solution per 50kg) given by slow I/V injection is useful for relatively minor procedures.

Detomidine (Domosedan 10mg/ml detomidine hydrochloride - max. dose 0.2ml per 50kg) is very useful despite the inco-ordination often seen. Attention should be given to the recognized contra indications and care exercised with elderly patients. Half the maximum suggested dose is often satisfactory and combination with butorphanol (Torbugesic 10 mg/ml butorphanol) enhances its effect at lower doses whilst providing post treatment analgesia. Maximum benefit is gained from sedation if a minimum period of 5 minutes post administration is allowed in a quiet, undisturbed environment.

Romifidine (Sedivet 10mg/ml romifidine - max dose 0.4ml per 50kg) would appear to have a similar effect to detomidine without inducing the same degree of inco-ordination. A longer post injection delay may be appropriate for full benefit to be achieved. The provision of tetanus prophylaxis should be considered after any surgery or wound treatment as a history of vaccination is often unreliable. Similarly, consideration should be given to post-treatment analgesia.

Phenylbutazone is generally well tolerated in the donkey and an average individual can be maintained on a dose of ½g BID for extended periods without undue risk.

Field anaesthesia

For situations where inhalation anaesthetic is not available, a number of techniques/drug regimes are described.

Successful and predictable field anaesthesia can be achieved by the following protocol.

Having established that the patient is clinically fit for anaesthetic an estimate of weight can be made.

For the Heart Girth Nomogram see Appendix 8.

In calculating drug doses a generous estimation would appear to facilitate both sedation and induction. A quiet environment and ensuring that adequate time elapses post sedation will encourage induction.

Acetylpromazine (ACP 10mg/ml at 0.15ml per 50kg) is given intramuscularly 30 minutes prior to sedation with *detomidine* (Domosedan 10mg/ml at 0.1ml per 50kg) intravenously. At least 5 minutes is allowed to elapse prior to induction. Timing this interval and avoiding any unnecessary patient stimulation is worthwhile.

Personal experience suggests that the inclusion of butorphanol (Torbugesic 10mg/ml butorphanol) at 0.2ml/50kg in addition to detomidine enhances and prolongs the period of surgical anaesthesia.

Anaesthesia is then induced using *ketamine* (Vetalar 100mg/ml at 1.1ml per 50kg). Most patients will slowly subside into recumbency over the next 30-120 seconds, a further minute should be allowed before any surgical stimulation is contemplated.

If muscular rigidity persists for more than one minute a bolus of *thiopentone* (1mg/kg ie. 1ml 5% solution per 50kg) may be given. These top up doses of thiopentone can be repeated for 3 doses to prolong anaesthesia. Slower injection reduces the risk of subsequent apnoea and multiple doses will significantly prolong recovery.

The use of an indwelling catheter is to be strongly recommended if thiopentone use is contemplated.

A soft towel should be used to protect and cover the eyes. The eyelids remain wide open and spontaneous palpebral activity is maintained under *ketamine* anaesthesia. Increased lachrymation and deliberate sighing respiration indicate that anaesthetic is lightening. Monitoring of the anal reflex will assist in assessing the depth of anaesthesia - pinching the anal sphincter should cause closure of the sphincter, a brisk response and raising of the tail head indicate that spontaneous movement is likely.

The provision of an oxygen rich environment by way of a nasal tube connected to an oxygen cylinder and flow regulator is recommended for more prolonged anaesthesia.

General anaesthesia

The protocol and techniques of anaesthetising a donkey follow standard equine principles.

One hundred and forty-five elective general anaesthetics have been performed at the Donkey Sanctuary over the last 2 years with a 0.7% 24 hour mortality. The common indications for anaesthesia include castration, dental disorders, tumour removal, ocular surgery, laparotomy, cystotomy and radiography.

Pre operatively donkeys are weighed, examined clinically and a blood sample is taken for routine haematology and biochemistry. They are fasted for 4 hours.

Our standard pre induction medication is as follows:

1 hour prior to induction

ACP @ 0.1mg/kg I/M i.e. 0.1ml/10kgBW of 10mg/ml ACP.

Plus

Pethidine @ 0.5mg/kg I/M i.e. 0.1 ml/10kgBW of 50mg/ml Pethidine.

10 mins prior to induction

Xylazine @ 0.5mg/kg I/V ie. 0.1m/10kgBW of 5% Rompun.

A quiet environment and maintaining contact with companions encourages sedation. An indwelling 16g catheter is placed by cut down venepuncture into the jugular vein.

Anaesthesia is induced in a padded box with thiopentone @ 2ml 5% solution/10kgBW.

Extension of the head facilitates passage of a 16mm diameter endotracheal tube in average sized donkeys.

Initial stabilisation of anaesthesia may require concentrations of up to 8% halothane and oxygen, with maintenance at 3%-4% in most cases. Nitrous oxide is not used.

Monitoring the level of consciousness in an anaesthetised donkey may be difficult and require regular, preferably continuous assessment by an individual experienced in equine anaesthesia.

It is advantageous to monitor several reflexes and cardiovascular and respiratory variables when monitoring depth of anaesthesia. Palpebral, corneal and anal reflexes, eye position and degree of lachrymation should all be assessed along with monitoring of cardiovascular and respiratory systems.

Despite close monitoring of the depth of anaesthesia some donkeys may react abruptly to surgical stimulation. It is useful to anticipate this eventuality by providing intravenous access at all times and having a bolus of extra thiopentone to deepen anaesthesia readily to hand. It is frequently observed that traction on the spermatic cord, particularly in mature stallions undergoing castration, causes slight reflex movement. It is unnecessary and may be dangerous to attempt to deepen anaesthesia to abolish this reaction.

Recovery is generally uneventful in a quiet hazard free environment.

Etorphine hydrochloride (Immobilon) is not recommended for use in the donkey. Enterohepatic recycling can occur earlier than anticipated and may be fatal.

Castration

The stature and temperament of adult entire donkeys, combined with the need to ligate the spermatic artery necessitate general anaesthesia. Before embarking on the anaesthesia consideration should be given to a number of factors:

(1) Age and health of the donkey - a full clinical examination is advisable with particular attention to signs of chronic respiratory disease.
(2) Tetanus prophylaxis - tetanus antitoxin should be administered to every castration and only omitted if there is definite history of previous toxid administration.
(3) The open wound may take a number of weeks to heal completely and the environment in which the patient is kept should minimise the risk of gross wound contamination. Pre operative intravenous crystalline penicillin may be recommended.

Following induction of anaesthesia 3 mls of 2% Lignocaine is injected into the substance of each testis and the patient restrained in either left lateral or dorsal recumbancy.

A standard closed castration technique is advocated. The scrotal ligament in some mature individuals is relatively strong and may inhibit easy dissection of the spermatic sac.

The spermatic sac and spermatic artery can be successfully ligated as indicated in Fig 1 using 5 metric (Vicryl) braided absorbable suture. It is essential to lay and tie the ligature securely around the vascular component. The sac is then transected 2 cm below the ligature using a Serra emasculator. Given adequate surgical cleanliness this technique has proved successful in over 200 castrations at the Donkey Sanctuary in the last 5 years.

Significant deposits of subcutaneous fat are found in the scrotal tissue of many obese and good condition donkeys. Careful dissection and removal of these deposits from around the wound improves the speed of healing.

Post operative treatment should include sufficient exercise to minimise

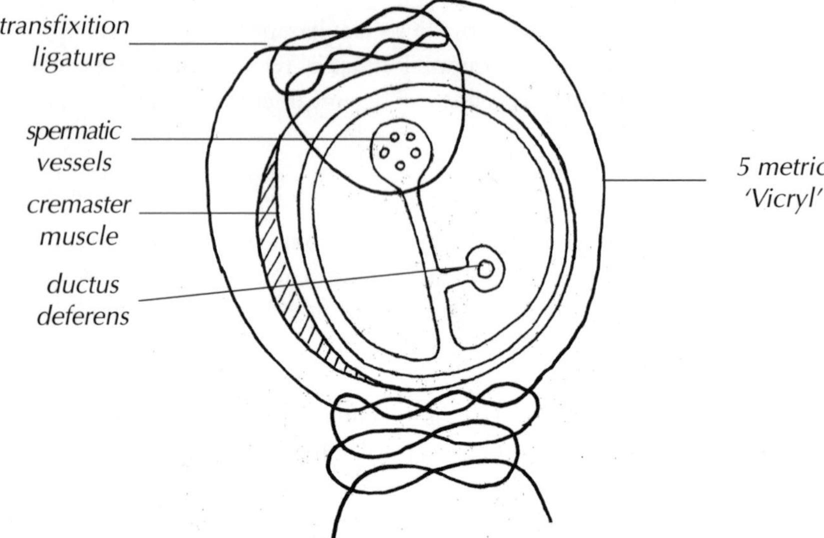

Fig 1. The spermatic sac and spermatic artery can be successfully ligated as indicated.

oedema formation, the prescribing of NSAIDs for analgesia and advice on good stable management.

Feet

Deep or chronic pedal sepsis with potential involvement of the pedal bone itself is not an uncommon problem. This can occur as a consequence of penetrating injury, chronic pus in the foot or laminitis. The characteristic features are a chronic or recurrent discharging sinus and radiographic changes in the pedal bone. These changes are most often seen on dorso-palmar/plantar exposures.

Investigation and treatment of these lesions can be successfully carried out in the standing patient. Initial sedation is often helpful and broad spectrum antibiotics administered. The tetanus status of the patient should be checked.

The palmar/plantar digital nerves are anaesthetised by an abaxial sesamoid nerve block using 2ml Mepivacaine (Intra-Epicaine, Arnolds), and a tourniquet of elastic cohesive bandage applied to the distal metacarpus and fetlock.

The hoof is then trimmed of all surplus wall, sole and frog to leave the surgical site exposed. Any infected or necrotic material is then debrided back with a hoof knife. It would appear to be important to leave a defect which will not trap infection and allow packing to encourage granulation from the bottom of the wound. Some surrounding healthy tissue may have to be removed, a curette and scalpel blade are often useful for excising corium or necrotic bone.

All infected material must be removed. The lesion can then be flushed and packed with swabs soaked in dilute povidone-iodine.

The healing and convalescent period may extend to three weeks or more and necessitate frequent redressing. The use of a surgical shoe with a removable aluminium sole plate is often superior to bandaging the foot. At the Donkey Sanctuary we use a glue-on shoe with a full bar plastic shoe to which the sole plate is screwed. Any gaps between shoe sole and frog can be filled with commercial silicone solvent.

The surgical site is redressed with povidone-iodine soaked gauze daily packed tightly into the wound to encourage granulation from the bottom of the defect. A dry clean box is essential. Systemic antibiotics are prescribed for five days and phenylbutazone given, the dose and duration dependant on the degree of lameness.

The success rate for this type of treatment is high in cases which do not show evidence of chronic laminitis and associated pedal bone remodelling on radiography.

The use of the abaxial sesamoid nerve blocks to facilitate the aggressive early treatment of cases of pedal sepsis, particularly in fractious individuals, may prevent more complex sequelae such as pedal osteitis developing.

Sarcoids

The equine sarcoid is a locally invasive fibropapilloma of the skin. They are very variable in appearance and sarcoids should be included in the differential diagnosis of any skin growth in the donkey. The often heavy coat of the donkey precludes early diagnosis of suspicious lesions unless thorough palpation is undertaken. This is advisable prior to treating single observable lesions as multiple, often remote sarcoids are not uncommon. Lesions vary in appearance from apparently well defined nodules to rapidly growing, ulcerated plaques of varying shapes with many differing intermediate forms. Biopsy of suspicious lesions should be undertaken with caution as there may be a risk of stimulating uncontrolled fibroblastic activity.

The specific aetiology of sarcoids has yet to be elucidated. A bovine papilloma like virus may be involved as BPV - 1/2 DNA is consistently isolated from lesions. Further non-intrusive research is being undertaken. Some authors propose circumstantial evidence that flies may be involved in transmitting an infective agent. Studies of the clinical records at the Donkey Sanctuary indicate that geldings are somewhat more at risk than females and that the highest proportion of clinical cases are seen between 2 and 5 years of age. Predilection sites include the paragenital region in the male, the ventral abdomen of the female and the head, particularly the peri-orbital region. Sarcoids may be found at any other site, the least common being the dorsal trunk.

Histologically sarcoids are characterised by interlacing bundles of spindle-shaped fibroblasts with variable numbers of mitotic figures and collagen fibrils.

Fibroblasts at the dermal-epidermal junction frequently line up perpendicular to the basement membrane in a palisade-like fashion.

The more nodular sarcoid resembles a fibroma with the more invasive ulcerated plaques being closer to a fibrosarcoma. Infiltrative expansion into the dermis and subcutis is seen around even apparently encapsulated and grossly well defined lesions.

Recurrence of lesions, at the original site, as satellite lesions, or on remote parts of the body, is the curse of sarcoid treatment. These regrowths are generally more aggressive in nature.

Small non-growing lesions that do not interfere with normal function may be best left alone and monitored for changing character. Similarly it must be accepted that some larger more aggressive lesions are beyond treatment and euthanasia will be required. Myiasis is a significant risk with ulcerated sarcoids and long coated donkeys.

Treatment by surgical excision can be curative if a wide margin of grossly normal tissue is removed around the mass. The mass should be handled minimally and not traumatised. Certain sites, notably the head and distal limb, are less amenable to surgery.

Cryosurgery with debulking of larger masses is more effective if a freeze-thaw technique is employed and repeated. The cycle is usually undertaken three times at each treatment. At the Donkey Sanctuary we use the portable Cryo Spray 60 (Mediforce, Bradford) and protect surrounding skin with bubble wrap over Vaseline petroleum jelly. Sloughing of necrotic debris may take up to two months.

The intra-dermal injection of BCG cell wall extracts have been effectively employed, particularly for cranial lesions. Inadvertent subcutaneous injection induces a marked purulent reaction. This is especially true if an adjuvant is used. Repeat treatments at weekly intervals until a response is noted is the usual protocol. Monitoring for anaphylactic reaction, pre-operative flunixin I/V and consideration of post operative analgesia are strongly recommended.

The use of radiation, implants, laser therapy and topical cytotoxic compounds is described elsewhere but we have little practical experience of these techniques at the Donkey Sanctuary.

3b
ULTRASOUND DEPARTMENT, THE DONKEY SANCTUARY

June Evers

In April 1995 the Donkey Sanctuary bought a Concept S Diagnostic Ultrasound machine with a 3.5mHz probe, a printout machine and a video machine linked to the main unit. This unit is portable and we can use it on the outlying farms.

The examinations carried out are non-intrusive and involve the liver, kidneys, heart and bladder. It is also used for pregnancy diagnosis using the probe externally, therefore early pregnancy is not detectable.

We are also in the process of building up a library of normal scans for comparison purposes.

The donkeys are usually examined standing and unsedated. They are encouraged to take an interest in a bucket containing a mixture of carrots and brown bread which distracts them from the preparations going on around them.

The donkeys tend most of all to dislike the noise of the clippers. It is important to clip as close to the skin as possible in order to obtain the optimum contact with the probe also using copious amounts of coupling gel.

For the heart, the major part of the examination is performed on the right side using the 4th to 6th intercostal spaces.

For the liver and right kidney the window used extends for about 20cm cranially from a point 3cm in front of the iliac crest and approximately 20cm in depth from the transverse spinous processes.

For the spleen and left kidney the window used is approximately 5cm in front of the iliac crest and extends 15cm cranially and 15cm in depth from the transverse spinous processes.

For external scanning in pregnancy diagnosis we use an area approximately 20cm in diameter, immediately in front of the udder.

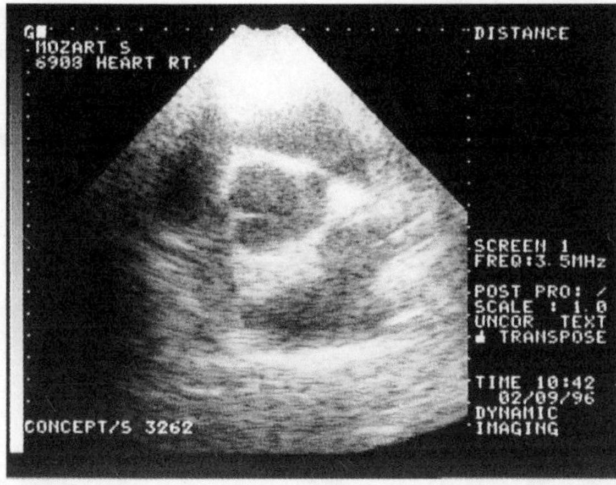

ABOVE Ultrasonograph of the heart of a donkey imaged from the right parasternal window. The aortic valve is seen in long axis in the centre field with the valve cusps imaged in the valve closed position. The left atrium is seen at 4 to 6 o'clock with the right ventricle apparent at 12 to 2 o'clock.

BELOW Ultrasonograph of a short axis view of the donkey heart imaged from the right parasternal window. The right ventricle at 10 o'clock is seen wrapping around the left ventricle in centre field. The thick left ventricular wall is imaged and in the anechoic centre the echogenic chordae tendinae are seen running from the free wall to the valves.

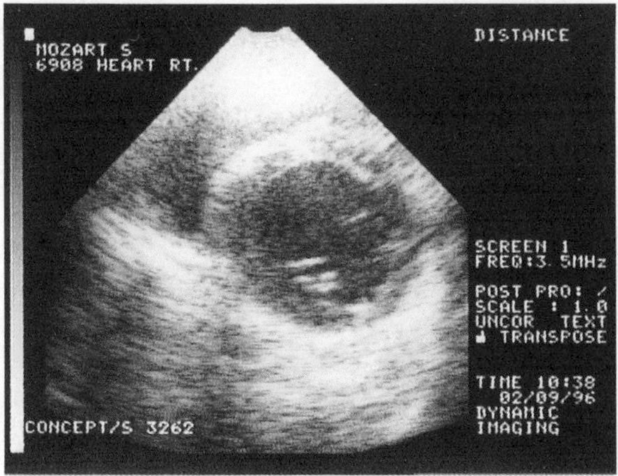

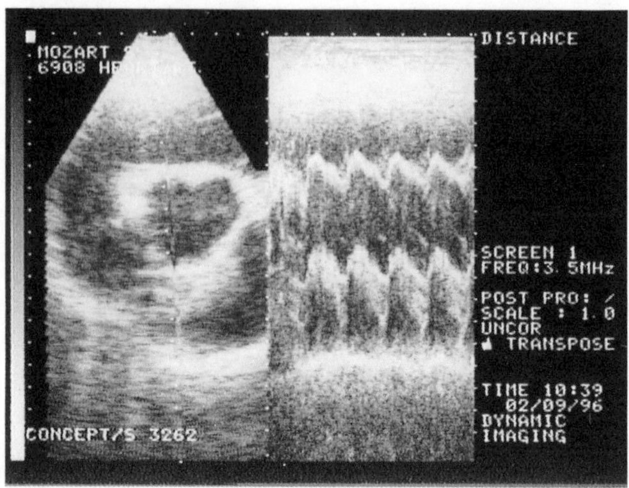

ABOVE Split image ultrasonograph with M-mode of a short axis view of the donkey heart imaged from the right parasternal window. The aortic valve is seen in centre field with the right ventricular outflow tract wrapping around from 7 o'clock to 2 o'clock. The M-mode tracing i.e. movement against time, demonstrates the range of movement accomplished by the ventricular walls and aortic valve aperture during systole and diastole.

BELOW Foetal heart.

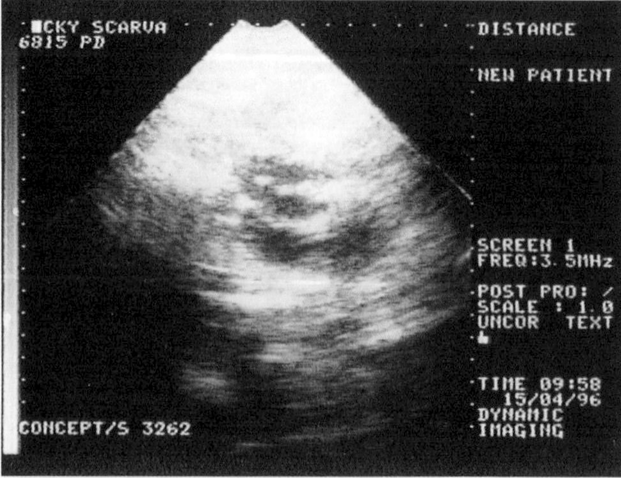

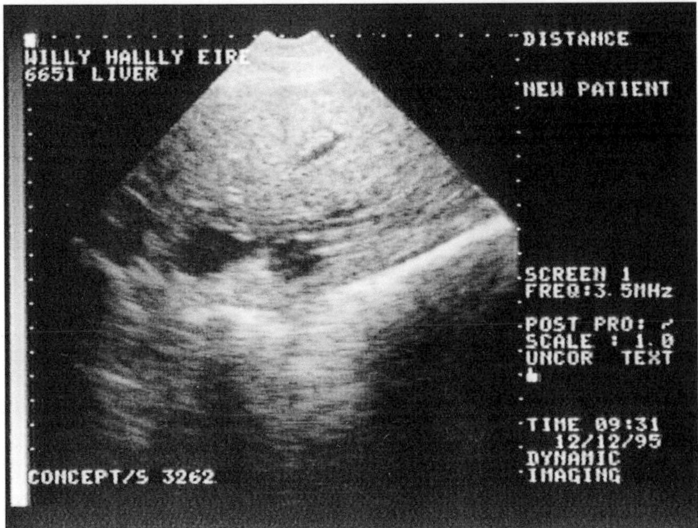

Liver.

JUNE EVERS qualified in radiography at Leeds General Infirmary. Whilst working at the Royal Devon and Exeter Hospital she gained her Higher Diploma of College of Radiographers. June was superintendent of the X-Ray Department at the Royal Devon and Exeter Hospital for fourteen years. She first joined the Donkey Sanctuary in a voluntary capacity in 1975 and was made a Trustee of the Sanctuary the same year. In 1996 June was made Assistant Administrator to the International Donkey Protection Trust.

4
PARASITES IN UK DONKEYS

Andrew Trawford

THERE ARE TWO MAIN GROUPS of parasites in the donkey: ectoparasites and endoparasites.

Some parasites have stages in their life cycle which enable them to be classified as both ecto and endoparasites.

Unfortunately there is little available literature to convey useful information on those parasites which affect the donkey and it is therefore often assumed that the occurrence, symptoms, pathogenicity, treatment and control of the following parasites are similar to the horse.

Specific references will however be given when literature on the donkey is available.

ECTOPARASITES

Lice	*Haematopinus asini*	the blood sucking louse (the most common ectoparasite of the donkey)
	Damalinia equi	the biting louse
'Sweet Itch'	Culicoides hypersensitivity	
Mites	*Chorioptes equi* *Demodex cabali, D. equi* *Psoroptes equi* *Sarcoptes scabei*	less common than lice but cases of mange are sometimes seen in donkeys rescued by the Sanctuary

Harvest Mites (Chiggers)	Trombiculidae	
Forage Mite	suborder Astigmata	
Fly Worry	Stable Fly (*Stomoxys calcitrans*) House Flies (*Musca* spp.) Head Flies (*Hydrotaea irritans*) Black Flies (*Simulium* spp.)	
Myiasis (Blowfly Strike)	*Lucillia, Calliphora, Phormia, Chrysomyi.*	
Anal Irritation	*Oxyuris equi.*	
Warbles	*Hypoderma* spp.	Rarely seen in donkeys
Ticks	*Ixodus* spp.	Rarely seen in donkeys fortunately

The two most common and important skin conditions of donkeys are caused by ectoparasites.

1. Lice

Two syndromes occur following louse infestation:

Anaemia: The blood sucking louse *Haematopinus asini* can infest donkeys in large numbers as it completes its life cycle in three weeks and remains on the host for all stages of the life cycle. General debility and weight loss occur if heavy infestations are not treated at an early stage.

Pruritus - skin irritation: The biting louse (*Damalinia equi*)
Irritation may be severe causing the donkey to bite and rub excessively. The self inflicted trauma to the skin is followed by dermatitis due to secondary bacterial infection. Interestingly the degree of irritation is not always directly proportional to the number of parasites. Frequently some donkeys develop an allergic reaction similar to the Type IV allergy dogs develop to a flea bite when just a few lice produce a severe reaction.

A mixed infestation of both sucking and biting lice is most commonly seen in the donkey.

Treatment

Pour-on anti-lice preparations containing 4% permethrin are very effective for treating the individual animal for both biting and sucking lice, but care must be taken not to reinfest the donkey due to poor management techniques. Grooming kit and tack should therefore be cleaned and disinfected at the same time as the animals are treated and any discarded hair carefully disposed of. Instructions for persons applying pour-on preparations include: wearing protective clothing, rubber gloves and boots.

Note

For animals showing allergic reactions it is important to repeat treatment, including all in-contact equines, to eliminate all lice. Treat severely traumatised areas by clipping the hair, scrubbing affected areas with chlorhexidine 4% (Hibiscrub) and applying topical treatment for dermatitis e.g. Dermisol.

2. Sweet itch

Hypersensitivity caused by flies (*Culicoides* spp.) produces one of the most difficult skin conditions to treat in the donkey. Lesions usually occur along the dorsal surface of the donkey from neck to rump and appear as a severe pruritic dermatitis.

Initially discrete papules appear on the skin causing hairs on the dorsal surface to stand erect. Gradually scaling and hair loss occurs especially on the ears and tail. Exfoliation of epidermal cells and serous effusion is followed by thickening of the skin and lesions associated with the self-inflicted trauma of rubbing.

Observations at the Sanctuary would indicate that a familial predisposition to sweet itch may exist. A warm moist environment during the summer fly season exacerbates the condition which may only be controlled by housing the donkey during the insects' feeding times or fitting a 'summer sheet' for protection.

Fly repellants are a useful control measure and some cases may be prevented from becoming serious by application of 4% permethrin at two week intervals, but do remember that 4% permethrin should not be applied to broken or damaged skin.

Problem fields or areas (tree cover, overgrown hedges, low lying or sheltered pastures) should be identified and avoided and low risk areas (open windy hill tops) utilised.

Other ectoparasitics include:

MITES

Although there are potentially four types of mites

Chorioptes equi
Demodex cabali, Demodex equi
Psoroptes equi
Sarcoptes scabei

these are rarely if ever seen at the Sanctuary even in the donkeys coming into isolation.

The widespread use of ivermectin for endoparasite control may account for the demise of this parasite but it should be included in the differential diagnosis of any skin condition producing hair loss, irritation, thickened skin with scabs and exudate.

Treatment

Pour-on preparations - as for lice.

Ivermectin 200µg/kg is effective and also treats endoparasites.

Harvest mites (*Trombiculidae*)

The larvae of these mites are capable of producing skin lesions and irritation. They are active for 4-6 weeks of the year in late summer and early autumn. Once having obtained a meal of lymph and disintegrated skin cells they progress to free-living nymphal and adult stages and the problem is therefore of limited duration.

Forage mites (*Astigmata*)

Free-living members of the suborder Astigmata are found in livestock bedding and stored foods and produce disease by inoculating or depositing irritant substances on the skin.

Outbreaks of infection have occurred at the Sanctuary following use of certain batches of straw bought in to the Sanctuary. Irritation usually occurs in the lower limbs and is treated using pour-on preparations. Application of topical pyrethrins is also being investigated. All affected straw should be burned.

FLY WORRY

'Fly worry' in general can also be a problem around eyes, lips, nostrils and genital areas.

Horse and stable flies will multiply in manure, rotting food stuffs, etc. Stable hygiene, proper and thorough disposal of muck and siting of muck heaps, etc., are all important in reducing these pests.

Myiasis (Blowfly Strike)
Wounds received during the summer fly season can result in a gross, ugly, maggot infested wound within 48hrs. All wounds should therefore be treated with insecticide Coumaphos 3% (Negasunt) or fly cream or be bandaged.

Remember to avoid routine surgery (castration) at this time of year.

Anal irritation
This condition may be caused by the rupture of the contents of gravid females of the pinworm *Oxyuris equi* (see details under endoparasites). This condition is very rare in donkeys in the UK.

Warbles
Although officially eradicated from most parts of Britain owners should remain vigilant for any lump on the dorsal skin with a breathing hole in spring or early summer. (Owners should not attempt treatment.) Consult your local veterinary surgeon as not only is this a notifiable disease but treatment at this stage may result in severe abscessation at the site of the larvae or even toxic shock.

Ticks
Fortunately for the donkey ticks prefer any other livestock rather than the donkey in the UK. Even abroad donkeys are rarely infected by large numbers of ticks. Tick borne diseases are also very rare.

Endoparasites

Endoparasites may be grouped into:

- Intestinal helminths - gut worms
- Lungworms
- Platyhelminths or Flukes which inhabit the liver

The disease picture or pathogenesis of each 'group' is also varied.

Intestinal helminths produce a wide range of clinical syndromes from those focused on the gastrointestinal tract such as diarrhoea and colic to more systemic conditions such as anaemia or poor condition.

The variation in clinical syndromes will occur according to the age, nutritional status and resistance of the donkey and also according to the species of parasite involved and the sheer number of that parasite in the host. The various species that commonly affect donkeys are:

1. Intestinal Helminths

	Clinical Syndrome
Ascarids (*Parascaris equorum*) Large Strongyles (*Strongylus* spp.)	Colic caused by obstructions related to *Parascaris equorum* and verminous migrations or arteritis largely attributed to the migration of *S. vulgaris*
Small Strongyles (*Trichonema* spp.)	responsible for the syndromes in late winter/early spring - cyathostomiasis
Pin worms (*Oxyuris equi*)	causing anal irritation, especially in young animals
Thread worms (*Strongyloides*)	usually seen in foals
Tapeworm (*Anoplocephala* spp.)	
Bots (*Gastrophilus* spp.)	

2. Lungworms

Lungworm (*Dictyocaulus arnfieldi*)

3. Platyhelminths or fluke

Liver Fluke (*Fasciola* spp.)

A detailed description of each parasite and its life cycle is not within the remit of this text since most of the information available refers to the horse.

It is perhaps more important to emphasise the diagnosis and control of individual or groups of parasites.

The diagnosis of endoparasitic infection can be made from routine examination of faeces for parasitic eggs. With lungworm infection, larvae are shed and require a different technique for identification (see Appendix 4 for the diagnostic technique). Since the eggs of *Gastrophilus* spp. are laid by flies on the legs of the donkeys, this is usually diagnosed by visual examination of the legs when grooming.

Identification of the eggs in the faeces does not however indicate the presence of a clinical disease and only when large numbers of eggs per gram have been identified can the possibility of clinical disease be considered. At the Sanctuary the occurrence of more than 200 epg in 25% of the herd is taken as an indicator for routine anthelmintic treatment, but this is more for control of pasture contamination than treatment of helminthiasis in the donkey.

Better indication of clinical helminthiasis may be given by weight loss, lethargy and depression, diarrhoea and, in more severe cases, colic and fever. Other laboratory diagnostic indicators include anaemia, changes in PCV (packed cell volume) and serum albumins and globulins.

With the advent of improved anthelmintic treatment regimes the incidence of colic due to the migration of the fourth stage larvae of large strongyles from the intestinal wall into the walls of the mesenteric arteries producing thrombosis and later aneurysm has diminished. The damage other species of these larvae can cause to the liver and other organs within the peritoneal cavity has also decreased.

Cyathostomiasis

Conversely anthelmintic treatment has produced a more dangerous scenario with the small strongyles (cyathastomes).

The effect of increased strongyle egg output in late spring/early summer results in increasing parasite contamination of the pasture with infective third stage larvae (L3). Although some larvae can survive winter conditions L3 development does not occur at this time and a large portion of larvae ingested over this period remain within the mucosa of the large intestine in a hypobiotic stage. Since these larvae are resistant to most anthelmintic treatments at normal dose rates given prior to winter housing, they survive in the wall of the caecum or colon in large numbers.

Acute verminous enteritis (larval cyathostomiasis) may then occur in late winter/early spring as these larvae emerge in large numbers simultaneously. Initially symptoms of abdominal pain, anorexia and depression are presented and hyperlipaemia quickly follows. Severe inflammation with sub-mucosal oedema and haemorrhage in the caecum and colon may result in severe diarrhoea but, in the donkey, death due to 'toxic shock' may occur before diarrhoea develops.

On post-mortem the mucosa of the caecum and colon is congested with gross oedema of the sub-mucosa. Ruptured cysts are numerous.

Treatment

2 doses of ivermectin at 200µg/kg 7 days apart combined with normal supportive therapy has had limited success. Donkeys in the same group and therefore considered at risk were given a treatment with fenbendazole at 7.5mg/kg for five days.

Control

Effective control of endoparasites at the Sanctuary has recently been changed primarily to slow down the development of resistance to anthelmintic and hopefully to reduce the incidence of cyathastomiasis.

Donkeys are treated prior to spring turn out with ivermectin at 200µg/kg. The faecal egg counts (EPG) are then monitored by random sampling 15% of the herd, initially eight weeks post worming and then every two weeks until the egg reappearance period (ERP) has reached the level of 25% of the herd having a faecal egg count of more than 200epg.

This has resulted in many herds receiving doses of anthelmintic only at spring turn-out and prior to winter housing since the minimum ERP was 22 weeks and in other herds was never reached during their summer grazing period. Regardless of epg all donkeys are wormed prior to winter housing with ivermectin.

One of the side benefits of the increased monitoring has been financial, in that the increased cost of labour and materials for the laboratory has been offset by saving on the cost of anthelmintic. It is also perceived that a few eggs will pass onto the pasture between doses and therefore some infective larvae will be ingested to stimulate immune response in the donkey.

The concept of good management in terms of stable hygiene, rotational grazing, proper pasture management and harrowing pastures is most important. The use of a biological vacuum (sheep) is still pertinent to ingest larvae on the pasture and is used on the Sanctuary land both in winter and early spring. Removal of dung at least twice a week in the summer is carried out mechanically. It is worth emphasising the need to carry out regular faecal sampling during the summer grazing period. If donkeys are at pasture during the winter months faecal sampling may need to be extended.

(Consult your veterinary surgeon regarding periodicity of faecal sampling/worming with regard to your own specific circumstances.)

N.B. The use of sheep may increase the incidence of the stomach worm *Trichostrongylus axei* but the pathogenicity of this species in donkeys is rarely a problem.

Resistance to anthelmintic

Frequent use of anthelmintics and sub-optimal dosing have been implicated in the selection for resistant nematodes.

Using the faecal egg count reduction test the efficacy of ivermectins, benzimidazole and pyrantel derivatives was carried out. The trials at the Sanctuary suggest that as yet no resistance to the ivermectins has been encountered in donkeys. There was however some indication that resistance to the benzimidazole and pyrantel derivatives was developing.

The following notes on Ascarids, Pinworms and Threadworms are for general information and are not specific to the donkey.

Ascarids (*Parascaris equorum*)

A large roundworm reaching over 10 inches in length. It mainly affects foals, with adult equines acquiring an effective resistance. The larvae are encapsulated within eggs on the pasture and can survive for years. They hatch after ingestion and their migration route includes the liver and lung. The larvae are therefore the cause of liver damage and respiratory symptoms, whilst the adults can physically block the gut, and even cause rupture of the small intestine. Infestations are usually derived from grazing foals on the same pastures year after year. Early infestation can result in mature adult worms in the gut within the first 12 weeks of life. Infestations respond well to most wormers; the first dose should be given at 8 weeks of age, and repeated 6 weekly until one year old. Control is better effected by choosing clean pasture for each new crop of foals and worming the dam before parturition.

Not recorded in donkeys at the Sanctuary.

Pinworms *(Oxyuris equi)*

These usually affect younger animals more than mature equines. The main damage is confined to anal irritation and stress from this irritation. Tail rubbing is therefore a frequent diagnostic feature. The eggs may not be found in the faeces, but can be recovered from the perineum using sticky tape. Infestations respond well to most of the common anthelmintic compounds. Control includes periodic steam cleaning of stables.

Rarely seen in donkeys.

Threadworms (*Strongyloides* spp.)

These usually only affect foals under 6 months of age, and infestations tend to disappear spontaneously after this age. Dormant infestations in pregnant mares are transmitted to foals via the milk.

Patent infestations in foals are diagnosed in the faeces, but diagnosed in mares in the milk, since larvae are not found in adult faeces.

Tapeworm (*Anoplocephala* spp.)

An increasing number of cases in horses suggest that *Anoplocephala perfoliata* may have increased in prevalence with a consequential increase in intussusception induced by parasite mediated inflammation of the ileo-caecal junction.

There is also evidence from a survey in the Welsh borders which suggests an incidence of 27% by faecal examination and 40% by serology of tapeworm infection.

At the Sanctuary less than 1% of donkeys admitted to the Sanctuary have evidence of tapeworm infection from faecal examination for tapeworm eggs and post-mortem evidence suggests an even lower incidence. The low incidence at the Sanctuary may be due to the poor habitat for oribatid mites (the intermediate host for *Anoplocephala*) on the Sanctuary farms.

At the Sanctuary treatment for tapeworm is only carried out on positive identification of tapeworm eggs in the faeces, when pyrantel (Strongid P) is given at 38mg per kg bodyweight (twice the dose rate for strongyles).

Donkeys at the Sanctuary are checked for hepatic disease (blood parameters) prior to treatment as dose rates at this level may be contraindicated in donkeys with liver problems.

Hydatid cysts

This is the intermediate stage of the double life-cycle of the tapeworm (*Echinococcus* spp.) of domestic carnivores. Infestation of the donkey occurs when it is forced to graze pastures contaminated by faeces from dogs, cats, foxes, etc. The ingested tapeworm eggs form large cysts in the liver of the donkey. These cysts can reach 5-7 cm in diameter and together can occlude large areas of the liver, causing severe dysfunction. Since infestations are largely only diagnosed at post-mortem examination, the opportunities for treatment are rare.

It is however interesting to note that the incidence of hydatid cysts on post-mortem of donkeys is much higher in donkeys admitted to the Sanctuary from Ireland and Wales suggesting a more intimate contact of donkeys with dogs, cats, foxes and other carnivores in these areas.

The cysts are seen in the liver and lungs of the donkey and can, in large numbers or size, affect liver and lung function. Control at the Sanctuary includes the regular treatment of the resident dog and cat population with praziquantel at 0.1ml/kg (Droncit).

In general control should include the prevention or removal of dog faeces from donkey pastures and preventing dogs and cats from ingesting raw offal.

Bots

Equine Bots (*Gastrophilus* spp) are flies that in their adult stage resemble bees. The life cycle of the bot fly is usually completed in twelve months. The eggs are laid by the adult usually on the legs of the equine. With this parasite the donkey fortunately is the least favoured host. The eggs are removed by the host licking and 1st stage larvae burrow into the tongue, gums and cheeks causing transient irritation.

The larvae then migrate via the pharynx to the stomach where they grow for up to 10 months before being shed in the faeces.

Stomach bots can cause mechanical blockage, colic or rupture of the stomach wall depending on the degree of infestation.

Treatment

Again ivermectin is the drug of choice since a single dose will effectively break the life cycle if given in late autumn or early winter when bots larvae have accumulated.

Lungworm (*Dictyocaulus arnfieldi*)

Without doubt the donkey's 'claim to fame' in the parasitic world is as the reservoir host of *Dictyocaulus arnfieldi* and every text book on respiratory diseases will include contact with a donkey as a causal agent for a coughing horse. Certainly the donkey tolerates even a large infestation of lungworms without apparent symptoms and the relatively low prevalence of patent infection in the horse means that the donkey is the source of contamination of pasture grazed by equines.

This situation, however, can be easily controlled if the care and attention that is paid to horses at pasture is also given to donkeys.

Ivermectin at dose rate of 200µg/kg will effectively eliminate lungworm from the donkey and with good dung pasture management it is possible to eliminate lungworm from the pasture. The Sanctuary farms, with over 3,700 grazing donkeys, have been free of lungworm for thirteen years.

Donkeys entering the Sanctuary with lungworm are isolated for a minimum of six weeks and treated with two doses of ivermectin (Eqvalan) at normal dose rates three weeks apart.

Since it is reported that lungworm larvae may survive in the subsoil for up to two years, pasture contamination must be considered. Harrowing permanent pasture will reduce larvae and ploughing/crop rotation eliminate larvae. Grass in hedgerows may however become a source of reinfection.

Diagnosis

Examination of faecal samples by Baerman Technique (see Appendix 4)

Treatment

Ivermectin is the drug of choice. Benzimidazoles have become increasingly less effective.

Liver Fluke (*Fasciola* spp.)

Of 60 post-mortem examinations performed on Irish donkeys transferred to the Sanctuary *Fasciola hepatica* was identified in 10 (17%). More recently of 200 faecal egg samples 17 (8.5%) were positive for *Fasciola* eggs. Blood samples taken from these donkeys before death indicated liver enzyme levels within normal range and it was noted at the post-mortem examinations that there was very little reaction to the presence of the flukes in the bile ducts or liver tissue of the donkey.

As previously mentioned, good pasture management includes using sheep on donkey pastures to reduce pasture larvae burdens. Patent liver fluke infection does occur in the donkey and control of the parasite is therefore recommended in order to prevent infection in sheep grazing donkey pasture, since liver damage in sheep is severe.

Treatment

Although not licensed for use in equines triclabendazole (Fasinex) at a dose rate of 12mg/kg bodyweight is effective.

Diagnosis

Since clinical symptoms of the disease are rarely seen, diagnosis is based entirely on faecal examinations for fluke eggs by modified sedimentation technique (see Appendix 5).

References

Catcott, E.J. (ed), Smithcor, J.F. (ed), *Equine Medicine and Surgery: A Text and Reference Work*, American Veterinary Publications, Inc, Illinois (1972)

Fowler, J.N., ' Parasites in UK Donkeys', *The Professional Handbook of the Donkey* - Second Edition; E.D. Svendsen (ed), 84-93 (1989)

Klei, T.R., Plowright, W. (ed.), Rossdale, P.D. (ed.), Wade, J.F., 'Recent observations on the epidemiology, pathogenisis and immunology of equine helminth infections', *Equine Infectious Diseases VI*: Proceedings of the Sixth International Conference, 7-11 July 1991, 129-136 (1992)

Martin, P.J., 'Development and control of resistance to anthelmintics', *International Journal of Parasitology* 17, 493-501 (1987).

Proudman, C.J., Ellis, R.N.W., 'Tapeworm infection in donkeys', *Veterinary Record* 18, 136, (1995)

Soulsby, E.J.L., *Helminths, Arthropods and Protozoa of Domesticated Animals,* Bailliere Tindall, London (1986)

Taylor, T.S., Craig, T.M., 'Lungworms in donkeys: evaluation of anthelmintics under field conditions', *Journal of Equine Veterinary Science*. 13, 3, 150-152 (1993)

Trawford, A.F., Tremlett, J.G., 'Efficacy of triclabendazole against *Fasciola hepatica* in the donkey, *Equus asinus*', *Veterinary Record* 139, 142-143 (1996).

Uhlinger, C., ' Preliminary studies into factors affecting the variability of egg reappearance period and anthelmintic treatment intervals in the control of equine cyathostomes', *Equine Infectious Diseases VI*, *op cit* 157-161(1992)

Urquhart, G.M., Armour., J., Duncan, J.L., Dunn, A.M., Jennings, F.W., *Veterinary Parasitology*, Department of Veterinary Parasitology, The Faculty of Veterinary Medicine, The University of Glasgow, Scotland. Longman Scientific and Technical, London (1987)

Waller, P.J., 'Anthelmintic resistance and the future for round worm control', *Veterinary Parasitology* 25, 177-191(1987)

Zayed, A.A.M, Meguid, A.A., Madbouly, M.H., 'Movement of stomach bot (*Gasterophilus intestinalis* and *Gasterophius percorum* larvae) in the oral cavity of donkeys (*Equus asinus*)', *Veterinary Medical Journal Giza* 41, 3, 53-57 (1993)

ANDREW TRAWFORD B.V.Sc., M.Sc., M.R.C.V.S., C.V.M.A. was born in 1944. He is currently the Director of Veterinary Services for the Donkey Sanctuary and I.D.P.T. He was educated at King Edward VI Grammar, Stafford, West Bridgford High, Nottingham and gained his veterinary degree from Liverpool University in 1969. His employment began in general practice in Lancashire. Andrew then moved overseas to Jamaica for seven years initially working as the Hospital Manager/Veterinary Surgeon for The Jamaica Society for the Prevention of Cruelty to Animals and finally establishing a private practice working with polo ponies, race horses and companion animals. He then moved to Canada to work as Director of Veterinary Services for the Ontario Humane Society where he gained his C.V.M.A. qualification. In 1979 he returned to England for two years where his initial contact as a veterinary surgeon with the Donkey Sanctuary began. Whilst with the Donkey Sanctuary he helped design the present hospital and laboratory complex, supervised its construction and purchased equipment for use within the building. Andrew then returned to overseas work in 1981 starting in East Malaysia for two years followed by seven years in Yemen Arab Republic working for the Overseas Development Administration (ODA), during which time he returned to the UK for a year to continue his education and completed his M.Sc. in Tropical Veterinary Science in 1988. On return from Yemen Andrew started work in Botswana as the Veterinary Officer for the Department of Animal Health and Production Government of Botswana, this job entailed secondment to the Department of Wildlife and National Parks to assist with chemical capture of White Rhinoceros and the capture of Wildebeest, Impala and Kudu for translocation to a sanctuary. Throughout his career his interest in and work with donkeys has been paramount.

Andrew returned to the Donkey Sanctuary in September 1994 and continues to travel overseas with I.D.P.T., assessing and developing the veterinary care provided for donkeys.

5
THE DONKEY'S FOOT AND ITS CARE

J. D. Reilly

DONKEY LOCOMOTION MAKES A SIGNIFICANT CONTRIBUTION to the hard graft of agricultural production in many parts of the Third World, and to a good deal of fun and companionship in the developed world. Yet relatively little is known about the anatomy and normal function of donkey feet and their particular afflictions. These appear, in many respects, to be quite different from those of the horse.

Before we discuss these differences, let us consider the general features of the equine hoof which is required to withstand the effects of the physical and chemical environment to protect the underlying sensitive tissues of the foot from damage and to transmit the forces of locomotion painlessly to and from the axial skeleton (Reilly and Kempson 1992).

Anatomy

The hoof is a highly evolved locomotion organ of epidermal origin. It has a complex three dimensional structure and consists of a horny capsule which encases bones, joints, blood vessels, nerves, ligaments, tendons and bursae, and connective and adipose tissue. The hoof horn capsule and its contents are collectively known as the 'foot'.

The visual parts of the hoof capsule can be divided into wall, sole, frog and white line (see figure 1).

The wall makes up the largest part of the hoof capsule and it has a major function in weight bearing. It is divided regionally into toe, quarters and heels and at the bearing border it is reflected at the heels to form the 'bars'. The major part of the wall grows distally from the coronary band and it has a cellular architecture, in that it is composed of a series of tubular and intertubular horn which can be seen microscopically when

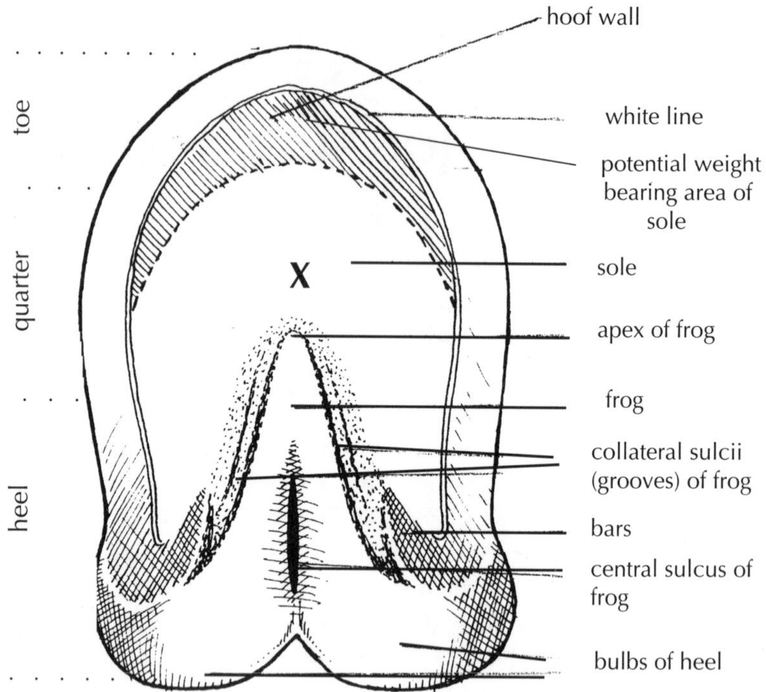

X centre of concave sole: site of thumb pressure test (see p. 84)

Fig 1. Structures visible on the weight bearing surface of the hoof capsule.

wall horn is cut in cross section (see figures 2 and 4). The tubules are produced from the cells overlying dermal papillae and the intertubular horn is produced from cells lying in the interpapillary regions. The full thickness of the hoof wall can be divided into three layers: stratum externum, stratum medium and stratum internum (see figure 2):

•The *stratum externum*, or periople, is composed of tubular and intertubular horn. It is believed to have a high lipid content and to act in water control and in protection. This part of the hoof turns milky white when wet.

•The *stratum medium*, comprises the larger part of the wall. It has well defined tubular and intertubular horn. In the pony it can be further sub

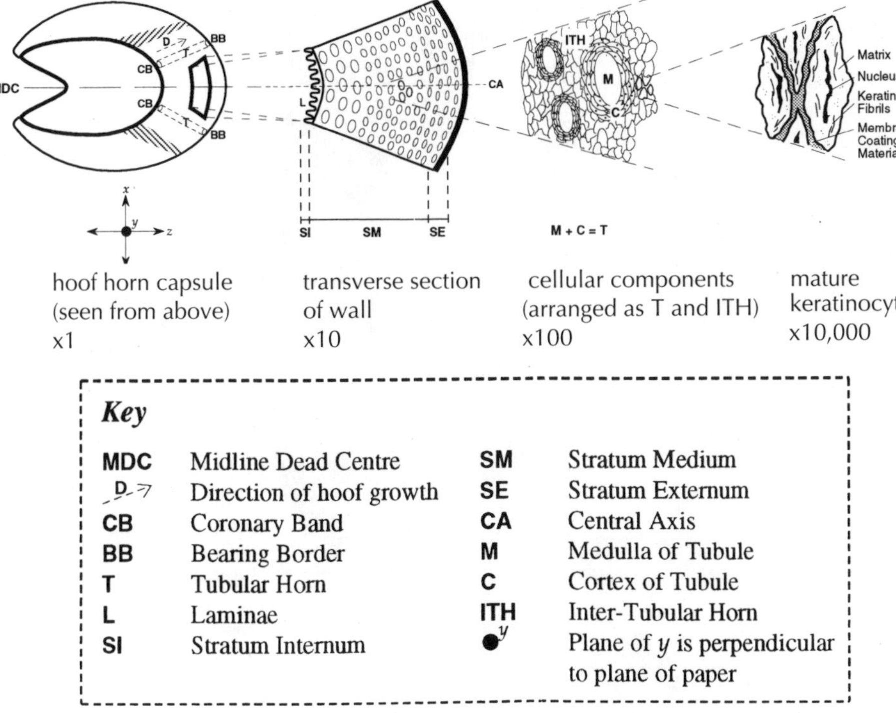

Fig. 2 Components of the hoof wall.

divided into distinct layers or zones, based on tubule density (Reilly *et al* 1996).

•The *stratum internum*, is composed of interlocking leaves of dermal and epidermal tissues known as the laminae (see figure 2). This forms a large surface area of contact to allow firm bonding between the hoof wall and, ultimately, the pedal bone via the dermal connective tissue.

These anatomical features of the wall allow it to effectively deal with multidirectional forces during weight bearing and locomotion.

The *sole* is also composed of tubular and intertubular horn and is produced from tissue overlying the base of the pedal bone. There is debate as to whether it should bear weight and, if so, how much. The sole is said to be concave under natural conditions and therefore does not bear weight.

The *frog* is a readily recognised 'V' shaped structure with its narrowest part pointing forward. In the middle of the frog is a groove referred to as

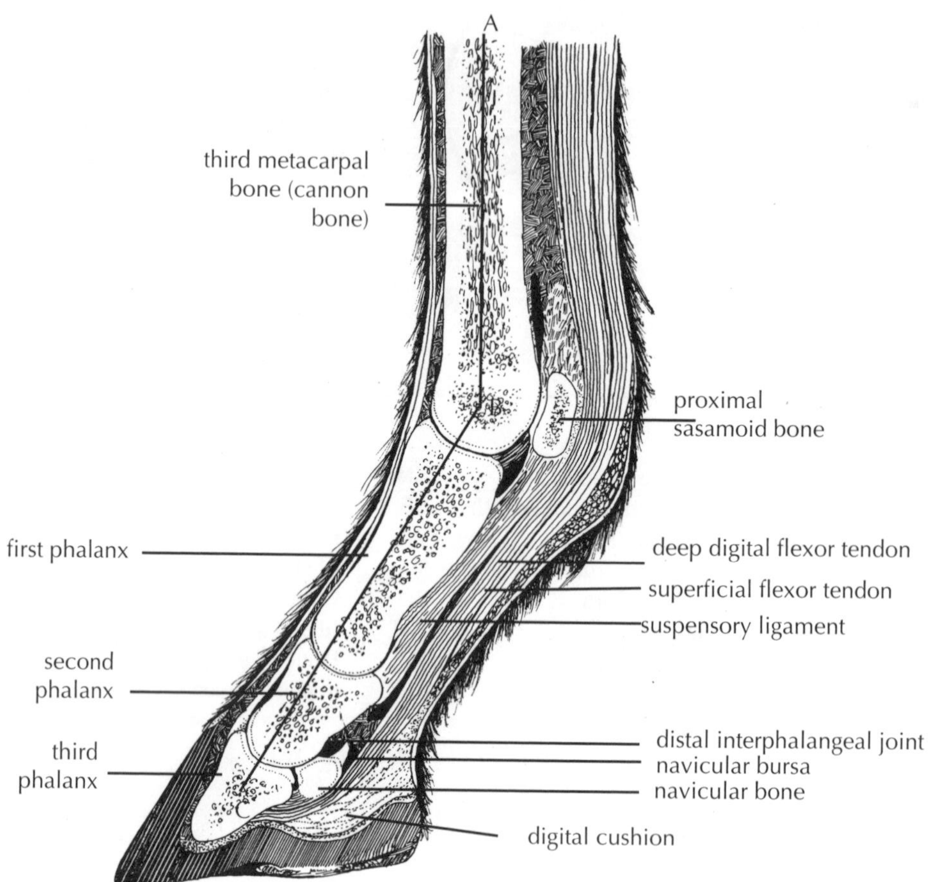

Fig. 3 Anatomy of lower limbs (internal view) with reference points (A B C) for hoof pastern axis (HPA). (Adapted from Adams)

the central sulcus. On either side of the frog, and between it and the respective bar for that side, is another groove called the collateral sulcus. The frog is made of a rubbery form of horn which is thought to function as an anti-concussive device, a non-slip device and possibly as an aid to blood circulation within the foot and limb. It may also help facilitate expansion of the heel under load. However, the frog is not the only 'expansion device' within the hoof capsule:

The *white line* forms the junction between the wall and sole and consists of an interdigitating component from each. It is thought to allow independent movement between the sole and the wall. If this were not so, the hoof capsule might suffer far more catastrophic consequences than are seen under load.

However, as with all complex designs, there are areas of compromise. The weaknesses in the design of the hoof capsule are that:

(i) the white line, while allowing stretch under certain circumstances, can also weaken and become a portal of entry;
(ii) the sole and frog are susceptible to penetration. Unfortunately they overlie very important structures that are only a 'nail's depth' away (see figure 3). Practical problems associated with these anatomical features of the hoof are discussed later.

There is little comparative work on donkey versus horse feet. What can be said is that donkeys' feet are, generally, smaller and more upright than those of the horse (Hifney and Misk 1983, Getty 1975) and their natural ground surface shapes are quite different. The donkey hoof is more oblong and the thickness of the wall at the bearing border does not taper radially as it does in the horse, but maintains a relatively constant thickness around the rim (see figure 1). This, together with the difference in shape, may indicate that either different amounts of movement of the two different hoof capsules take place during loading, or that different modes of movement are employed, or that the inherent properties of the hoof or foot tissues of the donkey are different to those of the horse. These questions are largely unanswered.

The donkey is also said to produce a greater thickness of sole than the horse (Hifney and Misk 1983; Somers and Svendsen 1986; Williams 1989). Donkey hoof horn appears to have different tubular characteristics to that of the horse. It is also reported to have fewer laminar leaves in the dermis (Hifney and Misk 1983).

Figure 4 shows stained cross sections of similar parts of the hoof wall clipping taken from a horse and a donkey and illustrates differences in staining pattern, distribution and size of the hoof wall tubules.

Further differences between the feature of the donkey hoof, compared to those of the horse are likely to emerge in the future and work currently being sponsored by the Donkey Sanctuary will help define them. Once we

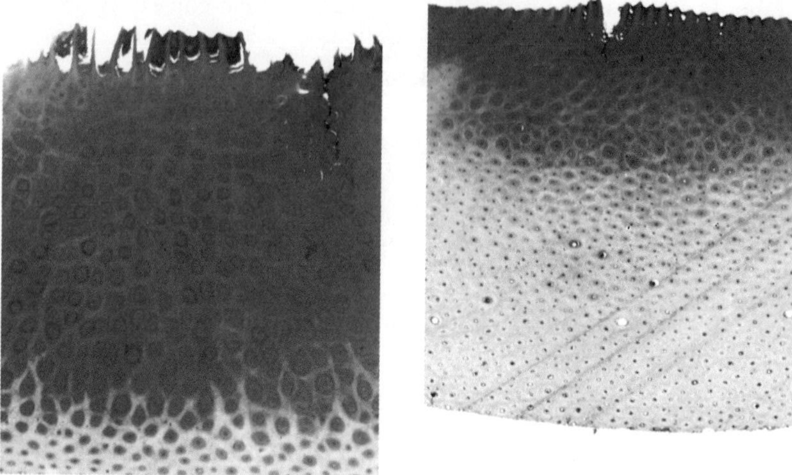

*Fig. 4 Comparison of donkey (*left*) and horse (*right*) hoof wall clipping: cross section as seen with the light microscope (Toluidene blue staining).*

know more about donkey horn *per se* and the differences between it and horse hoof are known, a plan to manage donkey horn effectively and for the greater good of the animal can be devised.

General care of the donkey's foot

The feral donkey, in its natural environment, has evolved to survive walking great distances over abrasive surfaces to obtain mouthfuls of low quality forage. Under these conditions, hoof growth and wear are generally compensatory. The domesticated donkey, in temperate climates, has no need to walk great distances and has an improved nutritional status. This means that growth and wear are not compensatory and thus the hoof capsule will become overgrown and unbalanced. This can lead to undue stress and strain on the hoof capsule, the joints and the tendons. Hoof overgrowth also compromises the blood supply to the donkey's foot (Bordalai and Nigam 1977).

There is therefore a requirement placed upon all donkey owners to ensure that their animals get corrective hoof care. It is essential that this is done by a qualified farrier who is registered with the Farriers Registration

Fig. 5 Trimming triad: happy donkey, happy farrier and happy owner (note: well lit, covered and concreted workplace).

Council. The feet need reassessing by a farrier regularly and frequently. A period of 6-10 weeks between inspections is recommended and, if this is not done, the consequences can be serious. (See section on overgrowth.) Mark on your calendar the projected dates for reassessment.

Handle your donkey

Any owner has a responsibility to provide reasonable care for an animal. In order to administer foot care, as with medicines and wormers, the animal needs to be handled appropriately. In view of the need to be seen frequently by the farrier throughout the year, the donkey must be trained to accept what is expected of it each time the farrier visits. This will mean that the owner needs to spend time, energy and patience on basic handling and reward. Don't make the time the farrier or the vet arrives the only time the donkey is caught and tethered. Do this frequently, but at irregular intervals, and use reward and praise. This will pay dividends in efficient use of time in the future, and dramatically increase the welfare of your donkey (see figure 5).

The farrier's needs

(i) See that the animal has been moved close by and ready to be tethered with a safe and fitted headcollar or halter.
(ii) Ensure legs and feet are dry and mud free.
(iii) Provide a clean, well lit, preferably concreted area, which is protected from the elements.
(iv) Stay with your animal and show an interest in what your farrier is doing. He will then work with enthusiasm.
(v) Seek and follow any advice your farrier can give you, particularly the date when the feet should be seen next.
(vi) Provide a cup of tea and prompt payment!

(Revised after Williams, 1989)

Following this advice will ensure that your donkey has received the best possible attention from your farrier and he will be happy to visit you again. This will foster a rewarding relationship between donkey, farrier and owner, resulting in optimal foot care and donkey welfare that will be a source of pride.

Trimming the donkey's foot

The aim of trimming the donkey's foot is to enable the animal to move with a sound and free action and to restore aesthetic shape to the foot and lower limb so that there is no undue stress or strain on the hoof capsule, joints, ligaments and tendons of the lower leg.

The theoretical mainstay of achieving this has been the adoption of the principles of maintaining the ideal 'hoof pastern axis' (HPA) and mediolateral hoof balance (MLHB):

1 Trimming and hoof pastern axis

The HPA is given by the line BC in figure 3. The reference points are:

(i) The proximal centre of the 3rd metacarpal (cannon) bone;
(ii) The distal centre of the 3rd metacarpal (cannon) bone;
(iii) The centre of the distal phalanx.

According to this principle, the cannon bone should be perpendicular to the ground and the line BC should bisect the three lower joints so that

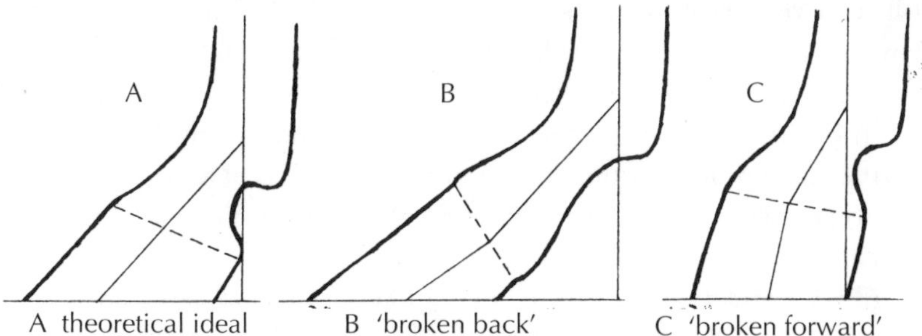

Fig. 6 Variations in hoof pastern axis.

the proximal, middle and distal phalanges represent a bony column in a straight line with no deviations. This line should make an angle with the ground of approximately 55-60° and should be parallel to the dorsal wall of the hoof. This cannot be too prescriptive, however, as the age of the donkey and its previous history will dictate what can be achieved.

Using these guidelines the three possible alignments of the HPA are given below and relate to figure 6.

(i) **The theoretical ideal** is aesthetically pleasing and is thought to create the optimum stress and strain situation viz the hoof capsule, joints, ligaments and tendons of the lower leg.
(ii) **A broken back HPA** occurs when the heels are too low and/ or the toe has been allowed to grow excessively long. Undue strain is then put on the palmar aspects of the foot which, in turn, may encourage abnormal wear of the hoof capsule. A misdirection of stresses through it and the bony column may then encourage formation of the 'Aladdin's slipper foot'.
(iii) **Broken forward HPA** occurs when the heels are too high and the toe too short. Excess stress is put on the lower limb joints, and concussion to the joints is believed to be increased.

There is also considerable debate as to whether donkeys naturally have a broken forward hoof pastern axis or not. This may be because the theory behind the adoption of the HPA system was developed for the horse and the donkey's foot does not necessarily comply. Supporters of the system will argue that the donkey should have the 'ideal' HPA and the notion that donkeys naturally have a broken forward HPA is a misconception. The arguments for the case are that:

(i) For the horse, the angle of the scapula and the ideal HPA are the same. For the donkey, although the HPA is steeper than the horse, when compared to the angle of the scapula they are, again, parallel.

(ii) A distracting feature of the donkey foot, that can lead to a misconception of a broken forward HPA, is the prominent band of soft tissue and hair that often bulges above the coronary band. If this is taken into account during visual assessment, then it has the effect of lowering the external angle of BC and should be ignored.

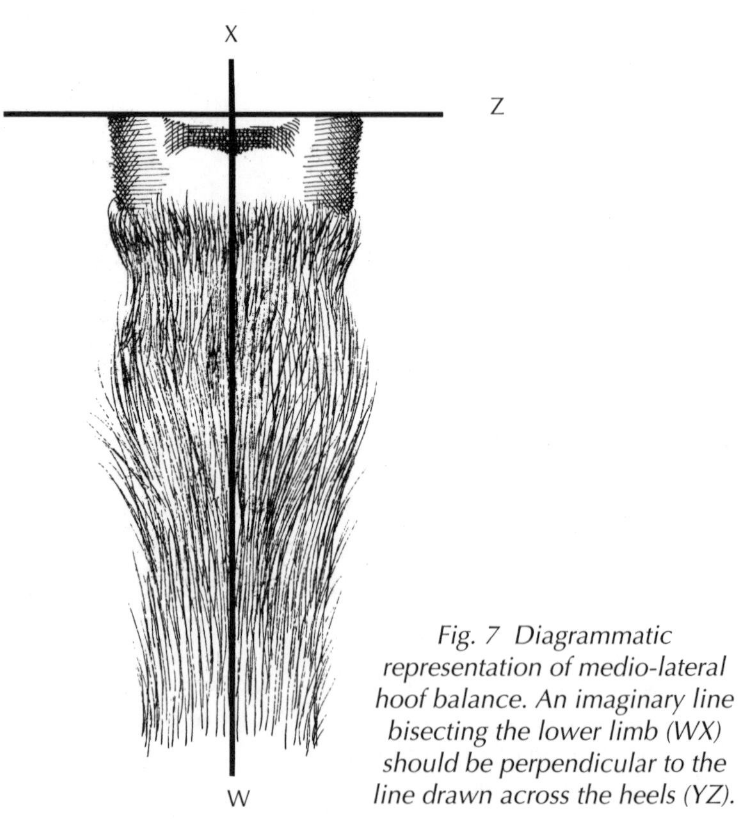

Fig. 7 Diagrammatic representation of medio-lateral hoof balance. An imaginary line bisecting the lower limb (WX) should be perpendicular to the line drawn across the heels (YZ).

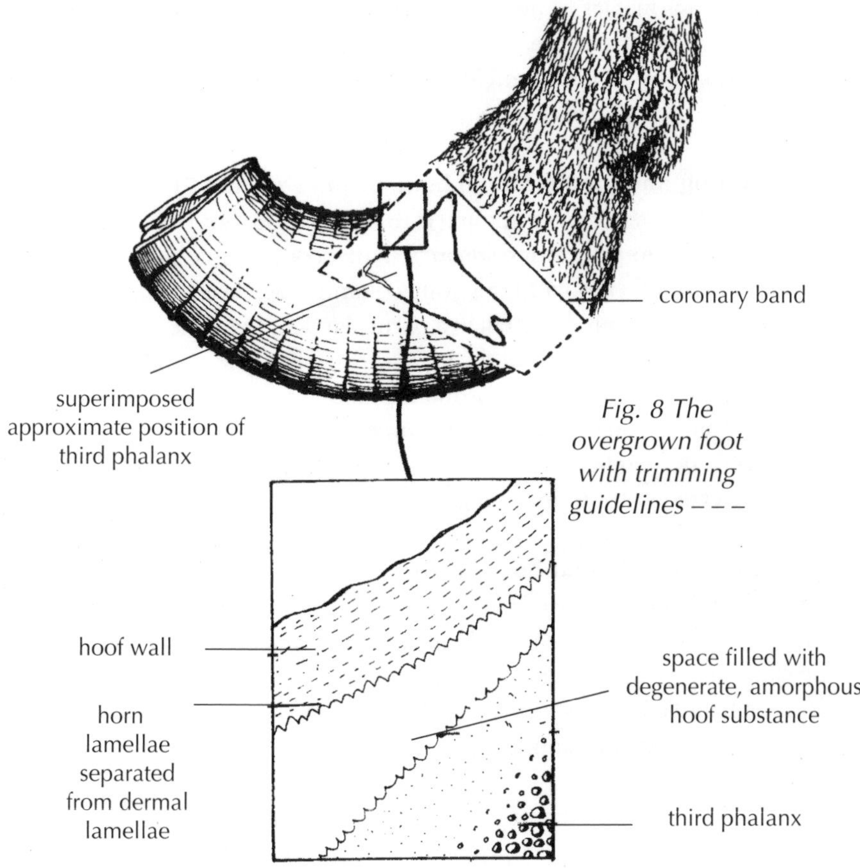

Fig. 8 The overgrown foot with trimming guidelines – – –

Fig. 9 Enlargement of anterior hoof wall (adapted after Fowler, 1995).

Research work being carried out at the Donkey Sanctuary and through the International Donkey Protection Trust should help resolve the natural HPA dilemma.

For horse and pony feet the assessment of HPA is often done visually, based on imaginary lines representing ABC in figure 3 superimposed on the external features of the lower limb. Because of the variety of configurations of donkey lower limbs, and the particular features they show, this can sometimes be quite difficult to carry out correctly. The only real way to tell the HPA in the donkey is to assess X-rays.

There are, in fact, a number of different presentations. Remember that the ideal hoof pastern axis represents the theoretical ideal and is the basis, if it can be achieved safely, for the donkey. Often the situation can be less than ideal and each case must be taken on its merits.

2 Trimming and medio-lateral hoof balance (figure 7)

The aim of this aspect of trimming is that, in the ideal and non-disfigured limb, the hoof hits the ground squarely so that comfortable weight transfer through the hoof capsule to the bony column is achieved.

As humans favour a footfall in a particular way, the same is true of the donkey. The result will be that the hoof capsule has grown and worn away according to natural weight distribution and the favour of the footfall. Thus, in time it is unlikely that the bearing border of the hoof capsule will be perfectly perpendicular to the long axis of the cannon bone. This needs to be corrected at trimming and is done thus:

Assessing mediolateral hoof balance

In order to do this one needs to flex the carpus of the forelimb or extend the hock and stand close in to the animal so that parallax is avoided. Support the cannon of the leg in a horizontal position so that the foot hangs freely and is not pulled towards or pulled away from you. In order to do this correctly, support the cannon with one or two fingers on the dorsal side midway along the bone.

To assess the balance of the hoof, get in close to the body of the animal and look along the long axis of the 3rd metacarpal bone and envisage an imaginary line along this axis (WX in figure 7). Next imagine a line at right angles to the long axis of the cannon, and drawn between the two heels of the hoof capsule (YZ in figure 7). Are the heels even or is one side higher? Be warned, this takes experience and practice to judge correctly. The often unequal 'flare' on the medial and lateral sides of the capsule can lead to false impressions of the height of the heels. This assessment is a job requiring the trained eye and skills of a registered farrier as are the subsequent decisions about how much to trim and from where.

3 Trimming the donkey's foot

It is important to have made a full assessment 'by eye' of the donkey's feet before any attempt is made to wield a hoof knife. Having now appreciated

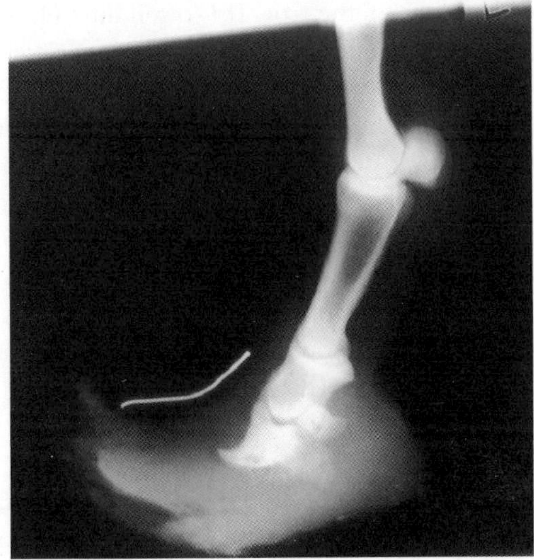

Fig. 10 Lateral radiograph of the distal limb of a donkey with marked hoof overgrowth and chronic laminitic changes.

the need to assess hoof pastern axis and the importance of mediolateral balance, the approach to physically paring the horn from the foot can be considered.

In general terms, if the foot appears very upright with strong heels and perhaps a broken forward HPA, then there is likely to be scope for removing more horn from the heel area. Should the toe be long and the heels low, perhaps with a broken back HPA, then it will be important to retain as much heel tissue as possible and concentrate on shortening the toe. If major changes in shape of the foot are required then, for the donkey's comfort, it is worth considering effecting the changes in a series of gradual stages rather than all at once.

(i) Trimming the sole

The donkey is said to grow far more sole than the horse or pony. Somers and Svendsen (1986) stated that the donkey grows nearly as much sole as new hoof wall in any one period. In order that the distal rim of the hoof wall actually bears the weight of the animal, then the solear material must be trimmed away first. This is best taken back in incremental amounts so that the solear surface is concave and all loose or necrotic tissue is removed, especially near the point of the frog. It is often difficult to judge how far back to pare and care must be taken not to be over zealous and penetrate the sole. Most farriers will pare back until the sole yields very slightly to 'thumb pressure' applied between the dorsal wall and point of frog (see figure 1). It is a source of debate as to whether the sole should be weight bearing. The sole should bear minimal weight. It is often unavoidable that the apex of the sole bears weight, either because it appears to have 'dropped' and is no longer concave in shape, or cannot be trimmed back any further under the 'thumb pressure' principle. Provided sufficient wall has been left for weight bearing, this should be acceptable. Soles that bear weight, especially if thinned, can lead to bruising and possible concussive laminitis.

(ii) Trimming the wall

The wall is trimmed paying attention to medio-lateral balance and how much heel needs to be retained to maintain, as closely as possible, an ideal HPA.

(iii) Trimming the frog

The function of the frog as an anti-concussive device is still a source of debate. For this reason, there is sometimes uncertainty as to whether it should be proud or trimmed right back. There may be an association between large bulbous frogs and donkeys with broken back HPAs. This may be because the frog has become hypertrophied as a result of undue stress and strain on the palmar aspects of the foot. These frogs seem to revert to a smaller size and shape once corrective farriery has been carried out.

There is also debate as to whether the frog has a function in assisting the circulatory system return in the blood from the foot. The donkey foot can appear to yield more readily at the heels than some horses and this too may 'massage' the distal circulation. The fact is that studies of relative movement or stiffness have not been carried out for donkey feet. Thus, the agreed compromise is to trim the frog to such an extent that it bears weight only when the foot is under load.

There is no doubt, however, that the sulcus and grooves of the frog are potential sites for harbouring dirt, stones and infections. The rubbery horn of the frog will often grow over these cavities and create a trap. These should be completely opened out during trimming so that they cannot clog.

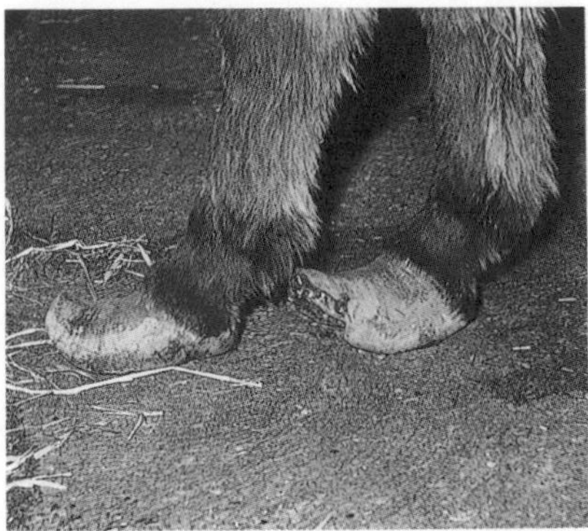

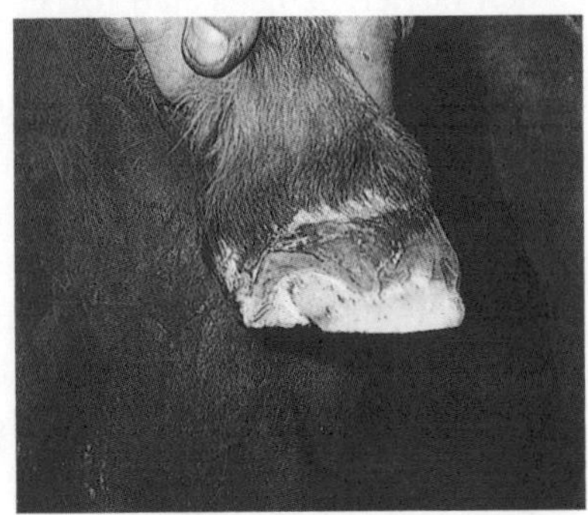

Fig. 11 Overgrown feet - pre and post trimming. The hoof wall has been cut away to remove degenerate horn filling the interlamellar space.

(iv) Trimming the bars

The function of the bars of the foot is another contentious issue. In practical terms, if the donkey is doing road work they should be retained and should be at the same height as the heel hoof tissue. However, if the donkey is on soft ground or deep litter then there is an advantage to trimming the bars back to sole level so that they do not become, like the frog, a potential harbour for muck, stones and infection.

(v) 'Dressing' the hoof wall

Once the foot is trimmed and cleaned, it is common practice for the farrier to take the foot forward at the carpus or hock and rasp the distal bearing surface. This can have advantages in that it will decrease flare and tidy up the cracked distal edges of the hoof capsule and even-up the wall width radially. It is fine for this to be achieved by rasping a bevel on the lower edge of the wall. However, the practice of excessive 'dumping' or rasping the distal two thirds of the wall in order to cosmetically improve the appearance of the HPA is to be avoided. This is because excessive rasping is likely to remove the outer layers of the hoof wall, both perioplic and parts of the stratum medium. This could increase the propensity for uncontrolled moisture changes across the wall which may lead to cracking.

(vi) Trimming grossly overgrown feet (figures 8 and 9)

When farriery is neglected for an extended period the hoof will become overlong, distorted and frequently twisted. Abnormal forces are imposed on the limb with over extension of the lower limb joints.

In order to trim such a foot it is essential to appreciate that the overgrowth is composed entirely of insensitive hoof capsule encircling often degenerate overgrown sole and frog. The structural relationship between the coronary band and the third phalanx does not change. In a donkey that has not 'foundered' the extensor process of the third phalanx will approximate to the level of the anterior coronary band. However, it may be up to 1.5 cm distal to this point in severely foundered individuals. If in doubt a lateral radiograph with radio-opaque markers will define the relationship between the distal skeleton and the hoof capsule. Such cases often show signs of marked remodelling of the third phalanx on radiography (figure 10).

The overgrown hoof is removed in increments guided by the degree of 'give' in the sole to thumb pressure and an understanding of the above anatomical relationships.

Where abnormal mechanical forces have caused separation of laminal bonding and extensive 'stretching' of the white line it is often necessary to dress back overlying hoof wall. In such cases it is inevitable that the sole will bear some weight temporarily (figure 11). A clean deep bedded stable will reduce subsequent trauma and contamination of exposed laminar tissue.

Many individuals respond with surprisingly few problems to the new improved angulation of the lower limb. Post farriery analgesia may be advisable in some instances along with a follow up trimming at monthly intervals to promote the correct formation of the new hoof capsule.

Conditions of the donkey hoof capsule

Little is known about the aetiology and pathogenesis of hoof related defects in equines. There is a confused and imprecise terminology used to describe them (Reilly, 1995). The donkey suffers some syndromes that appear similar to the horse and others that appear peculiar to it. It must be remembered that the stoical nature of the donkey and its habit of laying down can mean that painful foot conditions remain unrecognised. Consequently lameness work-ups can be delayed. Owners must therefore remain vigilant and minimise the chances of lameness with attentive hoof care.

White line separation

In the absence of other conditions such as laminitis, the usual reason for this is mechanical. If the hooves are neglected and allowed to grow excessively long then the excess leverage at the toe can mean that the white line separates and part of the wall breaks away. This leaves a cavity in the white line allowing the entry of dirt, gravel and potential infective agents. This can lead to the cavity progressing further up the foot. White line separations are also seen at the quarters and heels. It is thought that undue shearing forces may be instrumental in causing separations at these points.

Treatment for this condition relies on resection of affected areas while restoring normal foot shape and balance.

Thrush

Thrush is an infection of the horn which results in separation of the frog and horny sole from the underlying tissue. There is a foul smelling discharge in the frog grooves and along any tracts that are undermining hoof tissue. Many types of bacteria and fungi have been isolated from these infections. Thrush is a result of poor management, lack of foot care and wet conditions underfoot. It can be very severe and extremely painful if live tissue is penetrated. Long standing cases can lead to time consuming and expensive treatment by veterinarian and farrier. All necrotic tissue has to be removed and the remainder kept clean and dry.

Abscessation

Foot abscesses are a common cause of acute and severe lameness in the donkey. Any penetration of the sole by a foreign object, or penetration of the white line, may result in a deep seated abscess. A separated white line is more prone to penetration and must therefore be avoided. Infections of the white line may tract up the wall of the foot and burst out at the coronary band.

Pedal sepsis is the most common cause of lameness in donkeys (Trawford and Crane 1995) and can lead to osteomyelitis of the distal pedal bone.

It is possible for penetrations of the sole (e.g. by wire, nails, etc.) to give rise to infections of the navicular bursa, navicular bone, deep digital flexor tendon or coffin joint, with serious consequences (see figure 3).

Veterinary advice should therefore be sought if a foot abscess is suspected and, indeed, for any lame donkey. The pus tract will require radical paring and all infected material must be drained. Tetanus antitoxin and antibiotic therapy along with foot cleaning and dressing will be necessary. Consideration should also be given to appropriate analgesia and general nursing care.

Seedy toe/white line disease/hollow hoof/onchomycosis

There is considerable debate as to the cause of this condition. Yeast, fungi and bacteria have been isolated from the lesion which can occur at the toe and around the white line to the quarters. There is debate as to whether the white line is involved primarily or secondarily and whether the condition involves the stratum medium of the hoof wall primarily or secondarily. There is debate as to whether it is an aerobic or anaerobic infection. The characteristic lesion shows areas of grey, crumbly horn which, in long standing cases, are associated with large, hollow, often triangular cavities within the hoof wall with the apex of the cavity towards the coronary band. The hoof wall may also bulge in the area affected.

Various fungicidal and bactericidal treatments have been advocated for this condition but the common feature of treatment is that the affected horn must be completely resected. Because of the degeneration of the wall, this is a painless operation. All powdery grey material must be removed on resection, otherwise recurrent pockets of persistence are found on subsequent trimmings. Sometimes the work required to do this is minimal, at other times an almost complete hoof wall resection may be necessary. The use of fillers is not recommended in case any residual infection is trapped in place. Aftercare is usually not too taxing providing there are no complications. The patient should be kept in a clean dry environment and resected lesions cleaned out regularly. In these cases only the sole is allowed to bear weight and it often responds by becoming thickened while the new hoof wall grows down. The only animals that cannot be treated in this way are laminitics that may have insufficient sole to carry weight.

Laminitis

Laminitis is a complex systemic disturbance that manifests itself, at the level of the foot, by 'bounding' digital pulses, changes in blood flow and degeneration of laminar tissue that may result in 'rotation' and/or 'sinking' of the pedal bone within the hoof capsule. Any combination of the feet

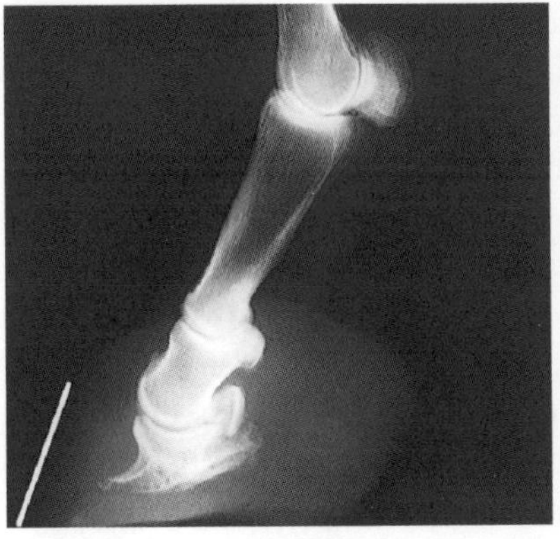

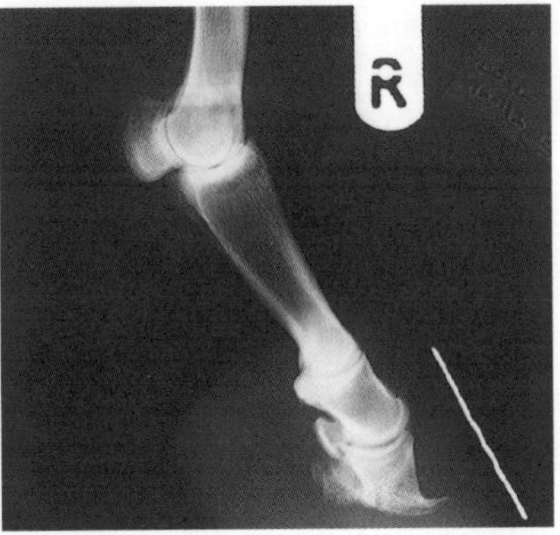

Fig. 12 Lateral radiographs of the distal limb of two donkeys with chronic laminitis showing extensive remodelling of the pedal bone and varying degrees of 'founder'.

may be affected at one time. It is usually preventable subsequently by changing management regimes and improving foot trimming and awareness of the owner.

The most common causes of laminitis in the UK are overlong feet, trauma on hard ground, incorrect diet, concurrent diseases, stress and pituitary tumours.

Laminitis is a serious condition needing immediate veterinary attention. The donkey should not be forced to walk but should be put in a stable with a thick shaving or paper bed. This may mean travelling the donkey by trailer from the paddock to the stable.

If the predisposing cause of the laminitis is known, this should be removed (e.g. move the animal from succulent pasture) or treated (e.g. respiratory infection, metritis or hyperlipaemia).

Foot bandages, well padded with thick cotton wool pads over the whole of the solar surface, applied to a clean, dry foot, often give some pain relief while waiting for the veterinarian to arrive. Animals which are 'rooted to the spot' and unable to walk should have only roughage and water brought to them.

Owners should know how to feel for digital pulses and palpate the coronary bands for ditches and depressions, in order to recognise the first signs of laminitis. Chronic laminitic feet may show diverging laminitic rings in the hoof wall, but these are not as obvious in the donkey as in the chronic laminitis horse or pony and many donkeys only show radiographic evidence of previous laminitic attacks (figure 12).

The attending veterinarian will give the donkey painkillers and possibly a drug to reduce blood pressure and anxiety. Heart bar shoes and frog supports are not applicable to donkeys because of the different relative anatomy of frog and pedal bone. Radiographically the point of frog is often about 2cm behind the fulcrum of the pedal bone so frog support or heart bars would exaggerate rotation. Sole support is therefore best. The feet are normally X-rayed with markers on the hoof wall to assess changes in the position of the pedal bone and any loss of bone density (see figure 12). It is imperative that further attacks are prevented so that the pedal bone is not permanently and irretrievably damaged.

Advice on body condition, feeding and restricted grazing may help reduce the risk of further attacks.

After a laminitic attack, the horn growth is usually rapid. Therefore, the feet should be trimmed every 3-4 weeks. The principles of trimming are the same as previously set out. However, trimming the soles of laminitics

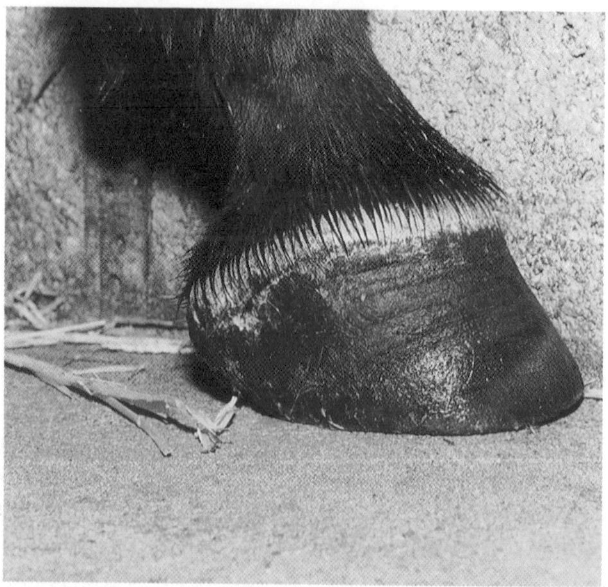

Fig. 13 A well dressed chronic laminitic foot showing diverging laminitic rings.

can prove problematic due to the increased prolapse, pressure and lack of concavity on the laminitic sole. Achieving concavity of the sole is not, therefore, always possible and 'thumb pressure' must also be used with care. Long-standing cases can have associated deep-seated solar abscesses with loss of pedal bone and chronic uncontrollable pain. This inevitably leads to humane destruction of the animal.

Concave dorsum syndrome

This is a condition seen relatively frequently at the Donkey Sanctuary. It can affect any combination of one or all four feet and shows a characteristic depression on the dorsum of the hoof capsule with a feathering of the horn distally. There may also be an apparent thickening of what appears to be perioplic horn.

The cause of the condition is unknown and lameness does not normally ensue. It may be a keratinising defect that is associated with destruction of keratogenous apparatus at the coronary band, possibly as a result of a history of chronically overlong feet and therefore excess pressure at this point.

References

Bordalai, C.C., and Nigam, J.M., 'Angiographic studies of the donkey foot (normal and abnormal)', *J Am Rad.*, XVIII, (3), 90-92 (1977)

Fowler, J., 'Trimming donkeys' feet', *Equine Veterinary Education* 7,(1) 18-21 (1995)

Getty, R., (1975) *Sisson and Grossman's The Anatomy of the Domestic Animals*, 5th Edition, W.B. Saunders Co., London (1995)

Hifney, A. and Misk, N.A., 'Anatomy of the hoof in donkeys', *Assiut Veterinary Medical Journal*, 10 (20) 3-6 (1983)

Reilly, J.D. and Kempson, S.A., 'Toward an understanding of hoof horn quality', in K Mortensen (Ed), Proceeding of the 7th International Symposium on Diseases of the Ruminant Digit, Denmark (1992)

Reilly, J.D., 'No hoof no horse?', *Equine Veterinary Journal* 27 (3), 166-168 (1995)

Reilly, J.D., Cottrell, D.F., Martin, R.J., and Cuddeford, D., 'Tubule density in equine hoof horn', *Biomimetics*, 4 (1), 23-36 (1996)

Trawford, A.F. and Crane, M.A. (1995) 'Nursing care of the donkey', *Equine Veterinary Education,* 7 (1), 36-38 (1996)

William, T.G., 'The donkey's foot and its care' Chapter 12, *The Professional Handbook of the Donkeys (2nd ed)* E. Svendsen (Ed), The Donkey Sanctuary, Sidmouth (1989)

JOHN D. REILLY, R.A.V.C. was educated at Seale Hayne Agricultural College, Devon, and Bristol and Edinburgh universities. John has worked in mixed veterinary practice in the West Country, in research as a Horse Race Betting Levy Board Scholar, and is now an Officer in the Royal Army Veterinary Corps.

He has a cross species research and clinical consultancy interest in hoof horn problems, and is supervising Donkey Sanctuary sponsored work investigating donkey hoof at De Montfort University, Leicester, where he is Visiting Research Fellow. He is married with three children.

6

NUTRITION

Fiona Taylor

LIKE THE HORSE'S, the digestive system of the donkey has evolved in adaptation to a grazing and browsing lifestyle. Nevertheless, there are subtle differences in the metabolism and physiology of the donkey which are reflected in the donkey's nutritional requirements. Having their origins in regions where vegetation is dry and sparse, donkeys are adapted to a high fibre diet and walking for long distances in search of food. Feral donkeys spend over half their day feeding and if domestic donkeys are given free access to good pasture, concentrate feeds or titbits, they will quickly become overweight. Even under these conditions, donkeys will actively seek out fibrous vegetation to supplement their diet.

DIGESTIVE PHYSIOLOGY

Donkeys, in common with all equines, are non-ruminant (single-stomached) herbivores which are capable of digesting large amounts of fibre in their diet, largely through a process of microbial fermentation within the digestive tract. They are often referred to as 'hind gut fermenters', since microbial digestion takes place in the enlarged caecum and large intestine after the food has first been subjected to the digestive processes of the stomach and small intestine. Roughage (which constitutes the major part of the donkey's diet) cannot be digested until it reaches the caecum and large intestine, whereas digestion of concentrate feeds takes place mainly in the small intestine.

Mouth

The process of digestion begins in the mouth. With its powerful, mobile and highly sensitive lips, the donkey can select and grasp suitable forage and guide it between the incisor teeth for cropping. In order to function effectively, the upper and lower incisor teeth should meet evenly; an overshot or undershot jaw will seriously impair the animal's ability to graze. At the back of the mouth, the cheek teeth are strong and hard with sharp, enamel ridges on the biting surfaces to give them an efficient shearing and grinding action. Uneven wear of the cheek teeth may result in the formation of hooks and sharp edges which abrade the gums, causing mouth pain, chewing difficulties, quidding and other problems. In extreme cases, the edges of the upper or lower teeth can overlap their opposite number to such an extent that lateral movement of the jaws is restricted. To prevent this, teeth should be checked regularly from five years of age and rasped if necessary.

Food is mechanically broken down in the mouth by chewing which, in donkeys, is particularly important for the subsequent digestion of fibre. Chewing also mixes the food with saliva, which serves to lubricate the food and assist its passage down the oesophagus to the stomach. Insufficiently macerated or lubricated food may lodge in the oesophagus causing choke. At the entrance to the stomach, movement of food is controlled by a muscular sphincter, which acts as a one-way valve. As with other equines, this sphincter is extremely strong in donkeys and will only rarely relax to allow the regurgitation of food or gas from the stomach.

Stomach

The stomach is a muscular sac which can expand to accommodate a variable amount of ingested material. In the adult donkey, the capacity of the stomach is relatively small (about 8-9 litres) and although it is seldom completely empty, most ingested food passes through within 1-2 hours. The digestive system of the donkey is adapted to the frequent intake of small volumes of food and, due to the small stomach size, it is recommended that donkeys are fed at least two or three times a day. Muscular contractions of the stomach wall result in churning of the food, which helps in the further break down of fibre, and mixing with the gastric juices. Protein digestion begins in the stomach but is limited due to the high rate of passage of food through the stomach.

The acid-buffering action of saliva allows some microbial fermentation to take place in the stomach. Excessive gas production may follow the consumption of rapidly-fermenting foods (such as grass cuttings or overfeeding with concentrates). Since the donkey cannot remove the gas by belching, this results in gaseous distension of the stomach and, potentially fatal, colic.

Small intestine

Semi-digested food from the stomach is released into the duodenum (the proximal portion of the small intestine) in spurts, under the control of the pyloric sphincter. The duodenum is the main site for digestion in the small intestine. Here, there are three fluid secretions which act on food as it emerges from the stomach:

- Pancreatic juice, from the pancreas, contains enzymes which act on proteins, carbohydrates and fat. Another function of the pancreas is to produce the hormone, insulin, which controls blood glucose levels.
- Bile is produced in the liver and transported to the duodenum via the bile duct. Like horses, donkeys have no gall bladder to store bile, but the bile duct is relatively distensible. Bile contains bile salts, which promote the emulsification of dietary fats to increase the surface area upon which the fat-digesting enzymes may act.
- Intestinal juice is produced by glands in the walls of the intestine and contains enzymes which complete the digestion of proteins and carbohydrates.

Digestion of the non-fibrous portion of the diet is completed in the small intestine and absorption of the simple products of digestion takes place along its entire length. These are amino acids (from proteins), monosaccharides such as glucose, galactose and fructose (from carbohydrates), and fatty acids and glycerol (from fats). Water, vitamins and minerals are also absorbed in the small intestine and the digesta becomes progressively more solid as it moves towards the caecum and large intestine.

Caecum and large intestine

The caecum and large colon are large fermentation chambers where micro-organisms (bacteria and protozoa) act to digest the fibrous portion of the donkey's diet. The microbes are able to produce the enzymes (which the donkey cannot) capable of digesting the tough, fibrous cell walls of plants and thereby release the plant cell contents for further digestion by enzymes from both the microbes and the donkey itself.. Microbial degradation of food results in the production of large quantities of volatile fatty acids (VFA). These products are absorbed in the large intestine and constitute a major source of energy for the donkey (particularly those on high roughage diets). Large quantities of water and electrolytes are also absorbed in the large intestine. In addition to digesting fibre and other nutrients, the micro-organisms of the large intestine also synthesise essential amino acids, water soluble vitamins of the B-group, and vitamin K.

Microbial activity results in the production of gases, which are either absorbed, expelled from the anus as flatulent wind, or further metabolised by the micro-organisms. Excessive production of gases, or obstructions of the digestive tract which prevent expulsion of these gases, can result in flatulent colic.

The nutrient content of the diet and the feeding regime are important factors in maintaining the balance of micro-organisms which make up the microbial population of the gut. Sudden changes in diet can, and do, result in digestive upsets (diarrhoea, impactions and colic) or other problems, such as laminitis. All dietary changes must, therefore, be made gradually. It is also preferable to feed on a 'little and often' basis (particularly roughage) in order to keep the microbial population relatively stable.

NUTRIENTS

Carbohydrates and fibre

Carbohydrates are the most important source of energy for the donkey. Non-structural carbohydrates, such as starch, maltose and sucrose, are digested mainly in the small intestine and the products of digestion (predominantly glucose) are absorbed into the circulation and transported to the liver. Structural carbohydrates are subjected to microbial fermentation in the caecum and large colon, the main products of which are volatile fatty acids, VFAs. The products of carbohydrate digestion are used as an energy source by tissues or stored as glycogen in the liver or muscle. Carbohydrates which are surplus to requirement are ultimately converted to body fat.

In addition to their requirement for carbohydrate as a source of energy, donkeys need a dietary source of long fibre for proper gut function. A certain amount of fibre is required to stimulate muscle contractions in the gut and to prevent impactions by breaking up the mass of gut contents. Fibre also serves to dilute the more readily fermentable material, and encourages the donkey to eat more slowly, which helps to prevent digestive disorders, such as colic.

Protein

Proteins are essential components of all living cells where they provide structure and regulate metabolic processes (as enzymes and some hormones). They are composed of long chains of amino acids, of which there are about 20 in naturally occurring proteins. Of these, 10 or 11 are considered essential amino acids, since they cannot be synthesised by the donkey in sufficient quantities to meet the demand and must be supplied in the diet. For normal maintenance, protein is required to replace that lost during the natural turnover of epithelial surfaces, hair and other body tissues, and in secretions. Additional protein is needed during periods of growth, pregnancy, lactation and for repair of damaged tissue.

Amino acids which are consumed in excess of requirement cannot be stored and are metabolised to supply energy or converted to body fat. When energy intake is low and the body fat and glycogen reserves are insufficient to meet the donkey's requirements, tissue proteins may be broken down to release energy. This results in muscle wastage.

Fat

Dietary lipids (fats and oils) are useful alternative sources of energy that can be readily utilised by the donkey. They also provide the donkey with essential fatty acids, such as linoleic and linolenic acids, and with the fat-soluble vitamins A, D, E and K. Fats provide twice as much energy as the equivalent weight of carbohydrate or protein. Essential fatty acids are important for maintaining skin and coat condition and shine. Dietary fat intake in excess of energy requirements is stored as body fat.

Energy

Energy is thus provided in the donkey's diet by a combination of carbohydrates, fats and protein (if present in excess of requirement). As with other animals, donkeys eat to fulfil their energy requirements, provided that the nutritional value of the feed is adequate and the capacity of the stomach is sufficient to hold the required amount. In general, a donkey is capable of eating up to 3% of its bodyweight per day in air dry feed, but will eat less if its energy needs are met with the smaller amount. If a feed is very palatable, however, the donkey is likely to overeat.

Minerals

Minerals are inorganic nutrients which have a wide variety of functions in the body. Achieving the correct balance in the diet is important since an excessive intake of certain minerals may be as harmful as a deficiency. Minerals may be classified as macro minerals (which are required in relatively large amounts) and trace elements or micro minerals (which are required in relatively small or trace amounts). Electrolytes are minerals in their salt form as found in the body tissues. The macro minerals are calcium, phosphorus, magnesium, potassium, sodium, chlorine (as chloride) and sulphur. The trace minerals include iron, copper, zinc, manganese, cobalt, iodine, selenium, molybdenum and fluorine.

Vitamins

Vitamins are organic substances which are required, in small amounts, for the regulation of various body processes. They may be classified as water soluble (B-group vitamins and vitamin C) or fat soluble (vitamins A, D, E and K). Water soluble vitamins are poorly stored in the body, with excesses being lost via the urine, so a daily intake is required. Fat soluble vitamins are stored in the liver and body fat so a daily intake is less critical. Because they are stored, however, the risk of toxicity is greater when intake is excessive and prolonged. The vitamin content of cereal and forage crops is depleted with age, during storage and after processing. Vitamin supplementation may therefore be of benefit when grazing is poor or during winter when conserved forage is fed.

Water

Water is perhaps the most essential of all nutrients since without it, life cannot continue for longer than a few days (or less in adverse conditions). An adequate supply of clean, fresh water is required to replace water lost from the body in urine, faeces, sweat, evaporation from the lungs and skin and in productive secretions, such as milk. Water intake may be reduced if the grazing is lush but the most important factors which increase water requirement are lactation (by 50-70% at peak lactation), environmental temperature (by 15-20% when ambient temperature rises from 15°C to 20°C) and exercise (by 20-300%, depending on the level of activity).

However, the donkey is thought to be more efficient in conserving water and may withstand water deprivation to a greater extent than other equines.

FEEDSTUFFS

There are two main types of feedstuffs available for equines, forages and concentrates. Forage feeds, such as grass, hay or haylage, provide both nutrients and roughage and may be sufficient to meet the demands of most non-working or non-productive donkeys. Concentrates, or 'hard feeds', are required by donkeys which are unable to eat enough forage to meet their nutritional requirements, such as those in work and those that are pregnant, lactating, growing or elderly.

Forage

Grass is the natural feedstuff for donkeys and is obviously of major importance. Pasture keeping not only supplies food, but also provides the donkey with an opportunity to exercise. The nutritive value of pasture varies according to the plant species present, soil fertility, climatic conditions and stage of growth of the plant. However, lush pasture is not ideal for donkeys and it is advisable to provide an additional source of high fibre roughage, such as straw. Over-eating can also be prevented by the use of temporary fencing to partition the field, by restricting access during the day or by sharing the available grazing with other animals. If fertilisers are used, one with a lower nitrogen level is preferable and will limit problems of obesity and laminitis. Pasture management for donkeys is discussed in more detail in chapter 17.

Hay is produced from forage (usually grass) crops by cutting, drying in the field and baling. It is not usually fed until at least six months after harvest since new hay is still green and fermenting, and could cause colic in donkeys. Older hay is more likely to become mouldy and the vitamin content deteriorates with time. Most donkeys do not require hay of the highest nutritive value, but mouldy or dusty hay should be avoided. The hay should also be free of toxic weeds. For example, ragwort is unpalatable when fresh but loses its unpleasant taste when dried in hay, so may be readily eaten by the donkey.

Haylage and silage are produced by the controlled fermentation of grass under anaerobic conditions. After cutting, the crop is allowed to wilt for a short period before harvesting. Haylage is wilted for longer than silage, giving haylage a higher dry matter content. The material is closely packed in towers (silos), clamps or plastic wrapping to exclude air. Commercially produced haylage is marketed in convenient vacuum-packed bales. Haylage, in particular, is a useful and palatable alternative to hay. Since the product is moist and dust free, it is of particular benefit to donkeys which are prone to respiratory disease. However, silage should be used with caution, since a number of outbreaks of botulism and subsequent deaths in equines have been associated with the feeding of big bale silage.

Straw is produced from the stem of cereal after the grain has been removed. It has a higher fibre content and a lower nutritive value than hay. Good clean oat or barley feeding straws are useful feedstuffs for donkeys and may be used to increase the fibre content of the ration. However, straw as the only forage source is unlikely to meet the donkey's nutritional requirements without some form of supplementation.

Grass cubes are prepared from grass, which is cut at the highly nutritious leafy stage, chopped and artificially dried, then cubed. This type of feed is a useful form of roughage for donkeys, and may be fed as part of the forage ration or as the concentrate ration.

Chaff is chopped hay or straw and may be used to add bulk to the donkey's ration. Molasses are often added to produce molassed chaff, which increases the palatability and fibre of the diet, and reduces the dust.

Cereals

Oats are the traditional and most widely used cereal for feeding equines and may be fed whole, crimped or rolled. Rolling and crimping may improve digestibility slightly, and can be useful for young animals and those with dental problems, but this advantage is outweighed by the deterioration in nutritive value after processing. Oats have a higher fibre and lower digestible energy content than other cereals and are often considered a relatively safe feed since chewing is encouraged and overfeeding is unlikely to occur. However, oats are well known for the stimulant effect that they have on the behaviour of some equines ('hotting up') so this may make them unsuitable for donkeys that are to be ridden by children.

Barley has a thick, fibrous hull which is relatively indigestible, so cooking, crimping or rolling is required, in order to rupture the seed case, before feeding. Steam rolling or micronisation improve digestibility of barley and is a useful means of preservation. Barley has a slightly higher energy content than oats, but less than maize.

Maize (corn) is a high energy feed which may be fed whole, flaked, extruded or micronised. If fed whole, however, the grains are hard and donkeys with poor teeth may find them difficult to crack. Maize is higher in digestible energy but lower in fibre (unless fed 'on the cob') and protein than oats. Since maize is energy dense, it is useful for feeding to thin donkeys or those in hard work, but only small quantities are required.

Wheat has small, dense grains with a high gluten content, which tends to form an indigestible pasty mass in the stomach if fed whole. For this reason, wheat is not commonly used alone for feeding donkeys but it is often found as a component of balanced compound horse feeds. In some areas, it is now also marketed as a branded horse feed in the form of dried bread.

Bran is a milling by-product of wheat, which has a relatively low nutritive value but is high in fibre. Bran is often fed to donkeys as a wet, warm 'bran mash' which may tempt a sick donkey to eat and provides a palatable vehicle for the administration of drugs. Its capacity to absorb water in the gut gives it mildly laxative properties. However, since bran is relatively deficient in calcium and rich in phosphorus, excessive feeding may cause skeletal deformities due to nutritional secondary hyperparathyroidism (big-head, bran disease, Miller's disease). Because this problem may contribute to the development of laminitis, the feeding of bran mashes to laminitic donkeys (or those prone to laminitis) has recently fallen into disrepute.

By-products

Sugar beet pulp and sugar beet nuts are by-products of the sugar refining process. These are very palatable, high energy, high fibre products which are useful for sick or convalescing donkeys. However, they are sold in a dehydrated form and they must be soaked before feeding, since they would otherwise swell with water and cause an oesophagal obstruction, and possibly choke. Sugar beet shreds must be soaked for 12 hours, pulp for 18 hours, and nuts or pellets for a full 24 hours before feeding.

Molasses, a sweet treacle-like liquid, is another by-product of the sugar industry and may be produced from sugar beet (beet molasses) or sugar cane (cane molasses). Both forms are high in energy and are useful for improving the palatability of feed and as a binding agent in the manufacture of nuts.

Compounded feeds

Compounded nuts are balanced mixed feeds in which the ingredients are ground and formed into pellets (cubes, nuts). They should be fed with a source of long fibre, such as hay or straw, and the feed may be bulked out with chaff. As with any new feed, compounded nuts must be introduced gradually into the diet to prevent the occurrence of laminitis, diarrhoea, colic or other problems.

Coarse mixes are compound feeds in which the ingredients are flaked rather than ground and pelleted, and should be supplemented with hay or straw. They are less dense than cubed feeds and it may be for this reason that they are preferred by donkeys with poor appetites. However, coarse mixes tend to be slightly more expensive than nuts, have a shorter shelf life and require more storage space.

Supplementary feeds

The salt requirement of donkeys varies according to their physical activity, and it is recommended that all donkeys should have free access to a salt lick (either as a block or in its loose, granular form). Trace mineralised salt, containing added iodine, iron, copper, cobalt, manganese, zinc and, sometimes, selenium are available and may be useful in some areas where trace element deficiencies of the soil may be a problem.

Vitamin and mineral supplements are added to the diet to increase the amount of a specific nutrient or nutrients in the diet. Many donkeys receiving compounded feeds do not require dietary supplements, but variations in quality of the diet and in individual requirements suggest that many donkeys would benefit from dietary supplementation.

Feed blocks are large blocks containing a concentrated source of nutrients, which are used to supplement poor grazing.

PRACTICAL FEEDING

Donkeys generally live for over 30 years and during that time, they may be kept as companions, for breeding, or as working animals (although the level of work varies widely). The amount of nutrients required daily by individual donkeys will vary considerably according to their life stage, level of physical activity, health status, environmental conditions and individual digestive and metabolic differences.

Because they are adapted to living in a much harsher environment, donkeys, in general, are able to subsist on a higher roughage diet than horses and ponies. In view of their apparently greater efficiency of food utilisation, it is likely that the nutrient and energy requirements of donkeys are of the order of 75% of those published for horses per unit weight. Many non-working donkeys in the UK are overweight because their feed intake is too high in relation to the amount of exercise they are given.

When formulating a ration for donkeys, the aim should be to maintain the donkey at an optimum weight and condition. Ideally, there should be firm muscle cover without excessive fat deposition, most noticeable as 'panniers' on either side of the thoracolumbar spine and as fat deposits around the buttocks. The nuchal fat crest (on the neck) may also be prominent in fat donkeys but once formed, it is resistant to dispersal despite overall weight loss and is, therefore, not a reliable measure of body condition.

It is often helpful to know the weight of the individual donkey. Veterinary staff at the Donkey Sanctuary have devised a formula from which the weight of a donkey may be estimated from measurements of its height and girth. To simplify using this formula, a nomogram has been constructed and the estimated weight can be read from a scale linking these two values (see Appendix 8). A pocket sized, laminated copy of the nomogram can be obtained on request from the Donkey Sanctuary. As a rough guide, an average sized donkey (9.2 to 11 hands) should weigh between 140-170 kg.

For most donkeys, the feed requirement for maintenance can be met from forage alone. Concentrate feeds are fed in situations where the donkey cannot eat enough forage to meet its requirements. During the summer months, the feeding regimen for donkeys kept at pasture depends largely on the amount and quality of the grass available. On lush, spring grass it may be necessary to either limit the time allowed for grazing or restrict access to the grazing area by using temporary fencing. Good quality feeding straw should be available *ad libitum* to satisfy the donkey's requirement for roughage and dilute the high nutrient content of the grass. When the grass is of high quality, the donkey may eat anything up to 1.5 kg of straw per day. If kept at grass over winter, supplementary feeding with hay or haylage will be required (at levels similar to stabled donkeys), since there will be little nutritive value in the grass and energy needs are greater to maintain body heat. When stabled, in air temperatures above 0°C, the average donkey requires approximately 2 to 3kg of good hay and 3 to 4kg of feeding straw per day. In terms of feeding value, 3kg straw is roughly equivalent to 1kg of hay.

These figures are guidelines only and adjustments should be made according to the size, physiological status and level of activity of the animal, and to environmental conditions. Donkeys under 4 years of age, elderly donkeys over 25 years, mares in the last third of pregnancy and first three months of lactation, and donkeys convalescing after surgery or illness have increased demands and may need extra hay or concentrates. Requirements also increase during periods of cold weather, especially if kept outdoors. In these cases, the amount of feed required may be up to 50% greater than for normal adult maintenance. Similarly, donkeys in regular work require extra feeding which can be provided as a concentrate feed. The average donkey in medium work will require an extra 0.25kg of pony nuts per half hour worked daily, which should be bulked out with a small quantity of chaff.

For donkeys with respiratory disease, especially Chronic Obstructive Pulmonary Disease (COPD), it is particularly important that they are not exposed to dusty or mouldy hay. Haylage is particularly useful as a feed for these donkeys since it is moist and dust-free. The Donkey Sanctuary finds that 2 bales of haylage are roughly equivalent to 3 bales of hay in feeding value to donkeys. Alternatively, hay may be soaked for 4 hours before feeding to avoid dust and mould inhalation but this can lead to leaching of some nutrients. Straw must be soaked for 24 hours before feeding.

Obesity is a relatively common problem in non-working donkeys in the UK. This has a number of detrimental effects but most importantly, overweight donkeys are at a high risk of developing hyperlipaemia following a period of stress and anorexia. For this reason, weight reduction in obese donkeys should be undertaken gradually over a period of time. Donkey Sanctuary recommendations are to aim for a weight loss of no more than an average of 2kg per month (approximately 1-2cm from the girth measurement). To accomplish this, food intake should be reduced to 90% of maintenance requirements and adjusted according to the response achieved. Feeding straw should always be available *ad libitum*. Moderate exercise will facilitate weight loss and, if at grass, access to grazing can be restricted as previously described.

The following are general guidelines which may be applied when feeding donkeys:

•Donkeys should be fed at least twice a day, at regular times, since the digestive and hormonal systems of the donkey are adapted to the frequent intake of small amounts of food.

•Changes in the feeding regime for donkeys (such as the introduction of, or changes in, concentrates in the diet) must always be carried out gradually. The microflora of the large bowel require an adaptation time to function effectively and an abrupt change in the feeding substrate may result in serious nutritional disorders.

•Amounts of feed should be determined by weight, not volume, since energy density varies between feeds and even between batches of the same feed.

•Avoid dusty or mouldy feeds which can give rise to respiratory disease or intestinal disorders.

•Access to a salt or mineral lick is advisable to account for variations in individual requirements.

•Clean water should be freely available at all times. When the donkey is hot after exercise, however, access should be restricted.

•Regular worming and dental checks are necessary to enable the donkey to make efficient use of its feed.

FIONA TAYLOR, B.Vet. Med., M.R.C.V.S. Graduated from the Royal Veterinary College, London 1981. She worked in a mixed, general practice in Nottingham for 1½ years before joining the Donkey Sanctuary in 1982 as their graduate veterinary surgeon. During the six years that she worked for the charity, she travelled extensively on behalf of the International Donkey Protection Trust.

Following a year out to travel around the world, she returned to general practice and worked in various locations around the UK as a locum. Although she maintains an active interest in veterinary practice, she now concentrates mainly on her work as a technical writer, predominantly in the field of companion animal nutrition.

7
HOUSING
David W.B. Sainsbury

Introduction

Housing may be the major capital expense to be faced by donkey owners, and buildings on traditional lines have become extremely expensive, so that methods have had to be sought to lessen these costs. This has led to an increasing use of non-traditional materials and the adoption of prefabrication, both worthy endeavours, but capable of leading the purchaser into considerable areas of risk. In addition there has been a trend towards the housing of donkeys under total cover, in relatively large numbers, which has created difficulties in environmental control and disease prevention that are not always easy to solve. Thus we find ourselves dealing with a dynamic subject where there are major decisions to be taken. I hope that this chapter will help the reader to make the right ones.

There are practical reasons why a donkey should be housed. The first essential of housing is to provide as healthy an environment inside as outside, and yet to give adequate protection from the severity of the elements. The second is to provide a good environment and facilities for the handlers.

A donkey must be kept clean and in good lean condition. It needs to be dry and carefully managed and handled. All these points are facilitated by good stabling. A list of the principal essentials for stables are as follows:

1. A reasonably uniform temperature, eliminating extremes as far as possible.
2. A dry atmosphere and freedom from condensation on the surfaces of the building.
3. Generous air movement and ventilation without draughts.

4. Sound, dry flooring.
5. Good drainage.
6. Adequate lighting, both natural and artificial.
7. Good feeding and water arrangements.

The environmental requirements

In order to provide the correct climatic environment in its housing and reduce the likelihood of disease, it is essential to have a basic understanding of the donkey's physiological needs. The principal elements of the climatic environment which affect the donkeys are ambient temperature, relative humidity, ventilation rate and air movement.

Ambient temperature

A donkey can readily tolerate a wide range of ambient temperatures, e.g. 0-30°C (32-86°F) without harm, depending on the degree to which the individual animal has been allowed to acclimatise, and provided the atmosphere is free from damp and draught.

Temperature *per se* can be a misleading guide to the suitability of the environment and should never be used as the sole criterion. In practice, there is a risk that, in attempting to keep animals warm, air flow and ventilation are restricted to a serious extent.

Relative humidity

The burden on the donkey, especially on the respiratory system, is intensified if the air is damp (i.e. the relative humidity is near saturation) and there is condensation on the internal surfaces of the building. The worst conditions are those of low temperature and high humidity, the optimal conditions for the viability and inhalation of pathogens. Few stables are sufficiently insulated, and any restriction of ventilation causes severe condensation on the walls, roof and windows.

Ventilation rate and air movement

Ventilation rates are based primarily on two points - the maximum rates to keep the building cool in warm weather, and the minimum rates to eliminate from the environment, even in the coldest weather, the humidity arising from the animals' exhalation and the evaporation of their excreta. Provided the minimum requirements are observed, there will be no problem with gaseous exchange. Quite a wide range of ventilation rates will satisfy the criteria - approximately a ratio of 10:1 from hottest to coldest weather which must be achieved without extremes of draught or stagnation. Accurate definition of these extremes is difficult, but a suggested range for air movement is from 0.15 to 0.5m/s (30-100ft/min), at a minimal ventilation rate of 0.2m^3/h/kg bodyweight (bwt) to 2.0m^3/h/kg bwt (0.05ft^3 min/lb bwt to 0.5ft^3 min/lb BWt).

The ventilation rates quoted here can be achieved accurately only if mechanical systems are installed and it is the location and design of air outlets and inlets that is critical in achieving adequate ventilation in traditional systems of natural air flow. Safe margins are 0.1m^2 (1ft^2) for the outlet, and for the inlet, a controllable area of up to 0.3m^2 (3ft^2) for each donkey.

Climatic environment and health

It is essential to produce an environment that helps the donkey to maintain physiological well-being, but there have been few investigations on which to base an objective approach. Recommendations, summarised below, provide a general guide to the required environment but, at present, they cannot be more precise.

Summary of the range of climatic environmental requirements for the stabled donkey

	Metric	Imperial
Ambient temperature	0-30°C	32-85°F
Relative humidity	30-70%	30-70%
Air movement	0.15-0.5m/s	30-100ft/min
Ventilation rate	0.2-2.0m^3/h/kg BWt	0.05-0.5ft^3/ min/lb BWt
Outlet ventilation area	0.1m^2/donkey	1ft^2/donkey
Inlet ventilation area	0.3m^2/donkey	3ft^2/donkey

Building and ventilation

It is essential that the buildings are well insulated to ensure adequate ventilation. This helps to eliminate dampness created by condensation and assists in maintaining equable and uniform conditions, reducing peaks or troughs of ambient temperatures or humidity. Good insulation also promotes air movement around the edge of the structure by preventing the warm, stale air from becoming chilled and therefore falling back towards the floor. There are a number of economical methods of installing insulation into existing buildings, depending on the basic construction.

The simplest ventilation technique, used since animals were first housed, relies on three natural forces:

1. Stack effect, i.e. rising warm and stale air
2. Aspiration, i.e. wind force across the roof of the building sucking air out
3. Perflation, i.e. air blown from side to side and end to end of the building

The following examples show how various buildings are served by these forces.

A roof extracting trunk or chimney, of dimensions similar to or greater than those shown in the table, provides the stack effect. Fresh air inlets replace the stale air and should be situated around the wall to give a uniform in-flow of air (Figs. 1 and 2).

A suitable design of chimney allowing the wind to blow freely across the top encourages the aspirating effect and the perflating effect is ensured if there are inlets on both sides of the building to give a through draught when required. The inlets must be designed to prevent down-draught, however. One of the best controls is an inward-opening bottom-hinged

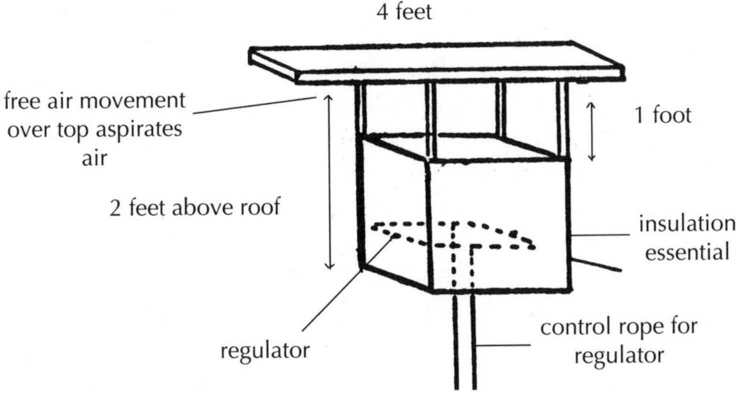

Fig. 1 Air outlet trunk (common dimensions shown).

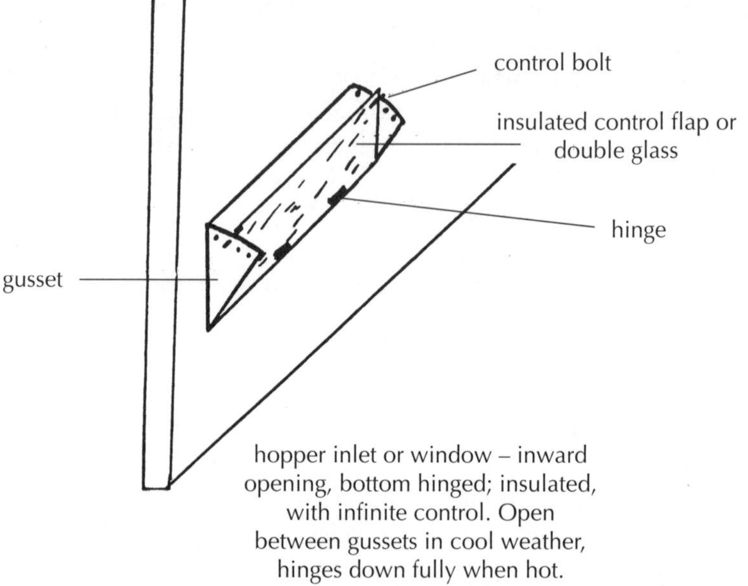

Fig. 2 Fresh air inlets.

control flap constructed of timber or another thermally insulated material. This construction deflects incoming air upwards in the cold weather if the flap is partly closed - or, in warmer weather, the air enters directly into the building, or blows across it. Ideally all ventilators should be fully controllable and their regulators easily reached. The inlets should be placed as low as is practicable without incurring the risk of interference by the donkeys. The best arrangement is one chimney trunk to each common air space with numerous air inlets to ensure a uniform intake of air around the building. Each stable should have its quota of half doors and windows, preferably of double glass, which can be opened for extra air flow in warmer weather. This system can be used to give a surplus of air flow with safety, if the air supply is draught-free, because the additional and faster air movement is well above the animal.

The arrangements described above may fail to function satisfactorily if the buildings are excessively wide or long, or are boxed in by other buildings which impede natural air flow. In these circumstances it may be necessary to use mechanical ventilation by installing extractor fans. This can be achieved with simplicity and economy by placing them at the base of the chimney.

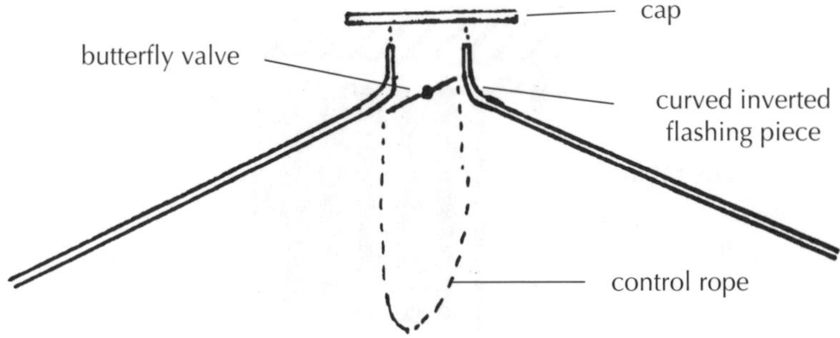

Fig. 3 Stale air extraction through open ridge controlled by butterfly flap.

Housing in covered yards

In a large building, containing a number of donkeys within a totally covered structure, there is a considerable danger of environmental pollution. Each building should be considered individually, so far as natural ventilation is concerned, because the air flow may be greatly influenced by the site chosen. The aim of ventilating a large covered building should be to ensure free air flow at all times.

The optimal method is to install a wide open ridge, from 0.3-0.6m (1-2ft) wide, protected with a flap to keep most of the weather out, but allowing the wind to blow freely across the ridge and thereby enhance the aspiratory effect (Fig. 3).

Other simple techniques of roof ventilation include the fitting of corrugated sheets, upside down and with a gap of a few millimetres between the sheets. This method, described as the 'breathing roof' is justifiably popular (Fig. 4). The 'Yorkshire' or spaced board (Fig. 5) traditionally a

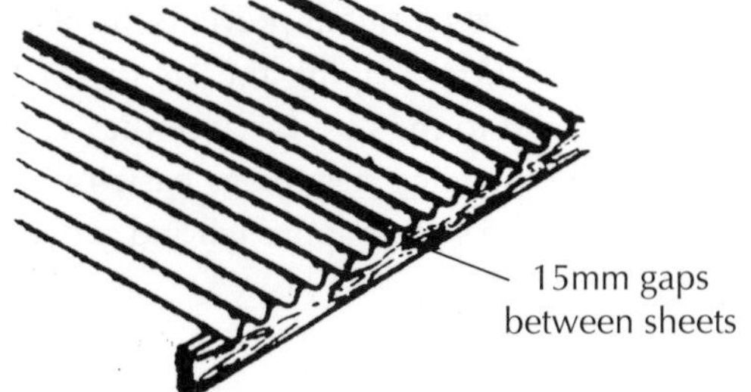

Fig. 4 Breathing roof.

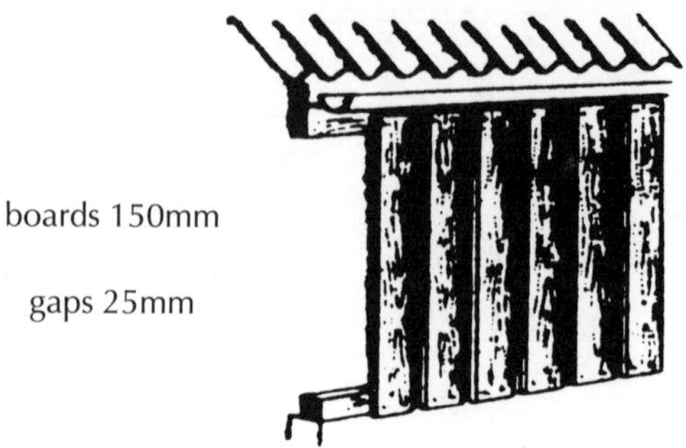

Fig. 5 Spaced boards.

walling of 150mm (6in) boards with 17mm (0.75in) gaps between, is a good adjunct to roof ventilation when used around the sides, at the top half of the wall and at the gable ends above the doorways. 'Hit and miss' sliding boards are a form of controllable spaced boarding in which one set of boards slides over the others, and recommended for building on an exposed site. Measures of restriction and individuality can be incorporated into the layout within the building as appropriate, and these can be ventilated by measures similar to those required for a single stall.

Monopitch house

An alternative type of house is the monopitch or lean-to building (Fig. 6) - an open-fronted shed, sloping from a low back to a high front, facing towards the warmest winds and the maximum sunlight. The pitch on the roof ensures a free flow of air towards the front and the generous air space promotes a good environment. The ventilation is completed with simple hopper flaps in the back wall and doors at the front. An extension to the roof, on the open side, gives protection to the animals and their attendants. The division of the building by cross-partitions prevents through draughts and provides a measure of isolation, helping the air to flow upwards. The cross-partitions need not add to the cost because they can also act as load-bearers for the roof. The building may be as basic or as elaborate as required but it is, fundamentally, a simple approach and avoids any real difficulties in environmental control.

The siting of the housing

The best site for stables is on well-drained land where there is a natural,

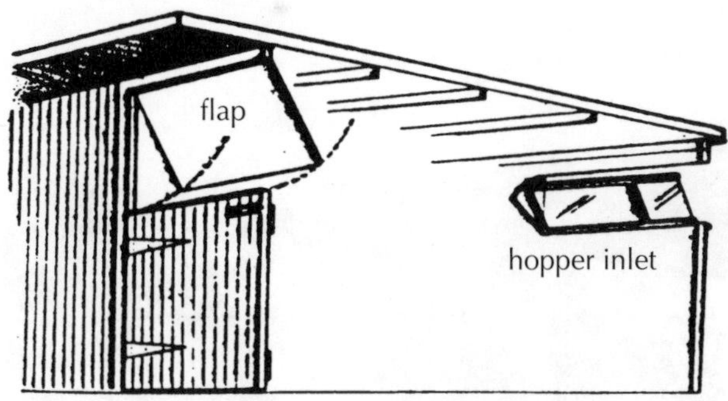

Fig. 6 Mono-pitch profile.

yet gentle, fall away from the buildings. The housing should be as protected as possible from cold and biting northerly and easterly winds, with the main doors and at least a substantial proportion of the ventilating (openable) windows facing south or west. When this is not possible, a second best is to protect the stables by trees or other buildings. A good south-facing slope is the best location. Avoid low-lying, damp and over protected locations where conditions can become extremely unhealthy in the damp weather of the autumn or the still, hot days of high summer. Low-lying hollows can also be dangerous frost pockets in winter.

The housing requirements

A stable block will consist of a series of boxes or stalls together with ancillary facilities. For example, within a unit there may be an isolation box for sick animals, a feed room, hay store, straw store, tack room, washing room with drying facilities and accommodation for the attendants, including a lavatory. There must also be some provision for clean manure storage situated conveniently, but not too close, to the boxes, and also office accommodation, plus garaging for vehicles and trailers. Obviously, the extent to which all these facilities will be required or can be provided, depends on the nature and size of the establishment.

In general nowadays donkeys are housed in loose-boxes and though there are some stalls in existence, it is now more usual practice to convert stalls into boxes. The essential dimensions of a loose-box are approximately 3.3m x 3.3m (10ft x 10ft).

Part of the Isolation Unit at the Donkey Sanctuary.

LAYOUTS

The simplest layout is a single row of boxes opening directly into the open air. This is a perfectly satisfactory design and can be embellished by adding a covered 'overhang' to the boxes to give protection to the donkeys and the attendants. This keeps the boxes drier and relieves them from excessive heating and glare from the sun and if they are constructed without supporting posts there are no hazards. Full advantage can be taken of the overhang if it is extended through to the adjoining service buildings, as it is a great help if most of the operations round the stables can be carried out under cover. The design discussed is probably the healthiest as it gives isolation between each box.

The totally enclosed unit

The more modern and popular system of housing large numbers of donkeys is in a barn. In this case the total approach is rather different. The barn is a large 'covered yard' - a lofty structure about 3m (10ft) to the eaves and rising to a ridge of about 8m (25ft). Inside, the boxes are placed in rows of two or four, depending on the width of the building. The rows are of the usual size with adequate passageways between them. So far as possible all ancillary services are also within or very close to this building. It is an arrangement much favoured in North America where the climate is not as equable as in Great Britain and where the harsh winters often bring deep snow.

Isolation box

It is wise to have at least one isolation box for sick animals in any sizeable unit. Such a box is essential if an animal is suffering from a contagious disease, but is also useful for donkeys requiring special treatment. The box or boxes must be quite separate from the rest of the establishment. The box should be readily accessible and the donkeys should not only be able to see people, and be seen, but should also be in sight of other animals if at all possible. An isolation box should be rather larger than the ordinary box.

The feed room

The feed room is used for storing fodder which is for immediate use, as opposed to the feed store, where the longer term supplies are kept. Its dimensions and that of the store will depend on the establishment's size.

Shelter with yard.

Interior of a large shelter at the Donkey Sanctuary.

Daily feeds are prepared in this room and it will contain separate bins for the individual feeds, e.g. oats, bran, barley, etc. There should also be a sink with hot and cold water and a tap to supply drinking water. In large establishments there may be chaff cutters and other machinery for the preparation of the feed.

Feed store

The feed store usually adjoins the feed room and is also close to the storage areas for hay and straw. The store will contain feed in bulk bins, sacks or bags. A very convenient arrangement is to build the feed store above the feed room so that the large quantities of feed can be moved down as needed. The movement of food up to the store will only be done occasionally, but installation of a mechanical system will make this task far easier.

Hay and straw stores

A totally dry building with hard, dry floors and free ventilation throughout is required for the storage of all bedding and feeds. Wet, damp or dusty bedding must be avoided at all costs in order to keep the risk of respiratory

Exterior of a large shelter at the Donkey Sanctuary.

disease and allergies at a minimum. The hay and straw barn should ideally be in close proximity to the feed room and feed store, but also sited in a position suitable for offloading bales from delivery vehicles. As well as storing hay and straw, this barn may be required for other forms of litter storage, such as peat, wood shavings, sawdust or shredded paper.

Being in a position to cope with bulk storage on site allows the purchase of good hay and straw at a time when prices are low and supplies readily available - essentials for good stable management.

Tack room and washing and cleaning facilities

The tack room is the most important service room in a group of stables. Within this room must be fitted the brackets, shelves and cupboards to take all the equipment. Closed cupboards and/or chests are useful for storing blankets and other clothing. The room should be well insulated and ventilated and have some form of heating and also incorporate washing and cleaning facilities.

Manure storage

The siting of a good manure store is important. It must be within easy access of the boxes but also with good road access for off-loading. If it is too close to the boxes it may create a smell nuisance and increase the fly menace.

The manure store usually consists of a concrete base with a fairly steep fall for drainage at the back to ensure that water and effluent do not run back on to the concrete access area. The rear and sides are usually sturdily constructed of blocks, bricks or reinforced concrete. Size will depend entirely on the period of storage envisaged. The more frequent the collection of the manure the better - both to avoid smell and fly nuisance and to reduce the size of the store.

Fences and gates

The whole establishment will require good fencing for the protection and safety of the donkeys and the staff. Post and rail fencing is ideal.

Construction

The roof construction may be of any suitable modern type but it is desirable to incorporate some thermal insulation. There are two ways of achieving this. The insulation can form an underlining to the exterior roof cladding, or a flat false ceiling may be installed. There is no great preference for either construction, but ventilation does tend to be better if there is a pitch on the ceiling rather than a flat ceiling which holds the stale air.

The outer cladding of the roof is usually corrugated asbestos or metal: it makes little difference which is used.

The exteriors of older traditional stable roofs are usually constructed of tiles or slates with an inner lining of timber. This is perfectly satisfactory, but is generally too expensive for modern use, as these materials are costly and also require more substantial supports.

Insulation of the construction of stables is not a traditional practice but some explanation of the importance attached to it may be helpful.

Insulation, or thermal insulation as it should be called, stabilises the ambient temperature by preventing too rapid rises and falls. It also prevents condensation which is especially harmful by its side effects to the respiratory systems of the donkeys and is also destructive to the building itself. Thermal insulation is also an important aid to ventilation by ensuring the warm air stays warm until it escapes from the building.

There are numerous ways of achieving good insulation. Examples of good procedures are as follows:

For the roof, an internal lining of compressed fibre board is surrounded by a vapour seal of polythene sheeting and above this 100mm of mineral wool or 50mm of expanded plastic polyurethane or polystyrene. There is then an air space and finally the outer cladding of roofing sheets, tiles or slates.

Insulated walls may be of similar construction but with a robust inner lining of rendered brick, block or timber. A layer of lightweight insulated concrete blocks can be incorporated or a cavity filled with expanded plastic insulation.

These measures will certainly add to the cost of construction but will assist in maintaining the good health of the donkeys and the longevity of the buildings themselves.

Walls

Traditionally constructed stables are usually built of brick, double thickness and uninsulated, but are not as warm or dry as the modern stable which is usually insulated and built of one of a number of different available materials. If brick is used, then it should be used with a cavity construction, preferably with the cavity filled with insulation, such as a polyurethane foam. Alternatively, the wall may be constructed of concrete blocks, which may be cement rendered, using load-bearing insulated construction, or of concrete panels or reinforced concrete poured in situ.

It is also possible to use various forms of prefabricated structures. Although traditional materials are often regarded as the best they are very expensive and cannot often be justified, whereas there are several useful and less expensive forms of timber and concrete prefabricated construction. When using these, it is best to have double linings, the interior lining being of stronger construction than the outer, as these will receive the full impact of the donkeys.

Materials used for all the internal divisions need to be of a strength similar to those used for external walls. They also may be constructed of brick or blocks, or by framing with the main framing built into the walls and the floors. This framing may be reinforced concrete or steel, which are certainly the most durable, or timber.

Donkey Sanctuary field shelter site.

Windows

Windows are most important in the modern stable. They need to be fitted at a high level in order to prevent damage and also because the light penetration is best in this position. It is helpful if windows can serve also as part of the ventilation system. This is most satisfactorily achieved if the windows are inward opening and have the bottom hinged with gussets to prevent draught blowing down on the donkeys' backs. The windows must be openable in stages, so that they allow maximum variation in ventilation.

Floors

It is impossible to exaggerate the importance of a really good floor surface. The general requirements are that the floor must be dry, reasonably smooth, non-slippery, non-absorbent and hard wearing. It must also have sufficient fall to take away the urine and any other fluids but not so much slope to increase the danger of slipping or encourage scuffing of the bedding to one side. A fall of not more than 1 in 80 is recommended. In stalls the fall is to the back, but in boxes it is best towards the door so that any fluid drains out to a gulley in the passageway. Very few buildings do have the correct slope, but it is absolutely essential that the floor is so sloped that after washing all the liquid flows by natural fall to the drains.

The ideal floor material would be Adamantine clinkers or blue Staffordshire checkered pavings, but generally these materials are considered so expensive that although very hard wearing and traditional, they must be replaced by concrete. Nevertheless concrete can be perfectly satisfactory if care is taken in its use. It should always be laid with a damp-proof membrane incorporated and there is much to be said for the addition of an insulation layer on particularly damp and cold sites. Thus the total floor construction from the ground upwards should consist of the following:

1. Ground, with all vegetation removed and well consolidated.
2. Hardcore or firmly compacted material 150mm (6in) thick.
3. Concrete 100-150mm (4-6in) thick.

The surface layer will wear much better if a good granolithic topping is laid.

Drainage

It is both unnecessary and undesirable to have complicated drainage systems in stables. The first essential is to have a good fall on the floor of the box to take as much fluid as possible to the outside. Considerable care and skill are required to achieve this, but it is well worth it. The main drainage system will be outside the boxes with gulleys to trap straw and other solid matter. Internal drain-inlets should be avoided, since they are more difficult to clean and can cause unpleasant smells and pollution. The design of the drainage system should ensure that careful consideration is given to easy clearing and rodding when, as inevitably will be the case, obstructions occur. Shallow and safe open channelling is much better than underground drains.

Care must be taken to comply with regulations that prohibit the contamination of rivers and water courses with effluent from drains and manure heaps. In order to be confident that regulations are not being contravened, since fines for non-compliance are characteristically heavy, it is wise to consult the local authority for advice.

Doors

Doors of loose-boxes and stables are best placed to one side of the box so that the animal can be kept warm and draught-free. Where two boxes adjoin the doors should never be placed next to each other.

Doors should not be less than 1m (3.3ft) wide or 2m (6.6ft) high. The door openings should have rounded external edges, as sharp edges can cause injury. The doors themselves should be side-hung to open outwards - an essential since an animal may prevent the door from being opened while lying down or when ill or cast. External doors to boxes which open directly to the open air are invariably formed in two halves.

It should be borne in mind that donkeys are very clever at opening doors and there should be at least two catches or bolts carefully chosen to be as safe as possible. The top door of a stable door combination is, in any case, a useful feature for additional ventilation and hooks and eyes should be fitted to enable the top part to be fixed open.

FITTINGS AND FIXTURES

Every box or stall will need mangers, water points, hay racks and tying up rings.

Mangers

Mangers for the feed are usually placed at about 0.7m (2ft) above the floor. They can be made from vitreous enamel, galvanised steel, stainless steel or timber with salt glazed channels and can be fitted either along the face of a wall or in the corner. There is no doubt that, in spite of its expense, stainless steel is the most perfect choice as it has a long life and is easy to clean. A manger may be combined with a hay rack or a water trough, but the latter combination is not recommended as the food tends to foul the water trough.

The manger is usually fitted on the wall of the box opposite the door. It is the best position for the animal and also for the safety of the operator, though it means that the attendant has the longest distance to walk for feeding and servicing. If it is also fitted diagonally opposite to the door corner, the donkey will be out of a draught when tied up.

Hay racks

Hay racks can either be combined with the manger or be entirely separate. The hay rack must be securely fixed to the wall. There has always been some dispute as to its best siting. If it is at a low level, the donkey eats in a normal position but if it is placed higher at, say, 1.3m (4ft) from the floor, dust and seeds can enter the donkey's eyes.

Water containers

Every box or stall requires fittings for clean, fresh water. The water can be provided in a bucket, or an automatic water trough may be fitted. If buckets are used then there should be a proper bucket holder secured to the wall. Troughs containing 2-3 gallons are made of galvanised or stainless steel and incorporate a ball valve, drain tap and overflow. All pipes and fittings associated with the water supply systems must be well insulated against freezing.

Rings

Rings are required for both boxes and stalls for tying up donkeys. Two or three rings per box or stall are usually adequate. One ring should be placed at about 1m (3ft) from the floor for tying the donkey to the manger, whilst another is put between 1.5-1.55m (5-5½ft) from the floor for general tying up purposes.

Electric points and lighting

At least one electric point is required in each box, and, as many of the major duties are carried out at night, it is much better to have points for two lights on each side of the box. The best light fittings are those with watertight, bulkhead covers, firmly secured to the wall and fitted with heavy prism glass or strong grilles. They should be placed 1.6-1.9m (5-6ft) from the ground.

Hygiene

Good housing is crucial to the achievement of good health in donkeys and this can only be maintained by ensuring good hygiene. This requires a regular programme of cleaning and disinfecting. It is not complicated and there are five principal procedures as follows :-

1. The accommodation should be emptied of all donkeys.
2. All the muck should be cleared out and removed from the premises.

3. Wash down with a heavy duty detergent sanitiser.
4. Soak in a Ministry of Agriculture approved disinfectant. Use disinfectants that are completely safe such as those based on iodophors, chlorine, organic acids or aldehydes.
5. Dry out before replacing bedding and the donkeys. The principal failure in cleaning and disinfecting techniques is to leave organic material in cracks and crevices. This is where bacteria and viruses persist. Also rodents and insects act as serious carriers of infection and must be exterminated.

D.W.B. SAINSBURY, M.A., Ph.D.., BSc., M.R.C.V.S., F.R.S.H., C.Biol., FI.Biol. is Honorary Director of the Cambridge Centre for Animal Health and Welfare, a Fellow of Wolfson College, Cambridge, and lectures at several universities and at the National Stud.

Many problems have arisen due to lack of care and consideration with regard to the housing of animals. Dr Sainsbury's interest in livestock housing in general has been a central enthusiasm of his career for over 40 years. He began research and investigation in livestock housing soon after he qualified in the 1950s and since that time an enormous amount of housing of all types has been built.

8
SOCIAL BEHAVIOUR

Jane French

Who hath sent out the wild ass free?
Or who hath loosed the bands of the wild ass?
Whose house I have made the wilderness,
And the barren land his dwellings.
The range of the mountains is his pasture,
And he searcheth after every green thing.
(Job 39: 5-6, 8)

Feral donkeys still live in these 'barren lands' so typical of their ancestors, the wild African asses, *Equus asinus*. And while the number and range of wild asses are now critically reduced, donkeys flourish in many countries. The success of the donkey (and its original domestication between 4,500 and 5,000 years ago) is due to its flexible social structure.

Studies of feral donkeys have shown that they form several types of social groupings. At one extreme, they live in coherent family groups or 'harems'. The 'harem' consists of breeding jennies with their young offspring and is controlled by a dominant jack. The harem stays together and occupies a defended area from which strangers are excluded. Membership of the harem only changes when adolescent offspring are excluded by the jack or when another jack becomes the harem boss. This type of social organisation is found in many other free-living equines, such as the mountain zebra, the plains zebra, the horse and the Asiatic ass.

At the other extreme donkeys live in a very loose social structure in which small groups are formed that rarely last more than a few days. There is no antagonism between groups and membership is very fluid. Mixing and splitting of the groups tends to occur when the donkeys in an area congregate for example at water holes, etc. The only permanent association is between a jenny and her foal. Dominant jacks do not have a harem but dominate breeding activity within a large area. Each adult donkey has a home range (i.e. the area in which the animal normally lives). The size of the home range is highly variable and may overlap the home range of other donkeys. This type of social organisation is typical of the wild African ass and Grevy's zebra.

The exact type of social structure adopted by a population of donkeys in any particular area will depend upon ecological variables; particularly upon the availability of food and water.

In arid and semi-arid regions the loose type of social structure predominates. The population lives in temporary groups that may be exclusively male, exclusively female, or include both males and females. Jennies are very rarely seen on their own: adults are with their foals; barren adults attach themselves to another jenny and her foal; and yearlings join groups. Young males also join groups but tend to become more solitary with age. Group size varies but the average size is three. The only stable group is a jenny and her foal. They remain together for at least 12 months. Colts tend to leave when the next foal is born but fillies may stay until they themselves foal.

Some jacks occupy an area over which they have exclusive mating rights. Other males are not excluded from these areas. Mating also takes place outside such territories; several males may pursue a female and the most dominant (often a territory holder) will mate with her. Jennies may prefer to mate with territorial males to avoid a wearying chase and the risk of becoming separated from their foals. Territory males may also be more attractive to jennies because they are obviously fit enough to dominate other males. There is some group cohesion since donkeys in an area will flee together if disturbed, although there is no order of leadership as there would be in a herd of horses.

In arid regions of Australia donkeys have been reported to congregate in large groups. These typically contain several dozens of animals but groupings of up to 150-200 are not uncommon in areas where donkeys are numerous. The jacks in these groups are not territorial and frequently fight over jennies that are in season. The smallest group seen is a jenny with her foal.

In more lush environments, donkey society is based upon three stable

Group of working donkeys turned out to browse in Eritrea. While the habitat is typical of that occupied by wild and feral donkeys, they are normally found in smaller groups.

groupings. These are: a dominant male with his harem and their offspring; a dominant male and several subordinant males with their harem and offspring; and bachelor groups of males. Bachelor males rarely mate. Subordinant males with access to a harem occasionally mate but most mating is done by the harem boss. The hierarchies within the groups are complex; dominance is not simply a function of such characteristics as age, sex, aggression or weight. Observations have found that in some groups separate hierarchies for males and females exist, and that foals that remain near to their mother share her rank. If the population is enclosed (on an island for example), harems have sole occupancy of a defended territory. If the population is not restricted physically, then the harem's cohesion is maintained by the dominance of the jack and the fidelity of the jennies.

These forms of social organisation are largely adaptive and produce the maximum stable population an area can support. In dry regions, donkeys range over large areas, are at low density (about one donkey in every three to four kilometres), and do not form harem type groups. Under these conditions, jennies are less likely to mate every season. This limits the size of the population and is adaptive in such areas where the supply of water and forage is unreliable.

Whatever their social organisation, the donkeys' daily routine will be determined by their immediate needs for food, water and shelter. Feral donkeys spend over 50% of their day feeding. Whilst their browsing habits allow donkeys to exploit unpromising habitats, forage is naturally bulky and of low nutritive value, and takes a long time to gather and process. Donkeys drink infrequently and irregularly. However, members of a group tend to drink together.

Donkeys move between feeding areas at a walk. Adults trot in response to most alarms and threats, during courtship drives, play, and when approaching water holes. Donkeys rarely break into a gallop; only when in close pursuit, during courtship or in play. Some feral donkeys travel long distances in a seasonal pattern following the ephemeral water sources.

Donkeys tend to alternate bouts of feeding with periods of rest. Most feral donkeys will rest in the hottest part of the day, be most active at dawn and dusk, and remain active throughout the night. Donkeys that are experiencing human harassment may prefer to be active during the night. Donkeys can rest whilst standing; resting donkeys stand with lowered heads, floppy ears and closed eyes. They also rest lying on the ground; either on their sternum (with legs tucked underneath the body and neck extended), or on their side (with all four legs extended). Foals tend to rest on the ground or leaning against their mother. As they get older they rest more in the standing position. In a group of donkeys resting is often a communal activity, with one donkey remaining on guard. Alert donkeys stand with their ears up and their weight distributed on all four feet.

Donkeys spend a small but regular part of their day in skin care. Donkeys frequently roll, shake and then groom after rest periods. This revives their sweaty or flattened coats, and removes some ectoparasites and moulted hair. Donkeys cannot reach every part of their bodies and so grooming often includes a rub against any suitable object, even other animals. Donkey groups and individuals often have favourite rubbing posts. Donkeys also groom each other. Within a group, each donkey has a particular grooming partner - usually a close relative. Grooming is obviously a pleasurable experience. Donkeys that lack other stimulation often groom very frequently. Rolling is often a communal activity with several donkeys gathering round a patch of bare earth to roll in quick succession. Donkeys will create their rolling areas by pawing the ground.

The frequency of elimination varies but occurs commonly after a rest period and in response to elimination by other donkeys. Donkeys tend to dung some way from their resting areas. They often cover other donkeys' excreta with their own; stallions tend to do this more than mares or geldings. This can cause problems in small paddocks as donkeys will not graze close to grass contaminated with urine or dung. Donkeys adopt a special posture for defaecation; they stand with their tail at forty-five degrees, and with their legs braced and spread backwards. Wild ass jacks prefer to defaecate on top of a previous pile of their own dung. This results in the build up of spectacular dung piles! These are indicative of a territory but do not seem to be territory markers as such.

Many behaviours that may be primarily non-social, like grazing, rolling, elimination, do also have a social facilitation and communication function. Donkeys will smell both urine and dung, for example, which suggests that these excreta have a communication function.

Although social behaviour occupies a small part of the donkey's day, its importance can be seen from the complex relationships that develop within a group. Donkeys have a fairly long lifespan (living about 15 years in the wild and 40 years as a companion animal) in which to develop and benefit from such relationships. Social behaviour depends on communication and this develops from the sensory capabilities of the animals concerned.

Donkeys are sophisticated visual communicators. They communicate much information by posture and slight postural changes. Donkeys have good night vision, panoramic vision, and devote a large area of their brain cortex to analysing visual information. They use sight to recognise individual conspecifics and predators at more than half a mile away, and to locate the best browsing. Donkeys are good at picking up visual cues. Because their eyes are located on each side of the head (rather than being close together and forward facing as in humans), they have a much larger peripheral field of vision and a relatively small binocular visual field. This wide field of vision has advantages in providing a good view of what is happening behind the donkey as it is grazing. Objects at the edge of the donkey's field will not be seen clearly which means that they can sometimes be startled by everyday items.

Donkeys have a wide range of vocalisations that have been influenced by domestication. The most obvious, and taking the most effort, is the bray. In the wild most braying is performed by territorial males. They tend to bray regularly soon after dawn and sometimes are answered by other jacks. Harem bosses bray to maintain contact with members of the group and advertise group possession of the area. They also bray before rounding up the group to move on to a new location. Subordinate males rarely bray in the presence of dominant males, unless several donkeys are braying at once. Jennies and foals rarely bray unless separated from the group, or in response to the braying of a stray group male. In domestic conditions, jennies often bray; particularly when in heat or with other jennies that are in heat, when waiting for food, and in response to other brays. Braying carries over considerable distance - in Mexico donkeys are called the mountain canaries! Braying can be used to advertise status and maintain group cohesion. The braying donkey's message is reinforced by the position of its ears. In a greeting, the ears are held back slightly (this is usually followed by a tactile greeting). For a challenge, the ears are flattened back. During courtship, the ears are up and pointing forward.

Donkeys produce other vocalisations: grunting and growling are agonistic; snorting is an expression of relief, disgust, excitement or nasal irritation. Whuffling is an affiliative vocalisation often used when donkeys are searching for each other, for example, grooming partners, and jennies to their foals. Jennies also make a lower-pitched anticipatory call as their foals approach.

Little is known about the acuity of the donkey's sense of smell. However, as they often investigate things by smell, this is probably an important sense. Donkeys have a secondary olfactory pathway that they employ to test odours. To use this system, they show a specific behaviour, the flehmen response. This takes the form of vigorous respiration, in which the nostrils are elongated and narrowed. The upper lip is twitched and curled back. This is followed by a deep inspiration and a forced expiration that sometimes ends in a snort. During flehmen, the donkey stands with his neck raised and often turned to one side. In the wild, flehmen occurs most frequently when a jack smells a jenny's urine. This suggests that urine contains information about a female's sexual receptivity as well as identity and status.

A donkey's sense of taste enables it to distinguish the edible from the inedible as it browses. Its varied diet suggests an educated palate. Donkeys use their sense of touch primarily through their sensitive lips that are covered by thousands of touch-sensitive hairs.

Both communication and social interaction are necessary for social cohesion within donkey groups. With the exception of sexual behaviour, social behaviour may be classed as either 'agonistic', that is behaviour that increases distance between individuals, or 'affiliative', that is behaviour that

A mild biting threat.

reduces the distance between animals.

Donkeys threaten two types of injury: biting using their heads, and kicking using their hind legs. In a mild biting threat, donkeys lay their ears back slightly and extend their necks towards their opponents. At the Sanctuary, mild threats are seen most often at feeders, and about half of donkeys threatened in this way will move away. In a stronger threat, the donkey lays his ears right back and opens his mouth slightly (ready to lunge forward and bite) and 80% of opponents will move away. Only one in ten agonistic encounters involves such full threatening postures. Only one in thirty bite threats develops into a fight. Bite threats are also used by jennies to discipline foals. A mild kick threat consists of laid back ears and turning of the rump towards the opponent. If the opponent remains, the rear hoof is lifted and the tail lashed before a kick is delivered. Donkeys move to avoid being kicked so that contact is rare; courting males, and combatant unfamiliar males are most likely to be kicked.

Escalating threats are only given by relaxed donkeys. If donkeys are startled they will attempt to kick or bite straight away. Donkeys also engage in trials of strength by pushing head to head or with entwined necks. Such trials may occur between serious rivals or be just for fun between friends. Play fighting also involves much rearing. A rearing donkey is vulnerable and off-balance, so rearing is rarer in serious fights. Serious fighting is rare since once a donkey moves away in response to a threat he is rarely pursued over more than a short distance. Fighting occurs most usually between males of equal status and strength. Combatants take a grip on manes and necks and attempt to bite fore and hind legs. Fighting culminates in rearing which puts both donkeys off balance. Fights rarely result in fatal injuries because the combatants are well matched, and have tough hides. In feral donkeys most fights (88.5%) occur between stallions and, as a result, stallions may have several battle scars, broken ears and missing tails.

As any approach may be hostile, certain behaviours are used to reassure and appease. Appeasement is always shown by subordinate animals as they approach higher status animals, by donkeys requesting grooming, and is very commonly shown by young foals. 'Jawing' is a submissive behaviour shown as the subordinate donkey approaches. It looks like an exaggerated chewing movement in which the lips never meet. The donkey moves its jaw up and down with its teeth mostly covered and the corners of its mouth drawn back. The donkey's ears are held out sideways and its neck is horizontal. 'Jawing' is probably an adaptation of a grooming movement.

Affiliative behaviour, which reduces the distance between animals, encompasses greeting behaviour, mutual grooming and play. Greeting posture is similar to threat posture but the ears are directed forward rather than back. Greetings are given by touching with the nose (nose to nose, nose to flank, nose to rump, nose to shoulder). Mutual grooming establishes close contact between particular pairs of donkeys (grooming partners), and probably provides both comfort and reassurance as well as skin care. A session of mutual grooming is initiated by an appeasing approach by one donkey. The donkey approaches with forward pointing ears (and occasionally with a slightly open mouth), and touches the neck of its grooming partner. If the grooming partner does not want to respond, it will walk away or threaten to bite or kick. If it is keen to groom, it will walk towards its partner. When grooming, partners stand head to tail and groom parts they cannot reach for themselves (often nibbling at neck, mane, forelegs and withers). These mutual grooming sessions can last from a few minutes to over half an hour. Sometimes one grooming partner grooms without being groomed in return. Jennies will groom their foals and courting males will groom jennies. These non-mutual grooming sessions tend to be much shorter.

Play is often seen amongst young donkeys. In play, donkeys will imitate a range of agonistic behaviours, such as biting, neck wrestling and rearing

A greeting posture.

but the ears are directed forwards to show friendly intent. Young foals spend much of their time playing; either exploring novel objects and their environment, or interacting with their mothers and (in donkeys that live in groups) with other foals. Young foals direct their exploratory play particularly towards their mothers; they will nip her many times mostly around her face and sometimes she will respond by engaging in a playful chase. Foals gallop fast to and from the mare, in irregular circles around her, sometimes for several minutes. As the foals get older, their mothers play with them less and foals spend more time in the company of other foals. In desert-dwelling donkeys, foals often have no opportunities to play with other foals and lead relatively isolated existences.

Whilst fullest expression of donkeys' social behaviour is seen in those that are organised into groups, sexual behaviour is seen in all types of social organisations. Although the different equine species can interbreed in captivity, the donkey's sexual behaviour is sufficiently different to discourage interbreeding in the wild. Donkeys require a long amount of foreplay for successful copulation compared with horses, the equines they are most likely to meet in the wild. Receptive jennies 'jaw' in response to the presence or bray of males. Their sexual behaviour is generally more overt than other female equids. Although individual jennies vary considerably in their behaviour, they often show more tail lashing, yawning, urinating and simulated flight when they are in season. They solicit mounting by backing into other donkeys with jumping movements of their hindquarters. They may show physical signs of being in season as well, such as a swollen red vulva and copious vaginal mucus. Some jennies attempt to prevent other females having access to the stallions.

Jacks are more aggressive and persistent in their courtship than other male equids. They are seen to 'drive' oestrus females; approaching them with head lowered almost to the ground and swinging in a snake like fashion, ears are flattened back and the upper lip extended. Typically a male tests a female's receptivity by sniffing her genitals and resting his head on her hindquarters or pushing his chest against her rump. Jacks also pursue and attempt to mount unreceptive jennies. Colts are capable of siring foals as soon as their testes descend but feral males do not achieve dominance (and therefore hold territories and do much breeding) until they are around four years old.

Jennies come into season once every 21-28 days, and remain receptive for 2-10 days. They may not come into season if they are in poor physical condition or if the environment is unfavourable. The wild asses in the Danakil region of Somalia, for example, breed only in the rainy season, and some feral donkey populations are also known to have a definite breeding and foaling season. The gestation period is about 12 months but the interval between foals in feral populations tends to be longer (16 to 18 months). In very poor environments, jennies may only produce a foal every three years. The age at which jennies become sexually active is very variable. There have been reliable reports of feral jennies conceiving when they were under a year old though most jennies are at least two years old before they have their first foal.

The donkey's behavioural flexibility enables it to adjust to a variety of social conditions. However, one relationship that is immutable and universal is that between a jenny and her foal. This relationship is essential for the foal's survival. It takes a few days to become established, during which time the jenny is very protective towards her foal. She always positions herself between her foal and other animals. She maintains close physical contact and often nuzzles and grooms her foal. Once the foal is familiar

Jennies maintain close physical contact with their newborn foals.

with his mother, he is allowed contact with others but, if danger threatens, the mother calls and searches for her foal. Whilst young foals rest, their mothers remain close by but as foals age they take the initiative in remaining near to their mothers. Members of groups that contain several jennies with their foals tend to rest close together but the adults never all rest at the same time.

After the first few days it is the foal that takes the initiative in suckling. This is particularly so in arid areas where lactating jennies increase their risk of starvation and predation by the necessity of staying close to water (they must drink 2-3 times a day). These jennies only allow the first suckling bout; thereafter foals are rebuffed and can suckle only after several attempts.

In less arid areas, jennies allow foals unrestricted suckling for the first five days and occasionally may invite older foals to suckle. Foals that want to suckle adopt a special approach to their mother. On approach, the foal vocalises softly, lays back his ears and sometimes tosses his head. If the jenny intends the foal to suckle, she will stand with a back leg flexed. When the foal reaches his mother, he noses and nips her face. He then turns and pushes his head against her udder and noses at the teat. While the foal suckles, the jenny will sniff him and will nip his back leg if he sucks too violently. If she does not want to suckle, she will continue browsing or will walk away from her foal. If the foal persists, she will threaten him. Jennies are not averse to giving an importunate foal the odd nip or kick!

Wild ass foals suck every 3-10 minutes until they are 5 days old; by 10 days they suck every 20-30 minutes. Until they are about 7 weeks old, wild ass foals suck about 40-50 times per day. They suck for about one minute and consume between 178 to 263 grams of milk each time. On average very young donkey foals suckle every 15-20 minutes for about a minute. Suckling frequency declines with age. Foals nibble at vegetation in their first week but rarely eat it - the grass is usually dropped from their mouths. They also nibble at wood and other inappropriate objects. They will use a salt lick when available and eat their mothers' faeces. They begin to graze and drink water in their 4th week. They usually paw the ground before attempting to graze. Interestingly, desert dwelling adults are very effective at digging for water, using an action reminiscent of this foal behaviour.

Foals suckle at any time but most commonly after a period of separation, rest, or disturbance, or when other foals start suckling. Most foals have been weaned by 8 to 10 months of age. However, if there is no younger sibling, foals may continue to suckle well beyond their first year.

The bond between jenny and foal changes as the foal becomes increasingly independent. An older foal spends much of its time away from its mother and returns to her only when danger threatens. The rate at which the foal becomes independent is affected by the social and physical environment. For example, foals with playmates move farther away from their mothers than solitary foals, as do foals living in fields compared with foals in woodland.

Over the millennia, donkeys have developed highly flexible patterns of behaviour and social organisation. It is this very flexibility that has enabled donkeys to survive and thrive in many different situations. With the result that today, while some donkeys can still be found leading a wild ancestral life in remoter desert regions, they play a vital part in agriculture and transport in many countries, and are also ever-popular companion animals.

JANE FRENCH, B.Sc., Ph.D., graduated in Applied Biology from Bath University in 1978 and obtained her Doctorate from Cambridge University in 1982. She has been studying animal behaviour formally for nearly 20 years. During this period she has observed a wide variety of wild and domestic species. Her particular interest is in social behaviour.

She undertook a Research Fellowship 1987 to 1990 at Bristol University on donkey behaviour, sponsored by the Donkey Sanctuary. Thereafter she worked for a year as a behavioural consultant, followed by four years for the Donkey Sanctuary both in research and administration.

She currently works as a freelance consultant.

9a
BREEDS IN EUROPE
Marilyn Squance

THE HORSE AND DONKEY are separate equine species as is the zebra and they can all interbreed to produce hybrids. The crossing of a zebra stallion and donkey mare is recorded as far back as the 1700s and has become popular in America in recent years. The hybrid is referred to as a 'Zonk', 'Zeedonk' or 'Zonkey'. There is at least one 'Zeedonk' in the UK. In the early 1900s 'Zeedonks' were bred in Africa in order to produce a more disease-resistant animal as the zebra is immune to tsetse fly and African horse sickness. However, this breeding was probably only on a small scale. Between 1820 and 1830 mountain zebra/ass hybrids were bred at Windsor Park.

When two separate species are interbred the hybrid offspring are almost always sterile due to the different number of chromosomes inherited from each parent (donkeys 62 chromosomes, horses 64, Grevy zebra 46, burchelline zebra 44, mountain zebra 32). Equine species do not interbreed in the wild.

With the spread of the donkey throughout the world, distinct strains were encouraged to breed in order to satisfy the particular needs of various areas, for pack carrying, cart pulling, mule breeding, etc., and the requirements of the various terrains, e.g. sure footedness for mountainous areas, speed for flat land, etc. Sadly many of these breeds have become extinct with the decline of the use of the donkey, particularly in the Western world. When the idea was mooted of compiling a chapter to record information on European domesticated breeds still in existence I accepted the task with enthusiasm. After much frustration and despair, through the difficulty of obtaining such information, I offer what many might see as a feeble effort. However, not to be easily defeated and consoling myself

The zeedonk.

with the quote, 'A journey of a thousand miles must start with a single step' I have recorded the information obtained in the hope that I will be contacted by those that have knowledge of other breeds and the information can be gathered for the next edition of the Handbook. I am indeed most grateful to those who have helped provide the information on the following breeds.

FRANCE

The Grand Noir Du Berry

(The Big Black Berry donkey) The Grand Noir du Berry donkey was the draught animal 'par excellence' of the small farmer in the province of Berry. For working in the fields and vineyards, large, strong donkeys tended to be selected over the years; towards the middle of the 19th century these donkeys replaced humans to pull the barges on the Berry canal and, further on towards Paris, on the Briare canal and its offshoots. Some bibliographic sources have made mention of a supply of donkeys brought in from Algeria around the 1850s but in the absence of any official documentation, it is not easy to follow the origins of the breed. It was the Thiaulins de Lignières, an association for the conservation of popular Berry traditions, that became

The Grand Noir du Berry.

concerned at the disappearance of the donkey in their region and a gathering of donkeys was organised at their annual fair in 1986. This was the beginning of a new awareness as they were surprised that there were more of these big, black donkeys than they had imagined. From then on there were more and more donkeys every year at their Whit Monday donkey and mule fair at Lignières - 100 donkeys in 1990 and 220 in 1993. Since then a group of breeders and those interested in the Berry breed established a standard for the breed from the donkeys found at the fair, from the memories of older residents and from documentation such as old postcards. The Association Française de l'Ane Grand Noir du Berry was founded to promote the breeding and use of the Berry donkey and to establish a Stud Book. The census carried out in 1993 brought forth 80 donkeys (males and females) conforming to the standard. In 1994 six males were authorised for stud. The French National Stud has recognised the Grand Noir du Berry donkey as a breed since 1994.

At four years of age the male measures from 135cm (13.1 hh) to 145cm (14.1 hh) at the withers and the female measures a minimum of 130cm (12.3 hh). The coat is single coloured, from bay brown to dark bay brown and may go to black. There is no cross, no streaks or zebra stripes on the legs. The belly, shoulders and inside thighs are grey/white. In the adult the summer coat is short - it almost looks clipped. The muzzle is grey/white, sometimes edged with red. The eye is bright with a grey/white surround, sometimes edged with red. The neck is strong, the back straight and the hindquarters either rounded or sloped. In silhouette the donkey is very well proportioned.

The Provence

The Provence donkey is also known as the 'Migration donkey', the 'Aries donkey', the 'Crau donkey' and the 'Savoie donkey'. The oldest written record of the importance of donkeys in the sheep-rearing districts of Basse-Provence and the mountain pastures of Haute-Provence, the French Alps and the Dauphin region date from the 15th century. For almost five centuries donkeys played an essential role in the seasonal movement of sheep - carrying materials, food for the shepherds, salt for the sheep and even the lambs born on the journey. The shepherds bred a donkey with a solid bone structure, well able to carry heavy loads, with a docile temperament and good legs to cover the migratory routes.

The Provence Donkey Association was formed on December 22nd, 1992, in order to promote the knowledge and the use of the Provence donkey, to encourage breeders to rebuild a sufficient pure-blood herd and to prevent any further introduction of foreign blood. The decline of the Provence donkey was alarming. The use of the railway, followed by lorry transportation, had considerably reduced the donkey's role. A census in the Provencal departments recorded 13,000 animals at the end of the 19th century, 2,000 in 1956 and only 330 in 1993.

The Provence donkey was recognised by the National Stud as a breed on December 18th, 1995, and joined the Baudet de Poitou and the Grand Noir du Berry in being managed by the breeders and the National Stud. The National Stud maintains a genealogical list of all the known horse or donkey breeds on a central file at Pompadour.

In 1996 the official administration of the breed with the setting up of the Stud Book began. It is envisaged that approximately 300 males and females will be registered, many of the donkeys continuing to be owned by shepherds.

The Provence donkey is hardy and solid with strong bone structure, calm and patient, easy to saddle, to put to harness or to ride. He is very sure footed even on rough ground. At four years of age the male stands 120cm (11.3hh) to 133cm (13 hh) and the female 117cm (11.2hh) to 130cm (12.3hh). The coat is dove grey and can vary from light grey to dark grey and often has a hint of red or brown. There is a dark, well defined cross. The head is of strong bone structure, well set on the neck. Often the donkeys have white around the eyes. The forehead, the ears and the edge of the eyes almost always have a brown/red tint. The muzzle is generally white, sometimes circled with red. The limbs are solid with a strong bone structure and may be marked with black zebra stripes and there is often at least one diagonal stripe on the front hocks. The foot is quite large for a donkey. The back is straight, flanks are large and hindquarters solid.

Shows are held annually in February at St Martin-de-Crau and April at Brignoles in Var. In September of even years in Ardèche and September of odd years in Savoie.

The Pyrenees Donkey

Also known in the south and south-west of France as the Gascon. The Pyrenees donkey's descendents were the Catalan from Spain. Along with the Baudet du Poitou the Pyrenees donkey was referred to in documents of the 19th and early 20th century and both were used in the production of mules. The Pyrenees donkey is more fine boned than the Poitou and has a short, dark coat. As early as 1801, J.B. Huzard, in praise of these donkeys, wrote that 'just before the revolution, the mills of Toulouse, Montauban and Moissac were still being served by donkeys of an

The Pyrenees.

The Pyrenees.

uncommon size and strength' and in 1857 J.H. Magne also praised the capability of the breed 'which trots just as quickly as a horse pulling two people in a two wheeled cart and which can work just as well as the heavy draught horses while costing a lot less to feed'.

In the last century, Pyrenees mares were used to produce asses milk which was recommended by doctors at the time and the males were mainly used in mule production in the South of France or as draught animals.

The breed was credited as being the best adapted form of transport for rough terrain and an indispensable part of the agriculture of mountainous slopes.

With the rare exception of tourism, donkeys have not been used for work in the Pyrenees since the middle of this century. In the absence of reliable figures, it is assumed there are still between 1,500 and 2,000 donkeys on the French side of the Pyrenees range and The Pyrenees Donkey

Breeders Association is presently trying to ascertain how many of these donkeys are Pyrenees donkeys.

The coat of the Pyrenees donkey varies from shiny black, shaded black, to dark brown or chestnut. The area around the eyes, the base of the nose, the inside thigh and the belly are faded almost to white. The coat is short except up to the age of two years when it is fluffy. The height can be from 120cm (11.3 hh) upwards and the larger donkeys are very elegant.

The Pyrenees Donkey Breeders Association was founded in 1994 by donkey lovers worried about the disappearance of the breed. In 1995 the Agricultural School in Gers became involved and gave their support and the aim is to gain official recognition of the breed. A standard has been established together with an inventory and registration scheme for the Pyrenees area and the south-west. In August 1996, 18 stallions and 23 females were registered in Book A and 54 animals in Book B recording mares that, for some minor reason, do not conform to the standard.

Normandy

The Ane Normand was recognised by the National Stud in 1996 and 36 donkeys were microchipped. The Normandy donkeys were used on farms

The Normand.

The Cotentin.

for transporting milk, milled corn, hay, etc, and also used at seaside resorts.

The Association de l'Ane Normand held their 17th fete in 1996 at Cherisay when 254 donkeys attended.

At 4 years the male and female stand at 110cm (10.3hh) to 125cm (12.1hh). The coat is brown to mouse grey with a dorsal stripe. There are no leg stripes. The underbelly is grey/white.

Cotentin

The Cotentin is not yet recognised by the National Stud but the Association de Rehabilitation de l'Ane Cotentin is applying to the National Stud to hold a Stud Book of Cotentin donkeys. The Cotentin donkey is named from the region where it originated, which is within the Manche area of Normandy. A show is held once a year at Banneville-sur-Ajon (near Caen, Normandy) and, in 1996, 250 donkeys were entered.

The Cotentin donkey's use was on farms transporting hay, manure and apples for cider making. The male stands at 120cm (11.3hh) to 135cm (13.1hh) and the female at 115cm (11.1hh) to 130cm (12.3hh). The coat is ash grey, blue grey or dove grey with white underbelly. The Cotentin has a defined cross and some donkeys have leg stripes.

Spain

It was estimated that Spain had 2,000,000 donkeys in 1960 which was reduced to 200,000 thirty years later!

The Catalan

The Catalan stallion has been known for centuries for its value in mule breeding. In the 9th century documents report on the great height and exceptional characteristics of these donkeys. Its place of origin is Catalonia.

They have been exported in the past to many countries to produce bigger donkeys. General George Washington was given a stallion and two mares in 1785 after writing to the King of Spain, Charles IV, asking if he might purchase some Spanish donkeys of the best quality.

Spain was one of the last European countries to adopt coach transport but when the coach was established in the 17th century there was no attempt to breed a Spanish coach horse; instead mules were bred out of Andalusian horse mares by Catalan stallions.

At the end of the 19th century more than 400 stallions and 200 females were exported to North America and an unknown number to France, England, Canada, India, Australia, Africa, Italy, the Balkan States and Central

The Catalan.

and South America. This was for the purpose of improving donkey breeds in these countries and for mule production.

In the 1950s the North American army chose 300 Catalan donkeys and shipped them to America where their offspring are known as Kentucky Catalan donkeys.

It is difficult to define the geographical region of origin of the Catalan donkey. The area stretched from the Pyrenees in the north, to the Mediterranean, taking in the river basins of the Segre, Ter and Cardoner.

With the mechanisation of agriculture in the 1950s so the Catalan donkey population started to decline. In 1978 an equine fair was held in Bañolas and breeders in the region were encouraged to take along their Catalan donkeys. The Association for the Protection of the Catalan Donkey Breed was founded. The Association works with the authorities to encourage breeders to protect and improve the breed. A registration book has been set up and the Military Stud at Ecija has retained stallions and females with the correct Catalan characteristics in order to assist in the conservation of the breed. The equine fair continues to be held annually in Bañolas on the third Sunday of November.

The Catalan donkey stands at 145cm (14.1hh) to 160cm (15.3hh) for the males and 135cm (13.1hh) to 148cm (14.2hh) for the females. Its conformation gives it a graceful and long silhouette. It has an admirable temperament. It has a heavy head with a wide face and big, wide eyes accentuated by a short fringe of fine reddish hair around them. The back is relatively long with strong muscular loins. The breast is wide and deep.

The coat is dark, from black through its shades to dark grape. The underbelly, the tip of the nose and around the eyes are silver white. Between the white and the black of the coat, the hair is a reddish or chestnut colour which sometimes appears on the ears.

The Mallorquin

There are only a few pure blooded examples of the Mallorquin donkey remaining, owned by specialist breeders (12 stallions and 60 mares recorded in 1992). Its structural conformation is similar to that of the Catalan donkey but it is shorter in height and finer boned. The Mallorquin donkey was valued for mule breeding as far back as the 10th century. In 1726 the Captain General of the island of Mallorca told the Governor of Madrid that despite the 3,000 breeding horse mares in Mallorca, it would not be possible to provide the Regiment of the Strasbourg Dragoons with horses, because the mares were all being covered by donkey stallions!

The main geographical area of the donkey was the island of Mallorca but it did extend to almost all the other islands in the Balearic group in greater or lesser degrees. The females were used for reproduction and draught, carrying sacks of olives at harvest time and as a means of transport for breeders. The stallion was dedicated to mule breeding.

In 1990 a group of interested breeders and owners founded an association (ACRIPROASMA) to promote awareness of the breed and to guide breeders. The association has worked to define a standard, identify animals and set up a registration book. In 1993 the Ministry of Agriculture and Fisheries approved the standard of the Mallorquin donkey.

The Mallorquin donkey stands at between 145cm (14.1hh) to 155cm (15.1hh) for males and 125cm (12.1hh) to 135cm (13.1hh) for females. The coat is black/dark grape with shading of white/grey around the nostrils, under the mouth, eye and underbelly.

Zamorano-Leones

The Zamorano-Leones donkey was bred in the south-east of the province of Leon in the area of Zamora and used by farmers and for mule breeding.

The Zamorano-Leones.

Like other Spanish breeds its numbers decreased dramatically for many years. A Stud Book was established in 1940 but abandoned many years ago. The population has now stabilised (8,000 in existence) but there are few examples that correspond to the true conformation of the breed. Fortunately the Military Stud has retained stallions and females of the Zamorano-Leones and it is hoped that through the EEC further research can be carried out and a registration book and Stud Book eventually re-established.

The true Zamorano-Leones donkey is very robust with a long, coarse coat ranging from black to brown. The average height for a male is 151cm (14.3hh) but they have been known to grow to 157cm (15.2hh), weighing 350k. The female stands on average at 141cm (14hh). It has a large head and powerful neck with ears that tend to fall to the front or side.

The Andalucian

Known as the Andalucian or Cordobese donkey, the breed evolved in the fertile valleys of the Guadalquivir to meet the requirements of the Andalucian farmers who needed a steady, willing, patient and well developed animal that could also be used to produce mules, which were in much demand.

An agricultural census carried out between 1930 and 1960 showed a

The Andalucian.

population of between 900,000 and 1,200,000 donkeys. Its decline has been rapid and few can be found today. The Asociacion para la Defensa del Borrico Andaluz (ADEBO) in Rute (Cordoba) and Horstmann Stiftung in Lucena are pushing local government to adapt measures to improve and protect the breed which is in danger of extinction. The first steps will be taken by the Military Stud at Ecija to recover the breed and establish a register.

The standard to be achieved is a height of 145cm (14.1hh) to 158cm (15.2hh) for males and 135cm (13.1hh) to 150cm (14.3hh) for females. The head is of medium to large proportion and is carried well forward, giving the impression of energy. The coat is light dappled silver grey. The hair is short and fine. The donkey has a very graceful and fine movement and quiet disposition.

ITALY

At the beginning of this century there was an estimated million donkeys in Italy which by 1961 had depleted by 60% and has continued to fall.

The Martina Franca

Up until the 1920s experts referred to the Apulian breed, which included the Martina Franca, Marche, Romagna, Bailicata and Calabria sub breeds. All had similar conformation features and the Martina Franca is now referred to as a separate breed.

The Martina Franca donkey is found in the region of Apulia. It is known for its exceptional hardiness and strength, which makes the Martina Franca especially suitable for breeding mules. The climate in the hilly area of Apulia is cold in winter and the ground is often covered in snow, while its summers are very hot, which has led the breed to withstand extremes of temperature and produce very hardy foals.

The origins of the breed are not entirely clear but the Spanish Catalan donkey might have been introduced in the past. The Martina Franca stands 145cm (14.1hh) to 150cm (14.3hh) high and has a blackish coat. Its head is large and the neck muscular. The limbs are very sturdy.

The Martina Franca has been exported to many countries and the numbers have dropped considerably over the years. In order to prevent the race from becoming extinct, the Society for the Conservation of the Asinine Race of Martina Franca was formed and a centre established at Russoli managed by the Regional States Forests (Ufficion Foreste Demaniali

Regionali).

The Ragusa

The Ragusa, like the Martina Franca, can cope with harsh climates. It is a breed that is found particularly in Sicily and today continues to be used for riding in the countryside because of its sure-footedness on any terrain. The mules bred from these donkeys and used in wars in mountainous areas are fondly remembered for their patience and good temperament. The Ragusa donkeys are generally dark bay in colour with a lighter brown coloured underside. The males stand 140cm (13.3hh) to 145cm (14.1hh) and the females 135cm (13.1hh) to 138cm (13.2hh).

The Pantelleria

The breed is almost extinct but in the past the donkeys around Trapani in Sicily were sought after by many countries for use in the circus ring. They had extraordinary stamina enabling them to maintain a speed of 9 m.p.h. pulling light loads for several hours. In the past races were held at which donkeys reached 15 m.p.h. The coat is blackish or dark bay and is short and shiny with an oily touch, quite different to the coat of other breeds. The head is small and thin. The Pantelleria has a very graceful action and is a lively but nervous animal. The average height is 125cm (12.1hh) to 130cm (12.3hh).

The Amiata

A breed of fairly large donkeys that were found in the provinces of Tuscany. The breed is now preserved from extinction by the Pisa Horse Breeding Institute which retains some mares on the Cernaia estate near Grosseto. The Amiata is mouse-grey with a dark cross on the back and leg stripes. It is a strong, lively donkey standing between 135cm (13.1hh) to 138cm (13.2hh).

The Asinara

Donkeys have for centuries been found on the small island of Asinara which is separated from Sardinia by a short stretch of sea. The breeding of some of the donkeys is now controlled while the remainder are allowed to run wild. Most are pure white and often have blue eyes. They have a small stature, standing at between 80cm (31½ inches) and 100cm (9.3hh), and their features have

The Sardinian.

made them desirable as performing animals in circuses. Inbreeding has produced many cases of infertility in mares and the breed is now protected and breeding stock based at a state property at Follonica in Grosseto. The origin of the breed is uncertain and some consider it is a sub-breed derived from the Sardinian donkey.

The Sardinian

The shepherds used the Sardinian donkey to carry their belongings out to the fields daily and on the return to carry firewood. At least twice a year the sheep would be moved to another grazing area and the donkey would carry all the goods and food needed for the shepherd and his family. In the past almost all the people of Sardinia were involved in the growing of food on various scales and owned a donkey to carry the tools and produce. In some areas of Sardinia donkey meat was considered to be a particular delicacy.

The Sardinian donkey stands at the withers at between 85cm (33½ inches) and 115cm (11.1hh) and weighs 90 to 130 kilograms. The coat is grey with a white underbelly and there is a distinct cross on the back. It is a very small donkey but has solid legs and is very robust. It is known for its patience and gentle manner.

The Sardinian donkey has declined as new agricultural developments have been introduced. In 1965 some 27,000 donkeys were registered. At that time registration was required by law to combat the wide practice of animal rustling but the number is probably on the low side as many people did not bother to register their donkeys. Today there are estimated to be no more than 200 donkeys on the island. Sixty Sardinian donkeys are based in the park at Ortueri under the care of Salvatore Casula, the local Mayor. An agreement was reached between the Association for the Defence of the Sardinian Donkey and the communal administration of Ortueri and 60 hectares were made available for the donkeys where they forage in open spaces and woodland. They are cared for by the Circle of Farmers and free veterinary attention is provided by a vet at the Regional Institute for Hippic Development. With little funding they are trying desperately to prevent the extinction of this breed and are preparing a Stud Book.

The **Miniature Mediterranean Donkey**, so popular in America today, was bred from donkeys imported from Sicily and Sardinia. These donkeys must be under 91.44 cm (36 inches) at the withers to be registered by the American Donkey and Mule Society as miniatures. Like the Sardinian donkey they have a life expectancy of 30 to 35 years.

The donkey has been a neglected species for far too long and it is important that we encourage interest in these marvellous breeds that have toiled for man for generations.

References

Hemphill, S., 'Zebra Mules', *The Brayer Magazine*, USA.

Dent, A. ,*The Story of the Ass from East to West*, Harrap (1972)

With grateful thanks to the following organisations for supplying information: Association des Eleveurs d'Anes Pyreneens; Horstmann Stiftung; Equine Stud, Ministere de l'Agriculture, Madrid; Association de Rehabilitation de l'Ane Cotentin; Association de l'Ane Normand; Association Française de l'Ane Grand Noir du Berry; Association de l'Ane de Provence; ADEBO; Comune di Ortueri; Associacio del Foment de la Raca Asinina Catalana (French Branch)

MARILYN SQUANCE joined the Donkey Sanctuary in 1981 and has been part of Dr Elisabeth Svendsen's team involved in the development of the Sanctuary to the 5th largest animal welfare charity in the UK that it is today. Joining as Secretary, Mal Squance was then promoted to Dr Svendsen's Personal Assistant, a post she held for many years. In 1995 she was appointed Deputy Administrator of the Donkey Sanctuary and the International Donkey Protection Trust (a post she shares with Paul Svendsen).

9b
THE POITOU:
a breed threatened and saved

Robert Camac

EVERY YEAR, the International Donkey Protection Trust receives many requests for help to relieve the suffering of donkeys caused by cruelty, ignorance or neglect. However, one request to Dr Svendsen was of a very different kind. It came from Professor François Ramade of the Department of Zoology and Ecology at Paris University, asking the Trust to help to save a rare breed of donkey from extinction.

Poitou is the old name of a province of France about three hundred miles south-west of Paris. The Loire Valley lies to the north, and the wine-producing country around Bordeaux to the south. The capital, Poitiers, is in the east of the province, a fertile agricultural region growing cereals and sugar-beet. The west of Poitou, bordered by the Atlantic Ocean, is flat and green, with large areas of marshes and criss-crossed by thousands of canals. This area, the home of the Poitou donkey, is quite unlike the dry stony countryside usually associated with the donkey but, as I was soon to learn, the Poitou is no ordinary ass! For hundreds of years, it was bred solely to be used in mule breeding, an activity which made an important contribution to the French agricultural economy and for which Poitou had a worldwide reputation.

The adult male Poitou donkey is called a *baudet*, which is pronounced 'bo-day'. He stands 14 to 15 hands, and the main points of conformation are: a long heavy head and long ears, well covered with long hair; thick strong neck; long straight back; slightly prominent hips; short croup; long well muscled thigh; straight shoulder and - most important of all - large broad feet which are shod. The *baudet* is stabled except when taken out to cover a horse or donkey mare. (A donkey mare is called an *ânesse.*) The colour of the thick coat of the Poitou, which is matted and tangled, is

Baudet du Poitou.

brown-bay, the belly and inside of the thigh being light grey. The Poitou does not have an eel stripe. This is a useful point in distinguishing a pure bred animal from other donkeys whose owners try to pass them off as pure bred and obtain an inflated price on sale. The *ânesse* is about one hand lower than the *baudet*; the coat is not as thick and the pelvis and croup are wider.

Unfortunately, many of the old records have been destroyed, but those that still exist show that in 400 years the conformation has not changed. This is because the breeders recognised that the *baudet* sired the best mules and that the breed should be kept pure and not crossed with other breeds of donkey. These mules were in great demand both in France and abroad. A history of mule-breeding in Poitou in the Middle Ages refers to a letter from an Italian prelate called Leon to Guillaume IV, then Count of Poitou - 'Please send me one of your magnificent mules.' He had been repeating this request for six years!

The reason why the patient Leon described the mule which he so badly wanted as 'magnificent' is because it would have been sired by a Baudet du Poitou. The history of the Poitou is closely linked to the history of mule-breeding. Originally the *baudet* covered a mare of one of the French breeds of heavy horses, such as the Breton. In 1599 Henri IV gave Hunfroy

Bradley, from the Duchy of Brabant, an experienced drainage engineer, the right to drain 3,000 hectares of marshland in Poitou, a contract which lasted for about eighty years. He brought draught horses from Brabant with him. The mares proved to be ideal dams for mule breeding, for not only did the *baudet* cover them more easily than the other breeds, but their mule foals commanded higher prices and sold more readily.

The Poitou mule stands 15.1 to 16.1 hands. The breeding of these mules became so successful that in the 18th century the governing bodies of the national studs became alarmed and felt it necessary to make regulations prohibiting the covering of horse mares by *baudets* in order to protect the breeds of horses. In 1770 one of the directors wanted a law passed for all donkey stallions to be gelded! However, the government recognised the value of mule-breeding to the country's economy, and encouragement was given in the form of premiums for approved animals retained for breeding; subsidies were given to breeders and cash prizes awarded at shows. In addition, some animals were bought by the National Stud and in 1884 a Stud Book was opened in order to improve the breeds of both the donkey and the *mulassier* (the type of horse suitable for breeding mules), to establish and maintain the desired points of conformation and to safeguard the future of both breeds.

The Poitou was exported to many countries, including America, Russia, the Belgian Congo and North Africa, and the army bought large numbers of mules. However, by 1950 there was little demand for the Poitou, either in France or abroad. The mule could not compete with the tractor and the lorry, and mule-breeding ceased to provide a living for the breeder. The effect on the Poitou was catastrophic. Some breeders sold or killed their herds. There was little point in registering the birth of foals or the fact that animals had been sold. The Poitou donkey had become an endangered species, but no-one seemed to have noticed.

Research into the breeding of the Poitou donkey was undertaken by Annick Audiot, a former student of Professor Ramade. The results of her research were published in 1977, by the French Institute of National Research into the Rural Economy. The statistics revealed by her survey caused great dismay. It was discovered that in the 'départements' which now form the old province of Poitou, the number of *baudets* recorded between the years 1949 and 1977 had fallen from 218 to 12, and the number of recorded *ânesses* had fallen from 340 to 13. During the same period, the number of Stud Book registrations had dropped from 125 to 7. (In 1976 there had been only 2.) Causing even more concern for the future of the breed were the findings relating to fertility. In 73% of recorded services, the *ânesse* either did not hold or aborted, and of the foals which were born, over one-third were dead. The average life expectancy of a Poitou donkey is fourteen years, and with fewer animals surviving, the problems of the breed became more acute. The survey drew attention to these problems, which included a critical review of traditional methods of stallion management, stable hygiene and consanguinity.

Following the publication of these findings, the regional Parc Naturel contacted breeders, national studs, research scientists and local authorities and a meeting was held in November 1979.

A programme to save the breed from extinction was agreed: to take a census of all Poitou donkeys and open a Stud Book with sections for pure breds and part breds; to set up an experimental breeding unit to improve the breed and breeding methods; to trace and preserve the old archives and to attract public attention and support.

The project was to be shared between the remaining private breeders, who were to be responsible for the continued breeding of the pure breds, and various statutory bodies. The Parc Naturel was to set up and administer the technical and scientific committees and take charge of research, publicity and attracting tourists. Their executive in charge was Marc-André Philippe, a graduate in both Ecology and Rural Economy who, like Annick Audiot, came from a Poitevin family. This local connection is an important factor in gaining the confidence and the co-operation of the breeders of the region. With their scientific qualifications, M. Philippe and Mme. Audiot appreciated the necessity for the use of modern technology to save the breed. Because of their local connections, they were able to put their point of view to the breeders with tact and diplomacy.

The experimental breeding unit at La Tillauderie - the Asinerie - was under the joint control of the Parc Naturel and the local Haras (National Stud). At the Asinerie, a programme of cross-breeding is followed, in case the pure breds were to be wiped out, for example by an epidemic. Large Portuguese *ânesses* were imported and covered by a *baudet*. The male progeny are sold. The female progeny are covered as three-year-olds by an unrelated *baudet*, so as to produce a three-quarters-bred animal. This process is repeated until the Spanish or Portuguese blood is bred out. Unfortunately,

Baudet du Poitou leased to the Asinerie 1988.

it was this project which suffered the first setback when there were a number of sudden foal deaths, followed in the next year by the deaths of eight *ânesses.* In addition five foals died in 1988 in another stud.

The Asinerie then consisted of a group of old stone farm buildings around a courtyard and included seven hectares of land, leased from the late Mlle Auger whose stud of Poitou donkeys was founded over a century ago by her great-grandfather. Whilst accurate figures were not available it appeared that she, and her manager M. Jean-Luc Duguy, owned about half of the recorded Poitou donkeys at that time. Mlle Auger was certainly the doyenne of the breeders.

On my return from France in 1986, I reported to the Trustees of the I.D.P.T. and they decided that the Trust should help to save this unique breed of donkey. In 1987, M. Philippe visited England to see the facilities of the Donkey Sanctuary, and the outlines of a scheme of co-operation were agreed. In the following year, John Fowler, B.Vet.Med., M.R.C.V.S., who was then the Senior Veterinary Surgeon at the Sanctuary, and I paid three visits to France. At the request of the Asinerie, and with the full agreement of local breeders, blood was taken from twenty-six donkeys in order to report on their general health and to record the clinical points of difference between the Poitou donkey and the 'ordinary' donkey. More detailed enquiries were also made into the deaths of the *ânesses* in the previous year.

Our report inevitably reflected deep concern about the traditional, outdated methods of stable and stallion management still being practised. The I.D.P.T. put forward certain proposals and in August we returned to France, where a very important development had just taken place. A new association called la SABAUD had been formed with a former French Minister of Agriculture, M. Fouchier, as President, and the son of a former Poitou breeder, M. Moreau, as Vice President. Both were veterinary surgeons living in Poitou. La SABAUD stands for 'Sauvegarder le Baudet' (Save the *Baudet*). This aim was stated in the articles of the new association, together with the following statement: 'The present scientific knowledge which we have of the *baudet* is not enough to save the breed. We, the founder members, the sons of former breeders, realise from our experience that the private studs cannot, on their own, carry out the research which is required to save the breed.'

The articles specifically referred to the problems of in-breeding, recent cross-breeding with other breeds of donkeys, and conditions of stable management and breeding. The breed was obviously on the point of

Niort Show 1906: prizewinning Baudet.

close this section, and in future to register animals only if their sire was registered in Section A. At that time Section B included 250 female donkeys. This was considerably more than the number of females in Section A. It was thought that this posed a serious threat which could weaken the characteristics of the breed. It was proposed to reduce this number drastically by asking the breeders to agree to retain in Section B only 50 or 100 of the best females already registered.

As far back as 1979 a programme of selective cross-breeding at the Asinerie, using large *ânesses* specially imported from Portugal, had been agreed. This has been followed and foals of the 4th generation have now been born. The descendants of the 7th generation of cross-breeding will be able to be incorporated in the original race.

Important research has continued. Although the first attempts of embryo transfer have not been successful, it is hoped that the major problems can soon be overcome. It is also disappointing that, in spite of research, there are still too many abortions which cannot be accounted for.

However the most exciting recent event, a real success story, was the birth in 1995 of a filly, Galaxie II, the first Poitou foal to be born by artificial insemination, using frozen semen collected 3 days earlier. This entirely new technique was devised by Professor Tainturier and his team at the Ecole Nationale at Nantes. Eight more *ânesses* have been similarly impregnated. It is hoped to set up an Insemination Centre to collect sperm from as many *baudets* as possible. Some sperm will be retained at the Centre and some will be used on pure-bred *ânesses* taken to the Centre for insemination, or exported abroad in specially designed containers. This technique will also enable sperm to be collected from *baudets* in other regions in France and from abroad and stored at the Centre until required.

Interest in the Poitou from abroad has increased. The Commission from Poitou visited Germany and confirmed the registration of 10 animals in Section A and 9 in Section B. With the agreement of the German breeders 12 animals were struck off. In his report in 1996 the President of la SABAUD wrote, 'For the breeders to agree that inferior animals already registered should be struck out of the Stud Book, even though this resulted in a loss of 30,000 French Francs per animal, is a marvellous example of the determination to improve a breed.'

The Americans are showing further interest in the Poitou, mainly due to the contribution which the breed makes to mule-breeding. At the end of 1995 10 animals registered in Section A were either exported or about to be exported to the USA.

In Switzerland there are 6 animals in Section A, and the Parc Zoologique, just over the border at Mulhouse, has a herd of 15 Section A animals.

The work of the Commission in checking and identifying animals for the Stud Book continues. In England it is understood that there are 7 animals, 3 males and 4 females registered in Section A. The 3 males are Torrent at the Slade Centre based at The Donkey Sanctuary, Devon, Theodore at Marwell Zoological Park and Doré du Bourg at Banham Zoo in Norfolk. Two of the females which came from France are at Banham Zoo. The other 2 females, Danielle (Torrent X Jonquille) and Iolanthe (Theodore X Danielle) were born at the Slade Centre.

In his excellent book, *Sauver Le Baudet du Poitou*, Marc-André Philippe quoted from a work, *Christian Gaul,* written in 1109 by Eugène Ayrault which 'established the fact that the Poitou donkey was already well known and highly valued at that time.' Records confirming this go back even earlier.

Danielle, still only a yearling, at the Bath and West Show.

Only twenty years ago the Poitou donkey faced extinction. Thanks to the resolve of local and national associations to meet this challenge, to support received from other regions in France and from abroad, and finally to the policy of la SABAUD and the dedication of its officers, this ancient breed has been saved.

After a thousand years the Poitou thrives at the start of another millennium.

(In including this new chapter in *The Professional Handbook,* Dr Svendsen and Mr Camac wish to acknowledge their indebtedness to the past and present presidents of la SABAUD and the Parc Naturel Régional du Marais Poitevin, Mme Annick Audiot and M. Marc-André Philippe.)

10
DONKEYS ABROAD
Elisabeth D. Svendsen

THERE CAN BE NO COMPARISON between the working donkey abroad and its more fortunate relative in the UK.

Throughout the world, find a working donkey and you will find poverty and people living on, or below, the bread-line. In all parts of the globe, donkeys play a vital role in agricultural and family life. Owing to the poverty of their owners, veterinary care and adequate food are the exception rather than the rule, and so conditions at best are poor for the donkey; and little is known from a professional point of view as to the minimum amount of food and water on which they can live and work. Although all Third World donkeys tend to be over-worked and under-nourished, they are treated very differently from one continent and area to another.

European countries differ greatly. Parts of Spain give great cause for concern and in the past Greece has caused problems. Fortunately, the Greek authorities are rapidly controlling the situation now, and enormous improvements have been made over the last few years.

Working through The International Donkey Protection Trust, I have visited and worked in many countries. Throughout my travels, I have been amazed to find the average life expectancy of donkeys and mules in these countries is 11 years, whereas the average age expectancy of donkeys in the UK, taken from a number of 989, is 27.64 years. To the poor peasant, the death of his donkey is a major calamity and to continue his farming and transport of goods, to buy another donkey, he has to dig into any capital he may be lucky enough to have. The approximate cost of the donkey would be the equivalent of £40-£60 - in some parts of the world, a major expense. This early demise has been unquestioned, as no veterinary surgeon has been involved, because the poor are unable to afford the fees.

Simple research carried out during my working trips abroad, and followed up by official trials, has proved parasites to be the major cause of death.

The difference in the condition of animals treated by a simple worming dose biannually is significant. The scant food eaten is digested by the donkey rather than the parasite, so the animal is able to increase its bodyweight. This means a thicker cover of flesh over bone, which reduces the terrible saddle galls and injuries caused through rubbing, so frequent in working donkeys. A fitter donkey means it is more capable of doing its job and the fact that its life should be extended dramatically will be of major help to the poor of the Third World.

PROBLEMS ABROAD FOUND IN DIFFERENT AREAS

Spain

In Spain many donkeys are used as part of the tourist industry and many are abused. A Code of Practice (see end of chapter) has been drawn up jointly by the International Donkey Protection Trust and the World Society for the Protection of Animals and presented to the Spanish Government. The code was adopted in Tenerife as a test case and this has come into force and will help conditions in riding establishments. It is hoped that in due course this will be enforced throughout Spain. The Spanish donkey in Tenerife is larger than the average English donkey and in consultation with the veterinary profession a workable weight limit which could be enforced was agreed.

In areas such as Marbella and Mijas, large numbers of donkeys used in tourist excursions had to stand all day without water and shelter but, after pressure, these facilities are now provided.

Our charity has objected to photographs taken for postcards where donkeys are clothed and made to sit in unnatural positions as well as the use of donkeys on a merry-go-round, where they are tied and forced to walk a continual circle carrying tourists.

A great deal of concern and attention was focused, by our charity and the national press, on the annual Lenten fiesta held at Villanueva de la Vera. The carnival lasts for four days and it has been the custom that on Shrove Tuesday the men, called '*calabaceros*' (pumpkin sellers), lead their 'boss' through the streets of the village riding a donkey. The 'boss' was usually the fattest man of the village and the oldest donkey in the village

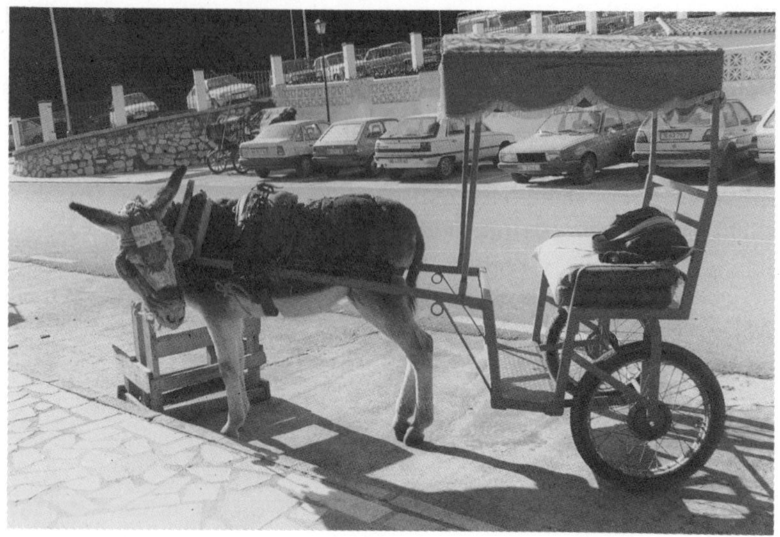

A burro (donkey) taxi in Mijas, Spain.

was selected. The man was put on the back of the donkey who was then dragged through the cobbled streets by a long, thick rope with over fifty knots in it. Youths and men each took a place at a knot in the rope and dragged the terrified animal through the village streets. The donkey fell frequently, partly because of the weight and partly because of the jerky dragging that he was subjected to. Each time the donkey fell he was kicked and poked and forced to stand again until, at last, after over fifty minutes, he was dragged into the market square. Eventually, when the animal was no longer able to stand, the crowd of men surrounding him would throw themselves onto the donkey chanting a song which included the words, 'Finally the donkey died and has left this miserable life....' The donkey was crushed by the crowd in 1986 and, although on first hearing that the donkey was killed we found it difficult to believe, we were given photographic evidence which showed the crowd on top of the donkey with only the donkey's leg protruding underneath. In 1987 Blackie, the donkey used in the fiesta, was rescued and the Donkey Sanctuary was asked to take him into their care. After undergoing his quarantine period we collected Blackie from Spain and he spent six happy years with us until his death in 1993.

The International Donkey Protection Trust attended the fiesta in 1988 and every year since then. In 1991 a petition with over a million signatures was presented to the European Parliament, carried on the back of a life-sized model donkey, which we named Blackie II. Blackie II had been offered to the villagers of Villanueva de la Vera in an attempt to persuade them to use it instead of using a live donkey, but unfortunately they refused to accept it.

Up to 1996, thanks to sending letters to everyone in the village and speaking at the local schools, things greatly improved. A donkey called Misty was used, and to a certain extent he was protected by his owner and the mayor's staff. However, the 1996 fiesta was a terrible event, in which the donkey fell at least 30 times, he was pushed and hit by a drunken crowd and nearly crushed to death during one of his falls when the crowd fell on top of him.

Help is once again being sought from not only UK charities but also from overseas animal welfare organisations, and in 1997 a concerted effort will be made to protect the donkey ourselves. Spanish members of the Intergroup on the Welfare and Conservation of Animals at the European Parliament, to whom I reported these terrible fiestas early in 1996, have agreed to play as large a part as possible in persuading the villagers to renounce this tradition of using a live donkey.

Greece

In Greece, from 1982 to 1985, with the support of the Agricultural Bank of Greece and the Ministry of Agriculture, the International Donkey Protection Trust set up worming trials to control the parasites in mules and donkeys. The donkey will always be part of the Greek peasant's working life, particularly on the isolated islands and in mountainous regions. The Greek Government has, in fact, taken responsibility for improving conditions and has allocated 150 million drachmas to the worming of animals. The majority of Greek people treat their donkeys well although the custom of adults riding the donkey will take many years to alter. Overloading is the main problem but the situation is improving rapidly. On Santorini, where the donkeys have to carry tourists up some 597 steps, conditions have improved a little. The government has installed a telpherage and a permanent veterinary surgeon is now based at Santorini. The Greek Animal Welfare Fund is working wherever it can and is gradually improving conditions for donkeys.

On the island of Patmos a donkey shelter is being set up, with advice from the International Donkey Protection Trust, by Prince Sadruddin Aga Khan and his wife, Princess Catherine, and their charity, the Bellrive Trust.

Turkey

Many donkeys are in use in the mountainous areas here, but the thousands of donkeys used up to 1980 on the coastal lowlands have been replaced by tractors. It was surprising to find that generally the animals were treated with sympathy by their owners, although recently we have received a few isolated reports of donkeys in poor condition. Ignorance, as in so many other parts of the world, is often the cause of distress to donkeys, and it is not unusual to see donkeys left hobbled for the night with their heavy wooden saddles still fitted.

Egypt

From 1992 to 1995 the International Donkey Protection Trust was able to run two mobile clinics working in the Nile Delta, where thousands of donkeys were treated by our teams and their owners were educated as far as possible on donkeys' needs. The charity worked under the umbrella of the General Organization for Veterinary Services, and this co-operation worked extremely well until, unfortunately, the G.O.V.S was privatised late in 1995. This meant that we could no longer work in Egypt, and to ensure that help continued to be given to the donkeys our mobile clinics were passed over, complete with all medications, to the Brooke Hospital, who are already established in Cairo and are able to continue working there. They have promised to give as much help to the donkeys as possible.

Cyprus

Dr G. Papadopoulos of the World Health Organization invited veterinary surgeons throughout the world to attend training courses arranged in the United Kingdom by the International Donkey Protection Trust. Dr George Efstathiou from Cyprus is one such vet and was most impressed with his visit to the Donkey Sanctuary. He invited us to Cyprus to see the conditions of donkeys for ourselves and to help in the setting up of a worming trial. The animals were found to be in a superb condition, and the very large, sprightly donkeys and mules were much valued by their owners. Most of the donkeys lived in the mountainous regions where their main task was to help in the grape harvest. The Department of Veterinary Services took over the task of treating the donkeys with anthelmintic and expressed their gratitude for drawing this need to their attention. Almost every donkey and mule in Cyprus is now dosed against parasites. The Department of Veterinary Services responds to all reports of cruelty referred to them, and has been known to prosecute owners when conditions are particularly bad. They are probably the best veterinary department in the world for responding to reports of cruelty and taking action. An excellent sanctuary has been set up by the Friends of the Cyprus Donkey near Limassol, and we have donated funds so that a field shelter can be erected.

South America

The donkey plays a vital role in village life in South America. One small village, perched high on a mountainside, had no water, the stream being at the foot of the mountains down two miles of tortuous zigzag road. At 6 a.m. each morning the donkeys gathered by the village well of their own accord. Their large wooden saddles were fitted on their backs and enormous empty water pitchers were slotted one on each side of the saddle. The village women arrived with armfuls of washing which they piled on the water pitchers and the whole procession set off down the track. On reaching the stream the women filled the water pitchers and, with a smack on the

Elisabeth Svendsen working in Peru.

Donkey brought for treatment in Mexico.

Our mobile clinic, San Bernabe, Mexico.

rump, the donkeys set off unattended up the track to the village while the women did the washing. As each donkey arrived in the village it waited patiently until one of the men arrived and emptied the pitchers into the well. The donkey then set off down the track and repeated the process. Four trips later, the donkeys waited by the stream, browsing, until the women called, and then they did a last trip with water, women and washing. This time the women unloaded the donkeys who then rambled off to graze and rest all night, completely free.

A recent trip undertaken by June Evers (Assistant Administrator of the International Donkey Protection Trust) and Andrew Trawford (Director of Veterinary Services) was to meet with Padre Vieira in Brazil, as he was apparently having problems with a large number of donkeys in the area. The situation, however, was found to be safe in his hands and the charity has been able to help with funding.

Mexico

We have been working over the last 12 years with the superb assistance of Dr Aline de Aluja from the Faculty of Veterinary Medicine of the National University of Mexico. Trial anthelmintic programmes have been carried out in isolated villages and the general health of the donkey and the knowledge of the local people has improved.

We now have two mobile clinics operating in and around Mexico City, after bringing in the International League for the Protection of Horses, as we were finding so many horses in trouble as well as donkeys. We now work in close harmony, sharing the work and costs. The market at San Bernabe still gives enormous concern to all. Despite the promised improvement in the market, both donkeys and horses, many with compound leg fractures, are still unloaded for sale and then re-loaded for an 80 mile trip to an abattoir. Neither charity has the automatic right to put down these animals, who are in terrible pain, and on a recent visit, June Evers reported that Dr Aline de Aluja was actually threatened by an owner carrying a gun as she remonstrated with him on the need to put down a horse in agony. We also work on the enormous rubbish tips, where donkeys are used by their impoverished owners to carry away reclaimed rubbish, and we help through education in schools.

Turks and Caicos Islands

The International Donkey Protection Trust was called to the island of Grand Turk in 1991, where there was a large feral donkey population trying to exist on almost scrub conditions and where, at certain times of the year, terrible drought is experienced. At the government's request a joint project was set up to put the donkeys in a specially prepared pound, with shelter, cover and food. This has not proved very practical and some of the donkeys have been shipped to Jamaica to ease the pressure on the island. A large majority of the remaining stallions have been castrated by a veterinary team in association with the vet from the neighbouring island of Providenciales to prevent further breeding.

Jamaica

Some years ago happy-go-lucky attitudes and ignorance seemed to cause problems for donkeys in Jamaica and the Caribbean. The tendency to hobble the donkey tightly by a front and back leg, or two front legs, causes both pain and immobility which makes the donkey an easy target for attack from children, dogs and flies. Raw sores are common and untreated because of the owner's poverty. Saddles, or improvised back packs, using nylon cord are frequently used in tying down large loads of cane or bananas; the cord tightens around the girth, becomes wet with sweat and then can cut deeply into the donkey's flesh.

Fortunately the situation has improved since our visit and the donkey is now regarded in a better light. We are hoping that the donkeys from Turks and Caicos will breed with local stallions, and the special care given to them will set an example to donkey owners throughout the island.

The Gambia

In Africa the donkey is experiencing something of a revival. The Gambia has seen an enormous upsurge in the donkey population in the last few years.

Tanzania

Unfortunately, in Tanzania the oxen were almost wiped out by rinderpest, and so donkeys were used for the first time to help with the ploughing. The International Donkey Protection Trust worked closely with the Tanga Draught Animal Project, training the agricultural officers in how to treat and look after donkeys, which included their training at the Donkey Sanctuary in the UK. These officers were then able to pass on their knowledge to local farms, and ploughing donkeys are now a common sight in that country.

Donkeys are slightly more resistant than horses to the tsetse fly, the cause of trypanosomiasis. Unfortunately, the life expectancy is brief, disease and the tsetse taking their toll. One big advantage of the donkey in ploughing is that frequently only one person is needed to control a donkey while several people are needed to work with oxen. The increase in the use of donkeys is also being experienced in other African countries such as Kenya and Ethiopia.

Ethiopia

Working very closely with the Veterinary University at Debre Zeit, the International Donkey Protection Trust has gradually been giving help to the millions of donkeys which are essential to agriculture in Ethiopia. Originally a team from the UK would fly out, taking much needed medical equipment, to liaise with the vets and to treat donkeys in the markets within a 30-mile radius of the Veterinary University.

Plans were drawn up to build a clinic close to the Veterinary University

Ethiopia.

but unfortunately political unrest forced suspension of this project until 1994. At this time it was decided to place a mobile unit in the area and in 1996 final plans were made for the building of a donkey shelter and clinic, which it is hoped will be operating in 1997.

The worst problems in Ethiopia are malnutrition, early death due to parasite infestation and acute back sores due to the total lack of any type of saddle or protection for the donkey's back from the load he is forced to carry. The charity arranged for one thousand 'soggies' (Kenyan-made rush pannier-type baskets) to be delivered to Ethiopia to help with this problem, which was organised by our Sanctuary in Lamu. This gave local people a useful income, and we hope it will show the Ethiopian people how, by using local materials, they can protect the donkeys' backs whilst carrying goods. In Ethiopia donkey dung is an important fuel, being flattened and dried and sold in the markets, thus adding yet another benefit to the ownership of a donkey.

Scientific trials carried out through the Veterinary University have proved the immense value of regular worming. Donkeys so treated are fitter, healthier and would appear to be living, on average five years longer, thus making a very worthwhile contribution to their owners, who are often

Ethiopia.

so poor that having to purchase another donkey, which is essential to their livelihood, can cause such a financial burden to the extreme extent that the weakest member of the family could well die.

Kenya

In Kenya the charity set up its first sanctuary abroad. The island of Lamu is part of the archipelago which stretches along the northern coast of Kenya, separated from the mainland by mangrove swamps. This district is served by a divisional veterinary officer and it was to him that the charity first went. It seemed there were almost 4,000 donkeys on the islands but it was almost impossible for him to visit or treat these animals in view of the financial restrictions and the amount of work in hand. The town of Lamu is Muslim and is known as the second Mecca. The streets are very narrow and normal vehicular transport will never be possible in the town. Every item brought to the island by boat has to be transported by donkeys and they are, therefore, a major necessity for everyday living.

When we first arrived in 1985 the state of the donkeys was poor. Many were starving and suffering from tetanus, trypanosomiasis and all had a severe parasite problem. The results of the anthelmintic treatment were so dramatic on the island that, on the second visit, the team were inundated with requests to dose those donkeys that had not received treatment on the earlier visit. The condition of the donkeys that had been treated was obviously superior to the others and the owners were highly delighted with the results.

After visiting regularly for two years it was decided to set up our first sanctuary in the area, in view of the long-term continuing use of the donkey, and it was officially opened on July 4th, 1987. Almost every donkey that is used to load and unload cargo walks past the gates and the drinking trough installed there has alleviated the daily suffering of many of the animals. Sick and ailing animals are taken in and there are four internal stables for those donkeys requiring prolonged treatment, and the outside exercise yard has plenty of shelter. Any donkey found in trouble wandering around the streets in a starved condition is housed and fed and the whole project has received the most enormous support from the local people. Regular visits are made to Lamu where a local manager, Abdalla Hadi Rifai, runs the refuge with a small staff. An extremely close relationship is maintained with the veterinary officer who calls regularly to administer any drugs required (provided by the charity) and to advise on difficult cases. A small

The Lamu Sanctuary.

laboratory is included in the building and regular routine checks are made on the health of the animals.

Our teams visit Lamu twice yearly, treating the donkeys on Lamu and the surrounding islands. A competition for the best kept donkey is held annually, and this has become one of the main social events there. Up to 200 donkeys are entered, and the attention paid to these donkeys to ensure they are in first class condition has proved to be a tremendous incentive to their owners, who in the past did not think that the welfare of their donkey was of any great importance. Every year, when judging, I have always made a point of looking at the donkeys' teeth to estimate their ages, and I was most surprised one year to find many of the donkeys being prepared by not only being bathed in the sea but also by having their teeth brushed with small scrubbing brushes - the owners thought that clean teeth would help them gain points to win the competition!

Work with the Kenya Society for the Prevention of Cruelty to Animals (KSPCA) to cover the rest of the country has also been undertaken, and the International Donkey Protection Trust now funds their donkey work. KSPCA officers have also received training in the UK.

THE WORK GOES ON

In almost all countries donkeys suffer by being worked too young, and damaged legs, feet and dipped backs clearly illustrate this. Constant loads that are overweight affect the older donkey too. Lack of nourishment is common and although many owners grow alfalfa grass to feed the donkeys, or allow them to graze on long hobble chains, others hobble their donkeys too tightly and they are unable to forage a wide enough area to maintain health. It is rare to find hard feed being given to donkeys. It is fair, however, to say that in some countries care of the donkey equals that of the children. The unnecessary use of bits in Arab countries prevents the donkey from supplementing his poor diet by browsing. Some extremely cruel and sharp bits are used, frequently crudely wired together, which can actually grow into the wounds they cause in the donkey's mouth.

Wherever possible the International Donkey Protection Trust aims to work with charities already established in other countries. This reduces duplication and ensures the maximum co-operation and benefit to the donkeys. According to the Food and Agriculture Organization of the United Nations in 1993 there were an estimated 44 million donkeys and

15 million mules in the world, so there is no danger of the work decreasing.

CODE OF PRACTICE FOR DONKEYS/MULES USED FOR COMMERCIAL AND TOURIST EXCURSIONS

GENERAL WORKING CONDITIONS

1. The maximum work rate of any donkey/mule shall be not more than six consecutive days, followed by one full day rest period. Donkeys/mules shall be used for not more than one and a half hours continuous work and this shall be followed by a minimum of half an hour's rest. A donkey/mule shall not be harnessed for more than eight hours in any one day.
2. Any tack that is used shall be in good repair and designed so as not to cause abrasions or injuries and shall be properly fitted so as not to cause any discomfort.
3. Each excursion group shall be led by a responsible and experienced adult. In addition, one assistant shall accompany every ten donkeys/mules in that group.
4. No donkey/mule shall carry excessive weight in consideration of the size, age and physical condition of the animal.
5. Lame or sick donkeys/mules, including those with sores, shall not be used for work.
6. The operator shall have a minimum of 10% reserve of extra donkeys/mules in sound health and suitable for immediate replacement of sick or lame working animals. A reserve donkey/mule shall be taken on all excursions as a replacement in the event of an animal becoming unsound during a trek.
7. Stallion jack donkeys shall not be used on touristic excursions and shall be kept in a separate area from excursion working donkeys.
8. A donkey in foal shall not be worked after the eighth month of gestation nor before the third month after foaling, or as specifically recommended. The operator shall keep records of all donkeys in foal or suspected in foal and shall display the same in a conspicuous area.
9. Donkeys/mules shall not be ridden until at least three years old and a weight limit of 38 kilos shall then be imposed until four years old. Working time shall be limited to a maximum of three hours per day until four years old.
10. A hoof pick shall be available during an excursion and where the

animals are shod, sufficient tools shall be available at all times to remove twisted or distorted shoes that may occur during the ride.

Health and Feeding

11. The feet of all donkeys on the premises should be inspected and cleaned out with a hoof pick at least once daily. Where it is the practice to shoe donkeys for working, these shoes must be correctly fitted by a farrier. The hooves of shod donkeys shall be trimmed and shoes re-fitted every 3/4 weeks or more frequently if necessary. Donkeys with loose shoes shall not be used for working. Where it is expected that a donkey will not be in work for a prolonged period the shoes shall be removed.

12. The minimum feeding cycle for donkeys/mules in work shall be two feedings per 24 hours, an adequate wholesome supply, consistent with keeping the animals in adequate condition for work, to be made available.

13. A sufficient feeding area shall be provided to permit all animals to eat simultaneously without aggression. Separate feeding areas shall be provided for slow eating animals and/or timid ones.

14. Donkeys/mules shall have continual access to fresh water when not in work.

15. Adequate protection from the sun, rain and wind shall be provided for all animals whilst not at work.

The donkeys/mules shall be routinely visited by a Veterinary Surgeon and/ or a designated inspector at a minimum of at least six monthly intervals or as he deems necessary, and his recommendations must be complied with. (The above Codes of Practice are issued by The International Donkey Protection Trust and the World Society for the Protection of Animals).

ELISABETH DOREEN SVENDSEN was born in Yorkshire on January 23rd, 1930.

1940-47	*Brighouse Grammar School - Matriculation*
1948-51	*Rachel McMillen Training College - 1st Class Froebel*
1951-53	*Teacher - West Vale School*
1953-55	*Company Secretary - W T Knowles & Sons Ltd*
1955-61	*Director - Modern Equipment Co. Ltd*
1961-63	*Director - Branch Thorn Industries*
1963-66	*Business Consultant, including Director, Ponsharden Shipyard*
1966-82	*Director - Salston Hotel Ltd*
1969-77	*Honorary Administrator - The Donkey Sanctuary*
1975	*Trustee & Honorary Administrator - The Slade Centre*
1976-85	*Chairman of the Trustees - The International Donkey Protection Trust*
1977	*Administrator - The Donkey Sanctuary*
1985	*Administrator - The International Donkey Protection Trust*
1989	*Trustee & Honorary Administrator - The Elisabeth Svendsen Trust for Children and Donkeys*

The above experience enabled Elisabeth Svendsen to have all the business knowledge necessary to successfully administer the charities she formed through her immense love of donkeys. The Donkey Sanctuary is the 55th largest charity in the UK and the 5th largest animal charity. Its administration costs are extremely low at 6.8p in the pound.

She was awarded the M.B.E. for her work in 1980, and an Honorary Doctorate in Veterinary Medicine & Surgery from the University of Glasgow in 1992. She has had 22 books published to date.

11

DONKEY WORK

Paul Starkey

Importance of working donkeys

Donkeys have been employed as working animals for over 5,000 years. For the past 50 years, estimates of the world population of donkeys have ranged from 30-45 million. There are now about 44 million donkeys in the world, with numbers still tending to increase (FAO, 1995). Over 96% of the world population are found in 'developing' countries. Donkeys have been declining in numbers and importance in industrialised countries. The numbers of donkeys in Europe have been falling steadily from 3 million in 1944 to fewer than 1 million in 1994. In contrast, in most developing countries donkey populations are increasing. In Africa, in particular, the geographical range of the donkey is spreading year by year. In several African countries, donkeys have become more important for both transport and agriculture in the past 20 years, and the trend continues.

The great majority of all donkeys in the world are maintained in order that people may benefit from their working ability. In a few countries (including Italy) donkeys may be prized for their meat. Although donkeys can be milked, this is not common. From a worldwide perspective, only a small number of donkeys are kept specifically for breeding, showing, companionship or for guarding sheep. Most donkeys are kept specifically for work. Their most common role is for transport, whether riding, pack transport or pulling carts. They may also be used for farm tillage. In certain countries they may be used for threshing, raising water, milling or other operations. The systems for owning and working animals varies from country to country. In most countries, donkeys can be owned and used by either men or women. Children are frequently given responsibility for working with donkeys.

The country with most working donkeys is China (11 million), followed by Ethiopia (5 million), Pakistan (4 million) and Mexico (3 million). Other countries with more than one million donkeys include (in descending order): Egypt, Iran, India, Brazil, Afghanistan and Turkey. More than half a million donkeys are found in Morocco, Nigeria, Colombia, Bolivia, Mali, Yemen and Niger. In some less populous countries (including Botswana, Mauritania and Namibia), the total number of donkeys may not be great, but their economic importance may be very high, with one donkey for every two or three people actively engaged in agriculture (Fielding, 1991).

Donkeys as pack and riding animals

Since the times of their earliest domestication, donkeys have been used for riding and for carrying loads on their backs. A well preserved painting from Egypt 4,000 years ago shows a man walking with loaded donkey (Clutton-Brock, 1992). The load-carrying abilities of donkeys are legendary, and the willingness of donkeys is sometimes badly exploited. Donkeys appear to be physically capable of carrying 100% of their bodyweight for short distances, although this is not to be recommended. For example, donkeys weighing about 125kg have been observed carrying 130 litres of water (130kg plus weight of containers). However, most owners expect their donkeys to carry more reasonable pack loads, and 40-80kg loads are more common, and will depend on the distance, the environment and the condition of the donkey.

In some parts of the world it is normal for adult men and women to ride donkeys, but elsewhere only children ride them. Most adult donkeys can comfortably carry the weight of an average person (say 70kg). Donkeys have carried many famous individuals in the past, including Abraham, Mary, Jesus and Nasreddin Hodja. While donkeys are quite capable of carrying people, their limit of comfortable load-bearing can be exceeded if people are very heavy, the ground conditions are steep or difficult, distances are great or the donkey is weak.

For riding and load-carrying, some form of saddle is desirable. While some people hang loads over the back of a donkey without any saddle, this puts pressure directly over the backbone (see Photo 1). A saddle provides stability and ensures the weight is carried on either side of the spine. Saddles do not have to be expensive or complicated. A simple wooden frame with broad, smooth boards that go on either side of the spine can

Photo 1 A simple, but unsatisfactory system for carrying water in Namibia. Although the rope joining the two water containers has been padded slightly, there is no saddle to take the weight off the spine.

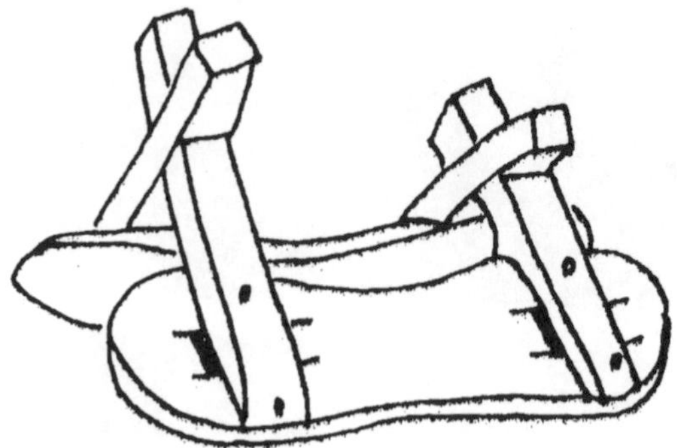

Figure 1 Simple wooden saddle to protect spine.

be effective (Figure 1).

Riding saddles have traditionally been made from leather over a wooden framework. However, a variety of materials can be used to make saddles. For example, in the Dominican Republic, the back of the donkey is first protected with a padded blanket (sometimes made from banana leaves)

Photo 2 Donkeys at market in Dominican Republic with simple saddles used for both packing and riding.

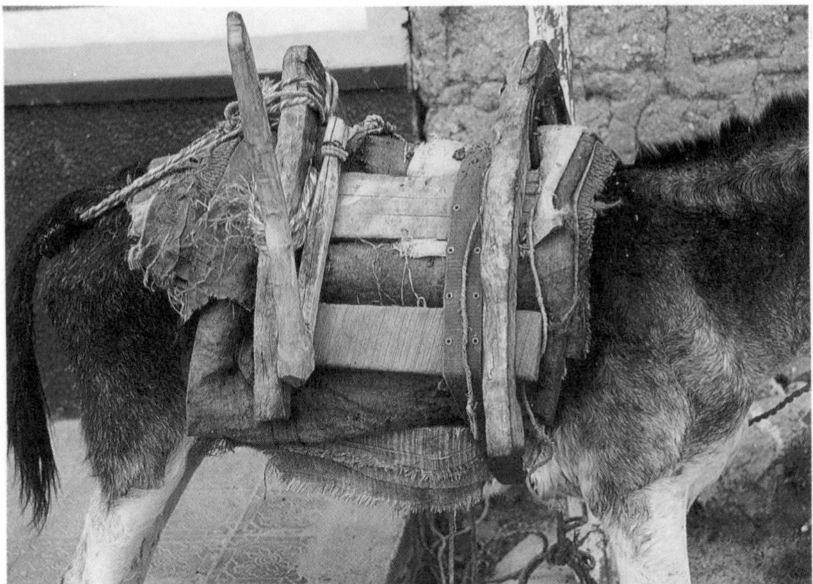

Photo 3 Simple wooden pack saddle in Nicaragua. The tied V-shaped pieces of wood over the saddle are for supporting firewood. Riding saddles are similar, but covered with leather.

and the simple saddle is made from banana fronds bound with wire and covered with goatskin. This saddle is used for both riding and load carrying (see Photo 2). In Nicaragua, several pieces of wood are used to make a frame that is then covered with skin (see Photos 3 and 4). In Ecuador, saddles carved from a single piece of wood may be used. A good saddle, correctly fitted, should prevent the problem of pack sores which cause distress to the donkey and reduce its ability to work well. A saddle is generally held in position with a broad girth strap around the chest of the donkey, and a 'crupper' around the tail.

Donkeys for cart pulling

The use of a cart enables a donkey to transport more than it can carry on its back. However, carts are only suitable for relatively flat, open terrain and localities with roads or broad paths. Most donkey carts have two wheels, as these are cheaper and simpler than four-wheel wagons. On a well constructed, well loaded donkey cart, most of the weight is taken by the wheels, so the weight on the donkey is not great. However, the load a

Photo 4 A donkey carrying water in Nicaragua. The weight of the water containers is supported by a simple wooden saddle, sitting on a blanket.

donkey can comfortably transport by cart depends a great deal on the environment. The force needed to pull a cart varies greatly with the slope of the land and the condition of the road surface. It may be easier for a donkey to pull a full cart on a flat, tarred road than to pull an empty cart up a sloping, rough track. The forward pull required by the donkey also depends on the type and condition of the cart wheels and bearings (which significantly affect the rolling resistance of the cart). The draft force needed to pull a cart forward generally falls within the range of 2-5% of total cart weight on tar and hard laterite roads. Thus, if a cart and load together weigh 500kg, this is likely to require a forward pull of 10-25kg force (kgf) or about 100-250Newtons (N).

In a flat area with reasonable roads, a balanced cart load of 400kg may be acceptable, as this may require a back load of 100-200N (10-20 kgf) and require a forward pull of 100-200N (10-20kgf). However, should the surface be loose sand, or the cart have poorly inflated tyres, a 400kg total load would be too much to expect a single donkey to pull.

Since donkeys are quite small working animals (compared with oxen or horses), it is particularly important that their limited energy is not wasted on poorly lubricated or inefficient cart bearings or poorly inflated tyres. Although traditional spoked wheels are still widely used in some countries, increasingly donkey carts are built using roller bearings and pneumatic tyres, similar to cars.

With two-wheel carts, the donkey may suffer if its load is not well balanced. If the load in the cart (including the weight of the operator and any passengers) is far forward, the load on the donkey's back may become excessive. A heavy load to the rear of the cart can lift a donkey right off its feet. Load balancing is not so critical with four-wheel wagons, since all the weight is taken by the cart wheels (Photo 5).

Most donkey carts have two shafts, and the weight of the cart is taken by a simple back saddle, with pads on either side of the spine (see Figure 2 and Photo 6). The ropes, rubber or chains that fit over the saddle may be permanently attached to the cart. There are some carts in use (particularly in eastern and southern Africa) where the weight of the cart is carried by the neck of a donkey (see Photo 7). It is undesirable for donkeys to carry the entire downward weight of a cart on a narrow neck strap or rope. This

Photo 5 Donkey with full collar harness pulling a four-wheel urban wagon in Cairo.

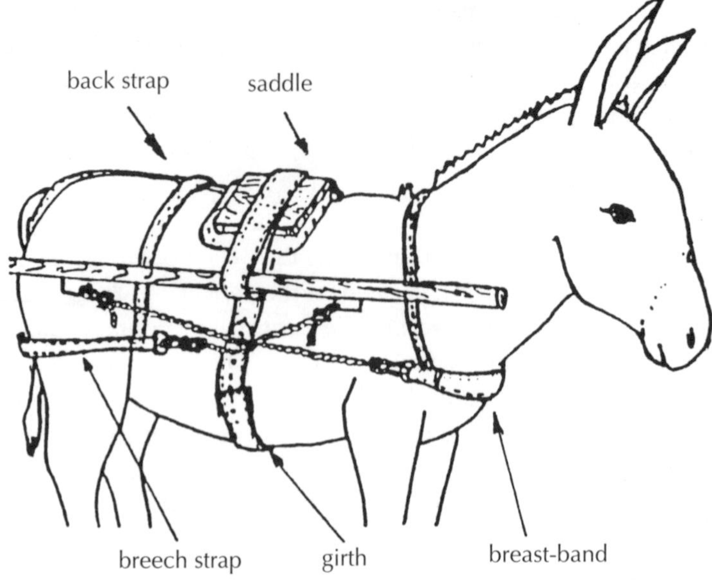

Figure 2 The arrangement of the breast-band, breech strap, and saddle for harnessing a donkey to the shafts of a cart (Source: FAO, 1994).

Photo 6 Spanish donkey with collar harness and simple load-bearing saddle.

Photo 7 Single donkey cart in Kenya. The simple harnessing system illustrates several problems. The weight is on the neck and not the back; there is no breech strap or braking system and the operator is standing forward, increasing the weight on the neck of the donkey.

causes the donkey discomfort and sores (Photo 8). It is better if the weight is taken by a well designed back saddle.

If a second donkey is to assist with pulling a two-wheel cart, it can pull traces from a breast-band (or collar) with a swingle-tree attached to the front of the cart. A third donkey can assist in the same way. It does not seem reasonable to expect a donkey to pull from a rope around its neck (see Photo 9).

Donkeys for tillage

While most donkeys undertake transport work, they can also be usefully employed for tillage operations. They are not as big or strong as oxen and horses, and so cannot be expected to undertake exactly the same work, unless they are hitched together in teams. However, with an appropriate implement, even a single donkey can be used for light tillage or weeding.

In some parts of the world, including many African countries, donkeys are increasingly being used for field operations. In some areas, including the Gambia and Namibia, they have replaced oxen as the main draft animals (Starkey, 1994). While oxen are stronger, donkeys are better at surviving drought conditions. Furthermore, donkeys are less likely than oxen to be stolen for meat. Donkeys can be inexpensive to buy, and so farmers who have lost their oxen through drought, disease or theft often try to perform tillage work with donkeys instead. At first, farmers may try to use oxen technologies, such as yokes, with donkeys (Photo 10). While this is understandable as a short-term measure, the use of ox yokes for donkeys is not desirable. Working donkeys should be fitted with breast-band harnesses or collars designed for donkey use.

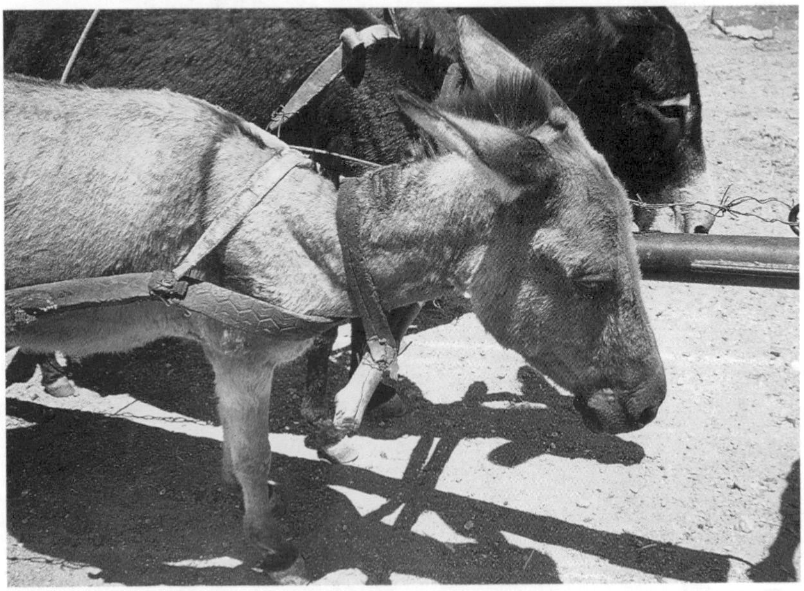

Photo 8 A problem with a donkey cart harness in Zimbabwe. The downward load is taken by a neck strap attached via a yoke to the draw-bar. The strap has been cutting into the neck.

Photo 9 A problem with donkey harnessing in Kenya. Although the central donkey seems correctly harnessed to the cart shafts, the side donkeys can only assist by pulling thin ropes around their necks. A solution would be for the side donkeys to be fitted with breast-bands, traces and swingle trees that pull from the front of the cart.

Work rates

A single donkey (weighing 120-180kg) is capable of pulling a draft load of about 200-300N (about 20-30kgf) for several hours. This represents about 12-25% of bodyweight. Greater force (in excess of 40% of bodyweight) can be exerted for short periods. Although a donkey may be willing and able to pull a heavy draft (e.g. above 20% bodyweight), it will tend to walk at a significantly reduced speed. Thus work rates will be slow. Highest work outputs are likely to be achieved with loads of about 15% of bodyweight, allowing a walking pace of about 1 metre per second to be maintained (Betker and Kutzbach, 1991). Thus, a donkey weighing 140kg can maintain a sustained draft of about 200N (about 20kgf) at a reasonable speed. Naturally, small donkeys cannot be expected to do as much as large donkeys.

Photo 10 Donkeys used for weeding in Zimbabwe, following the death of oxen. The donkeys have been temporarily fitted with an ox yoke, which should be replaced by correct harnessing.

Photo 11 Single donkey ploughing in Palestine. The harness is made from an inverted U of wood, pulling against a padded 'sausage' bent to form a collar.

Photo 12 Single donkey pulling a Houe Occidentale weeder in Senegal.

Single donkeys

Donkeys that are owned mainly for transport can assist greatly in soil preparation and weeding in vegetable gardens and small farm plots, including those managed by women and children. A single donkey may pull a small plough or cultivator, particularly if the soil is light and sandy (See Photo 11). The limited power of one donkey implies a draft force of about 200-250N (20-25kgf), so the width and/or the depth of cultivation cannot be great. A single donkey does not normally have sufficient power to plough a family farm much larger than two hectares.

In West Africa, a single donkey may pull a small tine-cultivator (e.g. *Houe occidentale*) for light tillage or weeding (see Photo 12). Single donkeys can also pull seeders (Photo 13). For this operation they may be better than a pair of oxen, since they can walk quickly in straight lines. A single donkey cannot be expected to pull a normal ox plough (draft about 500-800N, depending on soil conditions). However, such implements can be pulled by two or more donkeys harnessed together.

Teams of donkeys

The strength of two or more donkeys can be combined to allow them to pull ploughs and other implements. In Morocco, pairs of donkeys (and sometimes mixed teams of animals) pull long-beamed traditional ploughs. In Zimbabwe, 4 donkeys can comfortably pull a standard ox-plough (with a draft of over 1kN) for a four-hour work session (Pearson, Nengomasha and Krecek, 1995). In South Africa, teams of 8 donkeys can pull large, three-furrow ploughs in the light soils of Namaqualand (Starkey, 1995; see Photo 14). In Botswana, teams of up to 16 donkeys are sometimes used to pull heavy, two-furrow ploughs.

It is normal to work two donkeys side by side and this requires the swingle-trees of each donkey to be attached to a similar bar, known as an evener. If three donkeys are worked, an additional evener is required to balance the work (see Figure 3). Two donkeys can be worked in tandem (see Photo 15), with the harness of the rear donkey linked to the traces of the lead donkey. Larger numbers of donkeys are normally worked in tandem pairs (see Photo 14).

Photo 13 Single donkey pulling a seeder, Senegal. The breast-band harness is made from an old polypropylene sack. While it is very cheap and simple, a wider, softer band would be preferable.

Photo 14 Six donkeys ploughing in Namaqualand, South Africa. They are wearing locally made leather harnesses and halters.

Donkeys for other operations

Throughout the world, donkeys are mainly used for transport, and some light cultivation. In some countries they are also used to assist with some other operations, such as milling and water raising. In Egypt, donkeys may turn sakia irrigation wheels. In the countries surrounding the Sahara, some donkeys help to pull water from wells (see Photo 16). In Mozambique, some brick-makers use donkeys to turn clay-mixing devices (see Photo 17).

Photo 15 Women weeding with two donkeys in tandem in Tanga, Tanzania. The donkeys are fitted with muzzles to stop them eating the maize.

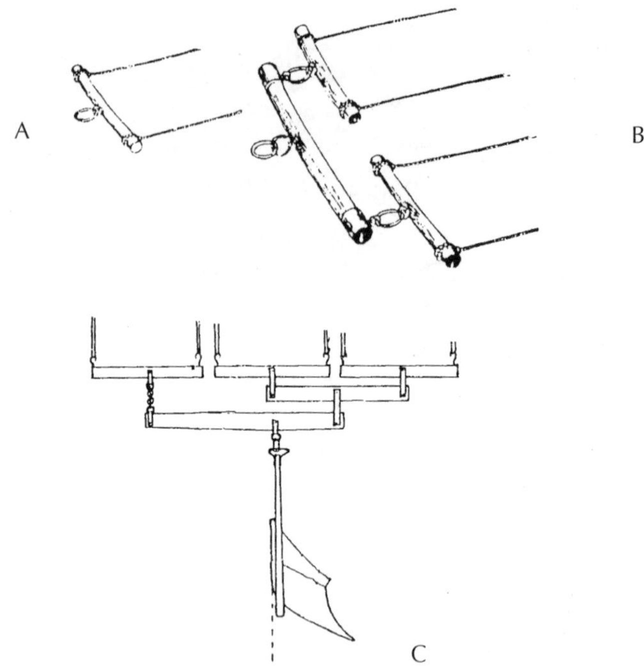

Figure 3 (A) Swingle tree for one donkey. (B) Swingle tree and evener for two donkeys. (C) Swingle trees and eveners for three donkeys.

Harnesses, hitches and implements

It is in the interests of both the donkey and the human user that donkeys are provided with comfortable and efficient harnesses. With a good harness, a donkey should be able to work more effectively, without the risk of sores that can reduce work output. In some ways, the willing donkey is its own enemy, for it seems to tolerate a wide range of poor harnessing systems. In some places, donkeys are expected to pull a cart or an implement from a thin rope around the neck. This is inefficient and cruel.

The simplest, effective harness is the breast-band, which can be made from a variety of materials. The breast-band should be broad enough to ensure there is a large surface area of contact. The inside surface should be smooth and soft to prevent rubbing. When relatively rough materials are employed for the band, an inner layer of softer material may be stitched to the inside. Formerly, leather was the material of choice for harnesses,

Figure 4 Adjustment of breast-band harness. Left: too low; Centre: too high; Right: correct (Source: Ellis, Ellis and Caxton, 1980).

and it is still widely used in some countries. One major advantage is that it can be stitched. However, leather rots and can be damaged by insects and rodents. Heavy-duty cotton, canvas webbing, industrial belting, old vehicle seat-belts, rubber from tyre walls and various sacking materials have been used, with varying degrees of success (Krause, 1994). Polypropylene sacking is cheap and available, but it is not a comfortable material for the animal.

The breast-band is normally supported by a strap over the shoulder or withers. A second supporting strap over the back may also be employed. Although there are great advantages in having the straps adjustable, this is not essential provided the harness fits the animal well (Figure 4). The joining of the shoulder strap and breast-band is important. It should be strong but smooth. Strong thread can be used, and outward-facing rivets can be employed. Wire is not recommended, as badly made or improperly repaired wire links are a major source of harness sores.

In a few countries, including Spain and Egypt, donkeys undertaking heavy work are fitted with full collar harnesses (see Photos 5 and 6). These are effective, but relatively expensive. Simpler collars, such as three-pad harnesses (see Photo 18) have been encouraged in some countries as a cheaper alternative, but uptake has generally been low. The advantages of the collars are counteracted (in the view of the owners) by the added complexity and expense. The good-quality, and very durable collars made in Europe and Egypt require many hours of artisan skill. Simpler collar-type harnesses can be made from a variety of materials, including old tyres or even padded motorcycle chains. If well padded and correctly sized and fitted these can be effective. However, a good breast-band harness is likely to be appropriate in most situations.

Many donkeys work effectively with their heads completely free, without bridle, bits and reins. Bridles and bits are mainly used to achieve accurate and rapid control by people riding donkeys, or using them for urban transport (see Photo 5). In some countries, the use of bits is obligatory for donkeys pulling carts in urban areas. Some traditional donkey bits in use can cause the animals discomfort or lead to sores (for example ring bits in Morocco) and these can be replaced by simple snaffle bits. The use of reins does not necessitate a bit, since reins can be connected to a simple bridle, whether made of leather or rope.

Although it is desirable that carts are fitted with brakes, most do not have them. Thus the donkey has to brake the cart itself. A breech strap or breeching around the rear of the animal assists the animal to brake, and to push the cart in reverse when manoeuvring. Breech straps are found on full harnesses in several countries including Egypt (see Figure 2 and Photo 5). Where breech straps are not used, braking may be achieved through the saddle and the back strap attached to the cart shafts, provided these are properly fitted. Injury to donkeys' necks and heads can occur during

Photo 16 Girl riding donkey that is raising water in Morocco.

Photo 17 Donkey churning clay at a brick works in Mozambique. The collar (from a motorcycle inner tube) is simple, but probably not as comfortable and effective as a good breast-band.

braking or hill descents if they are only fitted with neck bands or yokes. If the shafts of a donkey cart are short, the cart itself may hit the donkey during braking, causing avoidable injuries.

Restraint

When donkeys are not working, they are sometimes left to fend for themselves. However, to prevent them walking far, they are sometimes restrained with a hobble. No hobble is ideal, for it restricts the natural movement of the donkey. Some hobbles are much worse than others, and they can be very cruel (for example, if they are made of thin rope or wire that cuts into the legs). If hobbles have to be used, they should fit comfortably and not restrict the circulation of blood. A foreleg restraint (one leg tied in a bent position) should not be used as a grazing hobble.

Working life of donkeys

Donkeys can live and work for many years (donkey years) provided they are well maintained and free from major health problems. In some countries

Photo 18 Demonstration of three-pad harnesses at the University of Nairobi, Kenya.

(including parts of South Africa) traditionally maintained donkeys may live and work for 25 years. Local traditions speak of a person owning two donkeys in their lifetime, and say that if a young donkey is given to a newly married couple, it should still be working when the grandchildren arrive. However, in other countries, donkeys may have a life expectancy of only ten years, due to disease problems. Donkeys working in Asian brick kilns may have even shorter, hard lives.

Training, education and protection

Although donkeys are used in many countries, very few people ever receive training relating to donkey management and husbandry. Donkeys are seldom included in the syllabuses in schools, colleges or universities. Few veterinarians, animal health assistants or agricultural extension workers have ever had training about donkey utilisation. There are few technical books available at any level, in any language.

One reason for the lack of training and education relating to donkeys is the poor image of the donkey. In most of the world, donkeys are used by poor people with simple lifestyles, particularly in rural areas. They are not usually associated with education, advancement and urban development. The problem seems to be worsening and self-perpetuating, since national policies and educational curricula are determined by urban-based decision-makers with little or no knowledge of donkeys.

In many countries there is no legislation to protect donkeys from being over-exploited. Even if there is the necessary legislation, this is seldom used by government officials who have limited time, resources and motivation. Charitable animal-welfare organisations tend to be based in urban areas, and concentrate their limited resources on treating the symptoms of exploitation. Prevention of mistreatment through education should be the aim of both government and charitable agencies. This will remain a huge task as long as donkeys are neglected in national educational systems and suitable training materials are lacking.

The future of working donkeys

In many less industrialised countries, including much of Africa, donkeys are playing an increasing role in rural trade and transport. However, as countries industrialise and urbanise, donkeys tend to be replaced by other power sources. This has been seen in the United Kingdom, Ireland and the United States of America. Donkeys have been replaced by vehicles and motors for most operations. The donkey populations in these countries are only a small fraction of what they were when it was common for donkeys to work.

Although the same tendency of urbanisation can be seen in many parts of the world, the speed and pattern of change is very different. There are several countries that now encompass both an industrialised, urbanised economy and a large rural sector (e.g., Egypt, India, Mexico, South Africa, Turkey and several countries in the east of Europe). In these countries, the donkey populations remain high and donkeys continue to be very important in the rural areas (and sometimes for urban transport too). Often, the perception of the urban population and government officials in these dual-economy countries is that donkeys have stopped being important any more. In practice, donkeys remain widely used in the rural and mountainous areas of industrialising countries. Even in areas where bicycles, motorcycles and pick-ups play an increasing role in rural transport, donkeys may still be employed by some sections of the population for riding, pack transport and cart pulling. In some situations, the adoption of motorcycles by men releases the donkeys for greater use by women.

For a long time and in many countries of the world, donkeys have had a poor image, being associated with poverty and ignorance. This has been made worse in recent years by the international television culture, in which donkeys are seldom portrayed in the context of modern societies. Urban populations and the young increasingly associate donkeys with the old-fashioned - and the past.

Nevertheless, despite the poor international image and the inevitable increase in motor power worldwide, there is much evidence to suggest that donkeys will continue to be widely employed as work animals for the foreseeable future.

Networks and contacts

There are several national and international networks concerned with animal traction and all types of working animals, including donkeys. Many have pictures of donkeys incorporated into their logos. Members include those involved in development work, education and animal welfare. The networks link people concerned with improving systems for using working animals, for the benefit of the animal users and the animals themselves. They assist in information exchange through workshops and publications, and endeavour to promote favourable policies and technologies. Among the more active animal traction networks are ATNESA (Animal Traction Network for Eastern and Southern Africa) and RELATA (Red Latin-Americana de Tracción Animal). The addresses of these and some national networks are given in Useful Addresses at the end of this book.

References and bibliography

Betker, J., and Kutzbach H. D., 'The role of donkeys in agricultural mechanisation in Niger: potential and limitations', pp 223-230 in Fielding, D., and Pearson, R.A. (eds), *Donkeys, mules and horses in tropical agricultural development,* Proceedings of colloquium held 3-6 September 1990, Edinburgh, Centre for Tropical Veterinary Medicine, University of Edinburgh, UK (1991)

Clutton-Brock, J., *Horse power: a history of the horse and the donkey in human societies*, Harvard University Press, Cambridge, Massachusetts, USA (1992)

Ellis, V., Ellis, R., and Claxton, J., *Donkey driving,* J. A. Allen, London (1980)

FAO, *Draught animal power manual*, Food and Agriculture Organization, Rome, Italy (1994)

FAO, *FAO Production yearbook*, Volume 48 (1994) Food and Agriculture Organization, Rome, Italy (1995)

Fielding, D., 'The number and distribution of equines in the world' in Fielding, D., and Pearson, R.A. (eds), *Donkeys, mules and horses in tropical agricultural development*, Proceedings of colloquium held 3-6 September 1990, Edinburgh, UK Centre for Tropical Veterinary Medicine, University of Edinburgh (1991)

Jones, P., *Training course manual on the use of donkeys in agriculture in Zimbabwe*, Agritex Institute of Agricultural Engineering, Borrowdale, Harare, Zimbabwe (1991)

Krause, P., ' Harnessing techniques for donkeys used to draw carts', in Bakkoury, M., and Prentis, R. A .(eds), *Working equines*, Proceedings of second international colloquium held 20-22 April 1994, Rabat, Morocco. Actes Editions, Institut Agronomique et Vétérinaire Hassan ll, Rabat, Morocco (1994)

Pearson, R. A., Nengomasha, E., and Krecek, R. C., 'The challenges in using donkeys for work in Africa', paper presented at workshop on 'Meeting the challenges of animal traction' held 4-8 December 1995, Karen, Kenya. Proceedings to be published by the Animal Traction Network for Eastern and Southern Africa (ATNESA), Harare, Zimbabwe (1995)

Starkey, P., 'Harnessing and implements for animal traction', Vieweg for German Appropriate Technology Exchange, GTZ, Eschborn, Germany (1989)

Starkey, P., 'Donkey utilisation in sub-Saharan Africa: recent changes and apparent needs', in Bakkoury, M., and Prentis, R. A. (eds), *Working equines* (*op cit.*)

Starkey, P., (ed) *Animal power in South Africa: empowering rural communities*, Development Bank of Southern Africa, Gauteng, South Africa (1995)

Starkey, P., Mwenya, E., and Stares, J. (eds), 'Improving animal traction technology', proceedings of the first workshop of the Animal Traction Network for Eastern and Southern Africa (ATNESA) held 18-23 January 1992, Lusaka, Zambia. Technical Centre for Agricultural and Rural Cooperation (CTA), Wageningen, The Netherlands (1994)

PROFESSOR PAUL STARKEY is an international specialist in animal traction and a Visiting Professor at the Centre for Agricultural Strategy of the University of Reading. Through his work Professor Starkey aims to improve systems for using animal power in the world in order to enhance the quality of life of the people and the work animals themselves. His emphasis is on the humane employment of animals in environmentally sustainable agricultural and transport systems that benefit women and men, young and old.

Paul Starkey studied Natural Science at Oxford University, Education at Cambridge University and Tropical Agricultural Development at the University of Reading. He worked in Malawi for four years and for seven years in Sierra Leone, where he initiated a national animal traction programme. For the past fourteen years, he has worked as an international consultant on animal power for many international, national and charitable development agencies.

Professor Starkey has spent much time trying to achieve closer international liaison relating to animal power through networking and publications. He has been instrumental in helping to establish several national and regional animal traction networks. He has written and/or edited several books relating to animal power and prepared more than 100 other publications including journal articles, chapters and major reports. He has visited 100 countries worldwide, including almost all African countries. His photographs have been exhibited in several countries and have been used to illustrate many publications. Donkeys have been featured on the covers of several of his publications. He has prepared photographic exhibitions of donkeys and helped to organise an international workshop on improved donkey utilisation and management.

12
DISEASES AND HEALTH PROBLEMS of Donkeys Abroad

Feseha Gebreab

THIS CHAPTER PROVIDES AN INTRODUCTION to the diseases and health problems of donkeys abroad. Of the 41½ million donkeys known to exist in the world, 40 million, which is equivalent to 96.2%, are found in developing countries. Amongst the nations with the highest populations feature: China, Ethiopia, Mexico, Pakistan, Egypt, Iran, India, Brazil, Afghanistan, Turkey, Morocco and Nigeria (D. Fielding, 1991). Most donkeys seem to be associated with the highland and semi-arid zones as well as with semi-intensive and extensive agricultural production systems.

Donkeys abroad are working animals, mostly used for transporting on their backs various commodities ranging from basic household necessities such as fuel and wood to war hardware and ammunitions. In spite of the invaluable services donkeys provide, they are the subject of routine and frequent neglect and maltreatment. This has resulted in considerably reducing their work output, reproductive performance and most of all their longevity. Donkeys are vulnerable to an array of diseases of biological origin, and the one common entity leading to ill health, suffering and early demise is parasitism (Svendsen, 1994a). In Ethiopia, due to parasitism the average lifespan of the working donkey is rarely over 12 years and can be as low as 8 years in some (Svendsen, 1994b).

An attempt has been made in this presentation to provide a concise summary of the more important infections and conditions which cause ill health in donkeys overseas with particular emphasis on those countries where the contribution of donkeys is significant.

Colic

Generally speaking colic is less common in the donkey than in the horse. When it does occur it can take several forms: flatulent and sporadic, gastric dilatation, impaction and obstruction. In the flatulent form there is formation of large columns of gas in the large intestine due to excess feeding on lush green pasture, clover and other legumes. In gastric dilatation, the donkey will have a history of eating large quantities of wheat, maize, coarse straw, young clover, mouldy grain or hay. Colic due to impaction occurs as a consequence of feed being eaten hurriedly or the intake of excess low grade roughage leading to formation of large boluses. Obstruction is due to a foreign body, twisted bowel or strangulated intestine while spasmodic colic comes from rapid contraction of the muscles of the intestinal wall in response to poorly digested feed, exhaustion, overwork or the migrating immature larvae of *Strongylus vulgaris*. Colic in donkeys has the following clinical features: first and foremost there will be a change in behaviour characterised by a reduction in mobility, a loss of appetite and general depression.

Donkeys don't, as a rule, tend to roll or sweat and give the very obvious signs of colic that horse owners are used to. In the donkey it is dullness and depression rather than the exaggerated pain and rolling and thrashing that you see in other equines. In Mexico the cause of colic in donkeys is reported to be the ingestion of too much young green grass, or too much maize grain followed by watering and also by the ingestion of an insect known as praying mantis (Sims, B.G., et al, 1991). A considerable number of cases of impaction colic are observed in the working donkeys of Ethiopia fed on the fine residues of teff (*Eragositis abyssinica*) immediately after threshing. Infection of donkeys with *S. vulgaris* larvae is very probably the most common cause of colic in donkeys abroad.

Treatment: Preventive measures include adopting a strategic deworming procedure and checking teeth with a view to rasping when necessary. In the case of flatulent, gastric dilatation and impaction, carefully administer paraffin oil. The administration of tranquillisers and pain relieving drugs may also be necessary.

Saddle sores

Cases of saddle sore (back sore) have been reported in Ethiopia, Mexico,

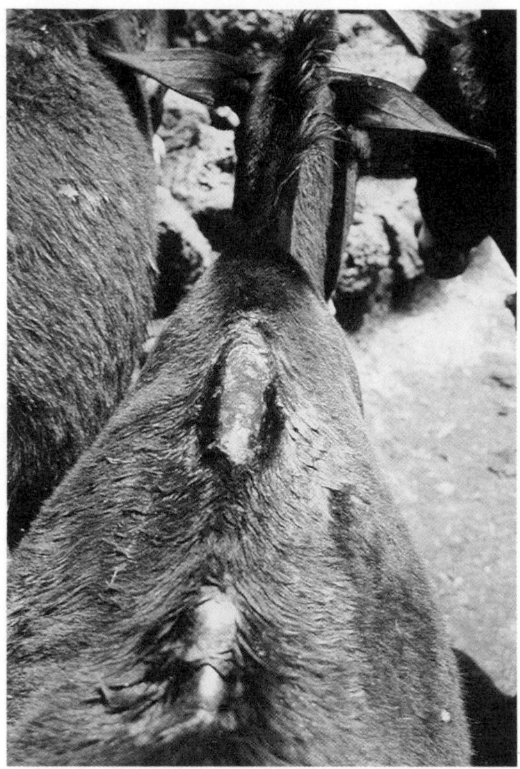

Saddle sore (back sore).

Nepal and other countries. In one study undertaken in Ethiopia, of the 2,020 donkeys examined, 680, i.e. 33.7%, were found to have saddle sores (Yilma et al, 1991). These were caused by the total lack of any type of saddle or protection for the donkey's back from the load. In other countries they are mainly due to poorly fitting saddles which cause excessive pressure and/or frictional rub. The signs are hair that is rubbed off and broken skin on the side of the withers or under the girth which often leaves raw bleeding sores that vary in size and are slow to heal.

Treatment: Rest the donkey from work and remove the saddle and girth. Check the saddle and girth in relation to the shape of the donkey and adjust the technique of loading to rectify the problem. If rest is not possible, sores on the withers or back may be protected from future rubbing by surrounding the sore area with a doughnut-shaped gauze pad or dressing. Apply zinc cream to the sore twice a day until signs of drying and healing appear. For advanced sores, clean the wound with peroxide, dry with clean gauze, dust with antibiotic powder or paint with gentian violet or use an aerosol spray containing antibiotic and gentian violet. Dermobion, a cream combining antibiotic and anti-inflammatory active ingredients, is also useful where wounds are exposed to self-trauma.

Other wounds

Lacerated wounds are one of the commoner types. Abrasions due to friction from improper harness and harnessing materials, such as nylon ropes and strips of car tyres, are other frequently encountered problems. In Ethiopia the main cause of lacerated wounds is hyena bites. Barbed wire and other sharp objects are also common causes of lesions. When lacerated wounds occur their edges are irregular, sometimes whole sections of skin and underlying tissue are taken away. Haemorrhage is variable depending on the type of blood vessel severed.

Treatment: For abrasions, clean and apply zinc cream twice a day until healing occurs. With a lacerated wound a decision has to be made whether the wound needs stitching or not. This will depend on whether the wound is fresh and whether there is sufficient skin present to appose the lacerated edges. If it cannot be stitched, clean the wound with water or apply peroxide, remove any hair, dead tissue, foreign bodies, and apply antibiotic powder as well as zinc cream. If the laceration is on the leg, cover the wound with gauze. When the bandage is removed clean with water, remove discharge, debris, etc. Continue similar treatment until fresh tissue has filled the cavity to skin level.

Thrush

Thrush is an infection caused by the Fusiforms bacterium in the grooves on either side of the frog. Sometimes the frog itself is involved. The predisposing factors that provide the breeding ground for infection are poor hoof care and damp, poorly drained yards where donkeys stand for lengthy periods in mud. In Ethiopia it is quite common during the long wet season. The clinical signs include a foul smelling, black tarry discharge in grooves on either side of the frog. The donkey may also be lame.

Treatment: Trim away any excess or infected frog, clean out discharge from grooves. Paint sole, including depths of grooves, with a solution of 10% formalin. Repeat treatment daily until condition has cleared up completely. Cleanliness is the keynote to prevention of thrush.

Cracked heel/Mud fever

This is a common problem of donkeys turned out in wet, muddy conditions. Constant wetting and chapping of the skin allows bacterial infection, especially *Staphylococcus aureus,* to gain entry. The heel area shows exudative dermatitis with scab formation. Oedema of the legs may occur and some cases may be extremely sore and lame.

Treatment: House affected animals so that the legs dry. Severely affected cases may need antibiotic treatment with penicillin and streptomycin. An equal mixture of sulphanilamide powder and liquid paraffin is also a very useful local treatment and this may be used as an antibacterial water-proofing agent when complete housing is not possible.

Pneumonia

This is an infection or inflammation of the lungs often seen in foals and in debilitated and stressed donkeys. It can be caused by viruses, bacteria, parasites, inhalation of foreign materials and drenching. Donkeys contracting pneumonia after drenching usually die or suffer permanent damage to lung tissue. Of the many predisposing causes, travelling, overcrowding, malnutrition and exhaustion are the commonest features in lowering a donkey's resistance to infection. Clinical signs include a donkey being off its feed, lethargic, rapid and shallow respiration, often with a cough, nasal discharge and high temperature. The breath may have a foul odour and moisture may be detected as the donkey breathes in and out.

Treatment: Place the donkey in a well ventilated area. If its temperature is high, position the animal in a cool dry corner. Provide fresh water and palatable nutritious feed. Administer broad spectrum antibiotics and rest the animal from work until recovery is complete

Anthrax

Anthrax is a soil borne infection caused by *Bacillus anthracis*. All mammals, but most commonly herbivores, are affected. The donkey may show acute anthrax and die within 1-3 days. Clinical observations are high temperature, severe depression, abdominal pain, followed by swelling under the jaw, chest, abdomen and in the lower limbs. When anthrax is diagnosed it is imperative that contamination from the dead body is prevented. The dead body should be buried 1-2 metres deep and covered with lime. The contaminated area around the dead body should be burnt, other surfaces should be treated with 10% caustic soda. In endemic areas donkeys should be protected by annual vaccination carried out a month before the peak risk period starts.

Tetanus

This is a neuromuscular disorder caused by a specific neurotoxin produced by the bacterium *Clostridium tetani.* The organism is present in the soil and faeces and gains entry into the body through a wound. In affected donkeys signs usually start as stiffness causing the donkey to move reluctantly, head and ears are extended, there is evidence of muscular spasms affecting the muscles of mastication and making eating difficult. Death occurs in almost all cases due to exhaustion, circulatory failure or pneumonia.

Prevention: In endemic foci the administration of tetanus toxoid provides substantial protection. A curative regime is tedious, requiring the administration of penicillin, tetanus antitoxin serum, as well as tranquillisers such as chlorpromazine and the provision of intensive care.

Strangles

This disease is characterised by abscess formation especially under the jaw, and inflammation of the upper respiratory tract with nasal discharge. The bacterium causing the disease is *Streptococcus equi.* The clinical signs are loss of appetite followed by slight cough and subsequently by bilateral nasal discharge. Lymph nodes of the head and neck are swollen.

Treatment: Since disease is highly infectious, isolate the donkey. Treatment is with antibiotics. Fortunately for the donkey morbidity and mortality is low compared with the horse.

Donkey with rabies.

Equine influenza

This lower respiratory tract infection of equids of all ages is caused by two antigenically distinct subtypes of the influenza A virus. Mules and donkeys are relatively resistant. The incubation period is one to three days with a clinical course of two to five days. Morbidity rates are high, up to 98%, but mortalities in uncomplicated cases are negligible and restricted to young foals and old individuals. The consistent clinical features are high fever, spasmodic dry cough, nasal discharge, laboured breathing and lymphopaenia. An outbreak in India in 1987 involved all categories of horses and donkeys without variation due to age, sex or breed. At some places donkeys were reported to have suffered more severely resulting in higher mortality as compared to horses and mules (Uppal, P.K., 1991). Effective vaccines are available for prevention. As for treatment, complete rest of the affected animals for a period of three weeks is recommended.

Rabies

Rabies is a viral infection of mammals transmitted in the saliva of a rabid animal. The most important hosts are carnivores and bats. In general, equine rabies is uncommon. In Europe, rabies in horses, mules and donkeys accounted for 0.3 to 0.5% of the total number of cases in domestic animals in 1979-1988. The mean number of confirmed cases in the three species was 74, 9 and 0.6 respectively. Nearly all the mule and donkey cases were reported in Turkey (Ramachandran, S., 1991). In general, mules and donkeys are resistant. A donkey strain was non pathogenic to rodents and dogs (Badali and Abou-Youssuf, 1968, as cited by Ramachandran, S., 1991). The author has seen one case of rabies in a donkey in Makale, Tgrai, Ethiopia in 1971. Vampire bat-transmitted rabies in donkeys has also been reported from Mexico (Sims, B.G., et al, 1991). In most clinical cases the early signs are drooling of saliva, spastic lip movement, hyperexcitability, leading to depression and anorexia. Rare cases become aggressive with biting, kicking and self-mutilation as overt signs. Paralysis develops primarily affecting the ability to swallow, then spreads to the hindquarters, with collapse and death in 2-7 days after initial signs.

Treatment: Rabies is invariably fatal. Isolate the donkey from other animals and people. Control measures have to be preceded by epidemiological studies to elucidate the disease pattern before the institution of appropriate strategies.

Sarcoid

Reportedly the most common skin tumour, representing 12.9% to 67% of all tumours of horses, mules and donkeys (McConaghy et al, 1994). Equine sarcoids are locally invasive, fibroblastic skin tumours that do not metastasize. Substantial evidence supports a viral cause.

Treatment: Sarcoids often occur in areas that are affected by repeated mechanical injuries. Because of their location and size, the tumours are frequently traumatised. Tumours may cause discomfort because of their location (e.g. eyelids) and by attracting flies. The following are available options in treating sarcoids: surgical excision, cryotherapy, immunotherapy, autogenous vaccines, topical chemotherapy, radiotherapy, hyperthermia.

Venezuelan equine encephalomyelitis

This is an aberrant mosquito borne viral infection of horses, mules and donkeys in Central America. In the 1970s in Mexico there was an epidemic of this viral disease (Uppal, P.K., 1991). All the types and subtypes of VEE virus are mosquito-borne and transovarial transmission in mosquitoes occurs. Mosquitoes infect horses, donkeys and mules and, in addition, contact transmission may occur between sick and healthy animals. It often manifests as an acute and fulminant form of myeloencephalitis after a short incubation period of one to three days. This is preceded by affected equines being anorexic and depressed. Diarrhoea is common and weight loss is rapid. Encephalomyelitis is featured by drowsiness and hyperexcitability. As the disease progresses convulsions become increasingly frequent and are followed by collapse, prostration and death.

Control: Equines at risk should be protected by vaccination and by applying movement restrictions on all horses, mules and donkeys. Inactivated virus vaccines are now available commercially. A modified, live vaccine (TC-83) is more effective in the prevention of VEE and is used annually.

PARASITES

Helminths

According to Lichtefels (1975) equids are host for helminths belonging to 28 genera and 75 species of nematodes, 2 genera and 5 species of trematodes as well as 3 genera and 24 species of cestodes. A considerable number of these are reported to occur in overseas donkeys. Table 1 (compiled by Pandey V.S. et al 1994) covering five African countries, supplemented by updated findings from Ethiopia and Kenya, shows the panorama and magnitude of the problem.

There is an overall similarity in the type of parasites seen in the donkeys in all these areas. In particular, the highly pathogenic large strongyle, *strongylus vulgaris* is common. There is more variation in the prevalence of the other large strongyles. The cyathostomes are also common in all the six countries, but there is a lack of knowledge pertaining to their differentiation at the species level.

Large strongyles

Three species of large strongyles are found in donkeys. In the six African countries where studies have been undertaken *S.vulgaris* and *S.edentatus* seem to be the most common. The third species *S.equinus* has a sporadic distribution. These species are important because they migrate in the circulation and vital organs and cause severe damage that is fatal in some instances.

Table 1. The percentages of donkeys infected with helminth parasites in some African countries

	Morocco[1] *n:597*	Tchad[2] *n:183*
Stomach		
Habronema musca	90	20
H.majus	85	15
Draschia megastoma	1	54
Total habronema	100	72
Trichostrongylus axei	100	-
Small Intestine		
Parascaris equorum	37	72
Strongyloides westeri	1	-
Anoplocephala magna	1	6
A.perfoliata	2	-
Paranoplocephala mamillana	1	-
Large Intestine		
Strongylus vulgaris	98	81
S.edentatus	26	8
S.equinus	-	11
Total Strongylus	100	89
Triodontophorus nipponicus	-	-
T.serratus	-	2
T.minor	-	37
T.tenuicollis	-	15
Cyathostomes	52	63
Probstmayria vivipara	-	-
Oxyuris equi	13	57
Gastrodiscus aegyptiacus	-	34
Liver		
Fasciola gigantica	-	1
F.hepatica	6	-
Hydatid cyst	12	-
Lungs		
Dictyocaulus arnfieldi	48	-
Hydatid cyst	4	-
Peritoneal cavity		
Setaria equina	29	89

[1].Pandey (1980a,b,c 1983), Pandey and Cabaret (1993), Pandey et al (1992a), Khallaayoune (1991), Abdelkarim (1991); [2] Graber (1970);[3] Vercruysse et al (1986); [4] Pandey and Eysker (1988, 1989, 1990, 1991), Eysker and Pandey (1989); [5.] Feseha et al (1991);[6] Mukhwana (1994).

Burkina Faso[3] *n:30*	Zimbabwe[4] *n:14*	Ethiopia[5] *n:6*	Kenya[6] *n:7*
90	86	-	-
93	64	-	-
47	79	-	-
100	100	100	-
+	64	100	-
43	50	33	20.7
+	7	-	-
27	-	-	-
-	-	66	-
-	-	-	-
100	100	100	-
90	-	100	57.6
60	-	17	-
100	100	100	-
37	71	-	-
47	79	-	-
-	-	-	-
-	-	-	-
100	100	100	15.4
-	29	100	6.7
30	43	100	-
57	14	+	-
-	-	-	-
-	-	17	-
-	-	-	-
-	-	83	-
-	-	-	-
-	29	-	-

S.vulgaris is the most common of the large strongyles and is considered to be the most pathogenic of all equine internal parasites.

Colic is the most frequent manifestation of large strongyle infection. It has been estimated that 90% of cases of colic are caused by thromboembolism secondary to *S.vulgaris* infection, but evidence is lacking (Austin, M.S. 1994).

S. edentatus is the second most pathogenic of the large strongyles and is relatively common. Damage from the parasite is usually minimal, but several thousand larvae may cause death within two weeks to two months.

S. equinus is the least common of the large strongyles. A few thousand larvae can cause severe illness and possibly death.

Treatment: *Strongylus vulgaris* and *S.equinus* are more susceptible than *S.edentatus* to the effect of anthelmintics. All three species are highly susceptible to ivermectin; and most of the benzimidazoles. Treatment of migratory larvae is best accomplished by administering a single dose of ivermectin at 200µg/kg of body weight. Some benzimidazoles like fenbendazole, oxfendazole and thiabendazole are effective against migrating larvae, but must be given at a dose of 10mg/kg and 440mg/kg of body weight respectively (Austin, M.S. 1994).

Small strongyles

This is the collective name given to some 40 species of small strongyles which are very common and belong to the genus Cyathostomum. Due to incomplete morphology, very few workers have identified these parasites to the species level. The most comprehensive list in Africa comes from Zimbabwe (Eysker and Pandey, 1989) where 11 species were found in donkeys. In a study undertaken in Ethiopia small strongyles belonging to the genera Cyathostomum, Cylicocyclus, Cylicodontophorus, Cylicostephanus, Poteriostomum and Gyalocephalus accounted for 46.5% of the small strongyles recovered (Feseha et al, 1990). It is now known that cyathostome larvae follow one of two general patterns of development:

- The first is progressive development in which third stage larvae exsheath in the gut and encyst within the mucosa or submucosa soon after infection. In the gut, the larvae then undergo continuous development to fourth stage larvae. Growth is complete when the fourth stage larvae emerge from the cyst and mature to adults in the lumen.

•The second is distinguished by a period of arrested development (hypobiosis) of early third stage larvae in the lumen of the gut, in the crypts of, or in the mucosa and submucosa of the caecum and colon.

Treatment: Treatment of larval cyathostomosis is difficult because normal doses of anthelmintics often fail to kill encysted larvae. Although ivermectin is recommended for removing encysted larvae, the normal dose (200µg/kg) is documented to kill only late fourth stage larvae in the luminal contents.

Other helminths such as *T. axei, P. equorum*, *O. equi, G. aegypticus*, *Habronema Anoplocephala*, etc, have been reported from a number of countries.

These parasite infections are important and merit attention either in their own entity or as contributors to polyparasitic disease.

ARTHROPODS

There are many arthropod pests that infest donkeys abroad, but report on their occurrence and importance is quite rare. The obvious ones deserving mention are presented very briefly:

Lice

The sucking louse (*Haematopinus asini*) and the biting louse (*Damalinia equi*) are found on donkeys. Lice are obligate and species specific ectoparasites. The complete life cycle is spent on the host, survival away from the host is limited. Lice are first evident on the head, neck, mane and tail. Restlessness, rubbing and damage to the coat would suggest that lice are present and, when the hair is parted, the parasites or their eggs may be seen. The major dermatological problems associated with infestation are pruritus and concomitant excoriation. Lice are easily controlled by treating hosts with residual insecticides. Ivermectin is extremely effective in controlling sucking louse.

Donkey botflies

Gasterophilus larvae in the digestive tract are arthropods reported frequently from different parts of Africa. Although six species are known to occur, only two of them, *G. intestinalis* and *G. nasalis*, are found throughout the continent as shown in Table 2 (Pandey et al 1994). *G. ternicinctus* was reported only from Burkina Faso (Kaboret et al, 1986, as cited by Pandey, 1994) and *G. inermis* only from Tunisia (Kilani et al, 1986, as cited by Pandey, 1994). Stomach bots can cause mechanical blockage of the stomach, colic, or rupture of the stomach wall and resultant peritonitis (Foll, D.Z., et al, 1990). Gastric lesions that are associated with larval attachment include deep pits in the stomach wall. In Ethiopia rectal prolapse is quite common in donkeys and has been ascribed to infection by *Gasterophilus* (Yilma et al, 1991). The infection rate detected was 50% (Feseha et al, 1991).

Table 2 Percentages of donkeys infected with Gasterophilus in some African countries.

	Morocca[a]	Tunisia[b]	Egypt[c]	Burkina Faso[d]	Tchad[e]	Zimbabwe[f]
n:	366	91	118	30	67	14
G.intestinalis	98	90	98	100	75	100
G.nasalis	96	70	86	87	54	7
G.haemorrhoidalis	70	-	-	7	-	-
G.percorum	-	48	-	87	9	-
G.ternicinctus	-	-	-	27	-	-
G.inermis	-	57	-	-	-	-

a. Pandey et al (1992b); Pandey and Cabaret (1993); Khallaayoune (1991)
b Kilani et al (1986)
c. Hilali et al (1987)
d. Kaboret et al (1986)
e Graber and Gruvel (1964)
f Pandey and Eysker (1988, 1990)

Treatment: Organophosphates are capable of eliminating totally the *Gasterophilus* population from the buccal cavity, pharynx and other sites of the digestive tract. Additionally trichlorophon (organophosphate) has an effect on ascarids and oxyurids, its metabolite dichlorvos eliminates strongyles from the digestive tract.

Donkey nostril flies

The nostril fly *Rhinostrus usbekistanus* has been encountered in the donkeys of Senegal, (Kaboret et al, 1996) and Ethiopia (Feseha et al, 1996). In the preliminary work undertaken by Kaboret Y, 1996, 33 donkeys infected with *R. usbekistanus* in Senegal manifested mild exudative inflammation with eosinophils. In the lungs emphysema, interstitial pneumonia and eosinophilic infiltration were the main pathologic features. Clinical signs are rarely seen in donkeys but should be the same observed in horses. This includes uneasiness, burying of muzzles in each other's manes or tails, snorting and shaking of heads. Old emaciated donkeys are more susceptible to the disease. It is possible for standard doses of ivermectin and organophosphate (dichlorvos) to control the disease.

CUTANEOUS CONDITIONS

Habronemiasis

Cutaneous habronemiasis, or summer sore, is a seasonal granulomatous skin disease transmitted by houseflies and stable flies. The spirurids *Habronema* and *Draschia megastoma* occur in the equine stomach. Skin disease is caused by the incidental deposit of infective larvae on moist mucous membranes or on pre-existing skin lesions. Systemic therapy with ivermectin at the recommended dose given twice, at three to six week intervals kills most larvae and produces rapid resolution of lesions.

Ascarids

Ticks and mange mites are uncommon in donkeys. Ticks are vectors of equine piroplasmosis (*B.caballi* and *B.equi*), but compared to cattle, the tick burden in equines is light. In a study undertaken by Feseha et al in Bahr Dar, Ethiopia, only 121 adult ticks were collected from 57 equines. Of these 83 were *Rhipicephalus*, 33 *Boophilus* and 5 were *Amblyomma*. The first two are the possible vectors of equine piroplasmosis. Very few mange mite infestation cases have been observed in donkeys in Ethiopia. Infestation by psoroptes has also been encountered in donkeys abroad (Abu Samara et al, 1987, as cited by Pandey, 1994), *B.caballi* from Egypt (Nafie et al, 1979 as cited by Pandey, 1994) and Kenya (Karanja et al, 1993, as cited by Pandey, 1994), *T.vivax* from Ethiopia (Feseha et al, 1992), *B.equi* and *B.caballi* from Ethiopia (Feseha et al, 1992).

In a study of equines, the great majority of which were donkeys, undertaken by Feseha et al in 1992 in Ethiopia, of the total number which tested positive for Babesiosis only 30.17% manifested clinical signs. The remaining 69.83% were apparently healthy. The major clinical signs observed were congested mucous membranes, lacrimation, depression and a rise in temperature from 37.6°C to 41°C. Haemoglobinuria was observed in only 7.5% of the cases. This can be ascribed to an immunity that is stable and maintained continuously by low grade infections. In the Gambia, where 63% of the farmers use mainly equines as draught animals (Cham, 1990, as cited by Mattioli, 1994), the major limiting factor was found to be trypanosomiasis (Sowe et al, 1990, as cited by Mattioli 1994). *T.congolense* causes chronic infection (Hard, 1981, as cited by Mattioli, 1994) with a longer persistence of the micro-organism in the blood, while donkeys infected with *T.brucei* die rapidly (Macheman, 1970, Stephen, 1970, as cited by Mattioli, 1994). In horses, *T.brucei* infections may be acute or chronic, often accompanied by oedema of the limbs and genitalia. In the study undertaken in Ethiopia 582 equine blood smears were examined by Feseha et al 1991 and 19 (3.29%), of which 15 were from donkeys, proved positive for *T.vivax*. This low incidence of infection could be due to the mildness of this type of trypanosomiasis in donkeys (Kyewalabye Kaggwa et al, 1989).

Trypanosoma equiperdum causes a venereal disease of horses and donkeys called dourine. It is confined to parts of Africa, Asia and South and Central America. The clinical signs are those of genital and ventral abdominal oedema, transient urticarial plaques and progressive emaciation. In many cases, the C.N.S is involved, causing an ascending motor paralysis which is ultimately fatal.

T.evansi causes an equine trypanosomiasis 'Murrina'. In some regions of South America, mainly Brazil, the disease called 'Cadera' is due to *T.equinum* another variant of *T.evansi*. 'Derrengadera' which is endemic in Venezuela and Mexico (Sims, B.G., et al 1991) is probably due to a third variant, *T.venezuelense.*

Treatment: Suramin and quinapyramine are the drugs of choice for the treatment of trypanosomiasis in equines, while imidocarb is the preferred one for equine piroplasmosis.

References

Abdelkarim, M., 'Variations saisonnières des populations vermineuses et gasterophiliennes chez les asines de la région de Settat (Chaouia)', Thèse Doctorat Vétérinaire, Institut Agronomique et Vétérinaire Hassan II, Rabat, Maroc (1991)

Austin, M.S., ' Large strongyles in Horses', Compendium on Continuing Education for the Practising Veterinarian, Vol 16(5), pp 650-657 (1994)

The Donkey Sanctuary, *Basic donkey health care manual*, p17, The Donkey Sanctuary, Sidmouth, EX10 0NU, Devon UK

Eysker, M., Pandey V.S., 'Small strongyle infections in donkeys from the highveld of Zimbabwe', *Veterinary Parasitology*, 30, pp 345-349 (1989)

Feseha, G.A., Mohammed, A., and Yilma, J.M., 'Vermicular endoparasitism in donkeys of Debre Zeit and Menagesha, Ethiopia. Strategic treatment with ivermectin and fenbendazole in donkeys, mules and horses in tropical agricultural development, Proceedings of a Colloquium on donkeys, mules and horses' (Eds. Fielding D. and Pearson R.A), University of Edinburgh, Centre for Tropical Veterinary Medicine, UK, pp 156-166 (1991)

Feseha, G.A., Nuria, Yideg, 'A preliminary survey on the prevalence of equine haemoparasites in Bahr Dar and surrounding areas', Thesis, Faculty of Veterinary Medicine, Addis Ababa University: p. 32 (Mimeo), (1992)

Fielding, D., 'The number and distribution of equines in the world. Donkeys, mules and horses in Tropical Agricultural Development' (Eds. Fielding D. and Pearson R.A.), University of Edinburgh, Centre for Tropical Veterinary Medicine, UK, p. 62, (1991)

Foil, D.Z., Foil, S.C., 'Arthropod Pests of Horses' *Compendium of Continuing Education for the Practising Veterinarian*, Vol 12 (5): pp. 723-730 (1990)

Graber, M., and Gruvel, J., 'Etudes des agents des myiases des animaux domestiques et sauvages d'Afrique équatoriale', Revue d'Elevage et de Médecine Vétérinaire des Pays Tropicaux, 17: pp. 535-554 (1964)

Graber, M., 'Helminthes et helminthiases des équidés (ânes et chevaux) de la République du Tchad', Revue d'Elevage et de Médecine Vétérinaire des Pays Tropicaux, 23: pp. 207-222 (1970)

Hawcroft, T., *A-Z of horse diseases and health problems*, Howell Book House, New York, p. 304 (1993)

Hilali M., Derhalli F.S., and Baraka A., 'Incidence and monthly prevalence of Gasterophilus spp. larvae (Diptera: Gasterphilidae) in the stomach of donkey (*Equus asinus*), Egypt. Veterinary Parasitology 23:

pp. 297-305 (1987)

Kaboret, Y., Pangui, L.J., and Vercruysse, J., 'Note sur la gastérophilose des ânes au Burkina Faso', *Revue d'Elevage et de Médecine Vétérinaire des Pays Tropicaux*, 39: pp. 211-212 (1986)

Kaboret, Y., Decommick, P., Pangui, J., Akapo, J., Dorchies, Ph., 'Lesions de la Rhinoestrose Spontanee a Rhinoestrus usbekistanieus (GAN 1947) chez les ânes (*Equus asinus*) au Senegal', Soumis a la Rev. Med. Vet. (1996)

Khallaayoune, K., 'Benefit of a strategic deworming programme in working donkeys in Morocco' in *Donkeys, mules and horses in Tropical Agricultural Development* (Eds. Fielding, D., and Pearson, R.A.) University of Edinburgh, Centre for Tropical Veterinary Medicine, U.K, pp. 174-180 (1991)

Kilani, M., Soussi, K., Dorchies, Ph., and Franc, M.,'Observations épidémiologiques sur les gastérophiles des équidés de la région de Tunis (Tunisie)', *Revue de Médecine Vétérinaire,* 137, pp. 537-540 (1986)

Kyewalabye Kaggwa, E., Lawal, I.A., 'Babesia equi and Trypanosoma Vivax infections in donkeys', *Revue d'Elevage et de Médecine Vétérinaire des Pays Tropicaux*, 42, pp. 205-210 (1989)

Lichtefels, J.R., 'Helminths of domestic equids. Proceedings of Helminthological Society of Washington', special issue, 42, p. 92 (1975)

Mattioli, R.C., Zinsstag, J., Pfister, K., 'Frequency of Trypanosomiasis and Gastrointestinal Parasites in Draught Donkeys in the Gambia in Relation to Animal Husbandry', Trop. Anm. Hlth. Prod., 26, pp. 102-108 (1994)

McConaghy, F.F., Davis, R.E., Hodgson, D.R., 'Equine Sarcoid: A persistent therapeutic challenge', *Compendium on Continuing Education for the Practising Veterinarian*, Vol 16 (8), pp. 1022-1031 (1994)

Mukhwana, E.J., 'Helminth parasites of donkeys (*Equus asinus*), Burchell's zebras (*Equus Burchelli*) and camels (*Camelus dromedarius*) in a selected area of northern Kenya' in Proceedings of a 2nd colloquium on working equines (Eds. Bakkoury M. and Prentis R.A.), Institut Agronomique et Vétérinaire Hassan II, Rabat, Morocco: pp. 45-50 (1994)

Pandey, V.S. and Cabaret, J., 'Stomach parasites of donkeys in Morocco: habitat and interspecific interactions', *Veterinary Parasitology,* 49, pp. 331-337 (1993)

Pandey, V.S. and Eysker, M.,'Parasites of the stomach in donkeys of the highveld of Zimbabwe', *The Veterinary Quarterly,* 10, pp. 246-248 (1988)

Pandey, V.S. and Eysker, M., '*Strongylus vulgaris* in donkeys (*Equus asinus*) from the highveld of Zimbabwe', *Veterinary Parasitology,* 32: pp. 173-179 (1989)

Pandey, V.S. and Eysker, M., 'Internal parasites of donkeys from the highveld of Zimbabwe', *Zimbabwe Veterinary Journal,* 21, pp. 27-32 (1990)

Pandey, V.S. and Eysker, M., 'Internal parasites of equines in Zimbabwe', *Donkeys, mules and horses in Tropical Agriculture Development* (Eds. Fielding D. and Pearson R.A.), University of Edinburgh, Centre for Tropical Veterinary Medicine, U.K, pp. 167-173 (1991)

Pandey, V.S., Khallaayoune, K., Ouhelli, H., Dakask, A.,'Parasites of donkeys in Africa', Proceedings of a 2nd colloquium on working equines (Eds. Bakkoury M. and Prentis R.A.), Institut Agronomique et Vétérinaire Hassan II, Rabat, Morocco, pp. 35-44 (1994)

Pandey, V.S., Ouhelli, H. and Verhulst, A., 'Epidemiological observations on stomach worms of donkeys in Morocco', *Veterinary Research Communications,*16, pp. 273-279 (1992a)

Pandey, V.S., Ouhelli, H., and Verhulst, A., 'Epidemiological observations on *Gasterophilus intestinalis* and *G.nasalis* in donkeys from Morocco', *Veterinary Parasitology,* 41, pp. 285-292 (1992b)

Pandey, V.S., 'Epidemiological observations on lung worm, *Dictyocaulus arnfieldi*, in donkeys from Morocco, *Journal of Helminthology,* 54, pp. 275-279 (1980a)

Pandey, V.S., 'Hydatidosis in donkeys in Moroccco', *Annals of Tropical Medicine and Parasitology*, 74, pp. 519-521(1980b)

Pandey, V.S., 'Seasonal prevalence of *Strongylus vulgaris* in the anterior mesenteric artery of the donkey in Morroco', *Veterinary Parasitology*, 7, pp. 357-362 (1980c)

Ramachandran, S., 'Viral conditions of Equids', in Proceedings of a Colloquium on donkeys, mules and horses (Eds. Fielding D. and Pearson R.A.), University of Edinburgh, Centre for Tropical Veterinary Medicine, U.K., pp. 114-125 (1991)

Reid., S.W.J., Fowler, J.N., Smith, K.T., 'Detection of the papillomaviral DNA in the sarcoid of the donkey', in Proceedings of a Colloquium on donkeys, mules and horses *(ibid)* pp. 135-137 (1991)

Sewell, M.M.H., Brocklesby., D.W., *Handbook on Animal Diseases in the Tropics*, 4th edition, ELBS with Bailliere Tindall, p. 385 (1992)

Sewell, M.M.H., 'Uniformity and Contrasts of the Helminth Diseases of Equids' in Proceedings of a Colloquium on donkeys, mules and horses (*op. cit.*) pp. 141-150 (1991)

Sims, B.G., Maldonado, S.J., 'Donkeys and Other Equines in Mexican Agriculture' in Proceedings of a Colloquium on donkeys, mules and horses (*op. cit.*) pp. 8-12 (1991)

Svendsen, E.D., 'Workshop summary: Donkey Parasitology', *Veterinary Parasitology*, 54, pp. 287-290 (1994a)

Svendsen, E.D., *The Professional Handbook of the Donkey* 2nd edition, The Donkey Sanctuary, Sidmouth, EX10 0NU, Devon, U.K., p. 56 (1989)

Svendsen. E.D., 'The main types of parasites affecting donkeys' health in various parts of the world', in Proceedings of a 2nd colloquium on working equines (Eds. Bakkoury M.E. and Prentis R.A.), Institut Agronomique et Veterinaire Hassan II, Rabat, Morocco, pp. 23-34 (1994b)

Uppal, P.K., 'Control of the 1987 Equine Influenza Epidemic in India and the present status of the disease', Proceedings of a Colloquium on donkeys, mules and horses (Eds. Fielding D. and Pearson R.A.), University of Edinburgh, Centre for Tropical Veterinary Medicine, U.K., pp. 126-134 (1991)

Vercruysse, J., Harris, E.A., Kaboret, Y., Pangui, L.J., and Gibson, D.I., 'Gastrointestinal helminths of donkeys in Burkina Faso', Zeitschrift für Parasitenkunde 72, pp. 821-825 (1986)

Yilma, J.M., Feseha, G.A., Svendsen, E.D., Mohammed, A., 'Health problems of working donkeys in Debre Zeit and Menagesha regions of Ethiopia', Proceedings of a Colloquium on donkeys, mules and horses (*op cit*) pp. 151-155 (1991)

FESEHA GEBREAB, B.Sc., D.V.M., M.V.Sc., was founding dean at the faculty of Veterinary Medicine, Addis Ababa University 1979-1988; chairman of the National Agricultural Research Council of Ethiopia, 1994 onwards; he is now Project Leader of Donkey Health Care and Welfare Project in Ethiopia, instructor in veterinary parasitology and clinical pathology, Faculty of Veterinary Medicine, Addis Ababa University and advisor to graduate students in the Faculty of Science of Addis Ababa and Alemaya University of Agriculture. He has written over 30 scientific publications.

13
PARASITES ABROAD
Elisabeth D. Svendsen

The International Donkey Protection Trust is a registered charity, operating from Sidmouth in Devon, which concerns itself with the plight of donkeys throughout the world.

On my travels in the early 1970s I regularly inspected donkeys and was surprised to find that the average life expectancy of a donkey varied from 9 years in Ethiopia to 15 years in Mexico. By contrast, the average age at The Donkey Sanctuary in the UK over a period of 7 years, taking a total number of 989 donkeys, has produced an average lifespan of 27.64 years.. Acknowledging the immense agricultural importance of the donkey in the Third World, it was apparent to me that helping the donkey to attain a longer lifespan, and to be fitter during its working life, would not only help the donkey but would have a substantial impact on the lives of the poorest people in the world, in fact, those who can only afford a donkey to assist them in every task of their working life. For two years I studied the problem, attempting to ascertain the cause of the early demise of donkeys abroad. Many factors had to be taken into consideration - nutrition, lack of water, excessive work and possible parasitic infestation. My trials led me, with a small mobile laboratory, to the most inaccessible parts of the world and, in fact, to the poorest areas of the Third World countries. The trials and tests carried out convinced me that parasites were indeed the main cause of the early demise, and the terrible clinical appearance, of donkeys and mules throughout the world.

One year's trial in North Africa convinced us that we had the correct solution in dosing the donkeys with anthelmintic but, unfortunately, political pressure forced us to retire from this trial and we next set up a trial in Greece. At this stage a protocol was set up, the object of which was to

Dr E. Svendsen administering anthelmintic in Tozeur, Tunisia.

demonstrate the efficacy of strategic anthelmintic treatment for the seasonal control of gastrointestinal parasites in working donkeys and mules. The body condition scores were set up as follows, and are still used today:

Grade 1	Very poor: emaciated. Ribs, spine and tuber coxae very prominent. Coat dull.
Grade 2	Below average: spine prominent, coat dull.
Grade 3	Average, good: spinous processes palpable but not prominent. Coat and skin supple, shiny and in good condition.
Grade 4	Over fat: spinous processes not easily palpated. Coat shiny, skin intact.
Grade 5	Obese: body well rounded with generous muscle and fat cover. Spinous processes not palpable. Coat shiny, skin intact.

We then chose approximately 100 donkeys and mules on three different islands and divided them into two groups - treatment and control groups.

All the donkeys assigned to the treatment group were given medicals and graded, and received anthelmintic treatment at strategic intervals over the course of two years. The anthelmintics used were pyrantel embonate and fenbendazole alternated between treatment intervals. At the time of dosing a rectal sample was taken from each animal, the results being recorded.

The control group received a placebo dose and a dung sample was also analysed. Each animal had to be easily identified with a special collar which was provided, giving a number, and the owner's full details were taken so that there could be no confusion.

This trial has been publicised, the results proving beyond dispute that donkeys treated by the strategic use of anthelmintics showed a 92% reduction in worm burdens and an overall improvement of 14% in body condition scores at the end of a two-year period. The results from Greece convinced the Agricultural Bank of Greece of the value of the trial and, in fact, 150 million drachma were allocated to a large worming trial to include all the donkeys in Greece. Follow-up visits were made to the islands where treatment was carried out and, in particular, to the island of Kea where all equines on the island were treated and the government subsidised anthelmintics for all other species in an endeavour to make the island parasite free. Once our official trial was completed, there was some concern that the local people might not adhere to the trial conditions without proper supervision but, nevertheless, the results were encouraging. The animals examined on our final trip showed a mean body condition score of 3.75 which was a very satisfactory average score and showed a great improvement on previous visits. Trials were then set up in other countries, starting in Mexico and moving to Kenya, Ethiopia, Cyprus and Egypt.

In charge of the trials in Mexico was Dr Aline de Aluja, under the auspices of the Faculty of Veterinary Medicine of the University of Mexico, and the results were conclusive. However, we did experience one problem after the first year of the trials. Local people were paid a small sum to compensate them for bringing the donkey from work in the fields to the trial area and, if their donkey was ill or had died, they would bring along any donkey they could find in order to receive the money. The veterinary team rapidly became aware of this as the results were inconsistent and a new identification system and control was introduced. Using our two mobile clinics in Mexico these trials have continued.

Eqvalan was used at the rate of approximately 20 ml per donkey and cultures produced evidence of the following infestations:

Strongylus equinus
S. edentatus
S. vulgaris
Strongyloides westeri
Trichostrongylus sp

Among the small strongyles: *Cylicocyclus, Poteriostomum, Cylicodontophorus, Cylicostephanus* and *Cyathostomum* were identified.

One of the other projects undertaken by the Trust was to give Third World veterinary surgeons the opportunity to visit The Donkey Sanctuary in the UK, and to see the work we do for donkeys here. So far, through the World Health Organisation, we have been host to Dr James Mzungu from Kenya, Dr George Efstathiou from Cyprus, Dr Ragheb from Egypt and Dr Yilma Makonnen from Ethiopia, as well as vets from almost every part of the Third World. During their visits the veterinarians were given the opportunity to visit one of the British Veterinary Universities for a week and Glasgow, with its very high reputation for parasitology, was the most popular venue. A full week there, a week at the Hereford School of Farriery and six weeks at the Sanctuary working with the veterinary surgeons in our very modern operating theatre and laboratories and with the donkeys themselves, all expenses and fares paid, gave these Third World vets an opportunity that they were very eager to take. Currently training visits are undertaken by vets employed in our overseas projects, or by special arrangement.

Professor Jimmy Duncan from The University of Glasgow Department of Veterinary Medicine, on one of his routine visits, followed up the association between our charity and the Faculty of Veterinary Medicine at Addis Ababa, and our desire to set up a worming programme there. Ethiopia has approximately 3.5 million donkeys which seem well adapted to low quality and quantity feed and, with a metabolism which copes with low water intake, had survived during the drought conditions better than any other draught animal. In fact the donkey is now one of the most important animals in the farming and transport system of rural Ethiopia. The biggest problem faced by donkeys in Ethiopia is general debility, bad sores and early death due to heavy parasite infestation. Parasite species found include:

D. arnfieldi
Gastrodiscus aegyptiacus
Strongylus equinus
St. vulgaris
St. edentatus
Trichonema spp
Habronema muscae

Also identified in smaller quantities were: *Fasciola hepatica*, *Anoplocephalid cestodes*, *parascaris equorum*, *oxyuris equi*, *Triadontophorus* spp, *Gyalocephalus* spp, *Trichostrongylus axei*, *H.microstoma*, *setaria equina*, *cylindropharynx asini* and *C.aethiopica.*

During worming trial visits to Ethiopia the writer and team found that there was a tremendous amount of work to be done for the donkeys in Ethiopia and an I.D.P.T. mobile clinic was set up in 1994 to provide free veterinary treatment for donkeys. A static clinic for donkeys is under construction at this time. One of the trials set up by our charity took donkeys from three villages into account and, using different anthelmintics, proved the value of using Eqvalan. It was found to be the most efficacious, not only for endoparasites, but for ectoparasites, but it had a further spin-off in that, surprisingly, body contact with treated donkeys gave control donkeys an improved immunity to the infestations, particularly with regard to ectoparasites.

A further two mobile clinics worked in three areas in the Nile Delta, Egypt and, once again, even one administration of Eqvalan improved the donkeys' general condition. Those donkeys under regular treatment became much stronger and fitter, and the terrible saddle galls caused by ill-fitting harness on thinly covered bones became less.

The charity is also working in Kenya, where a donkey sanctuary has been set up on the island of Lamu. Over the page you see a picture of Bahati taken into care on the point of death from a very poor owner. The next picture shows Bahati fully recovered being returned to her owner three months later. Over the next two years Bahati received no difference in food or working regime, but had anthelmintic administered twice yearly by our visiting team. The following photograph shows her with her foal on one of the team's visits to her owner's village of Matandoni.

Lamu is an island where donkeys are the only form of transport

Bahati being taken into care.

and in view of the inaccessibility of the island and its narrow streets there is no way that they could be superseded by more modern means of transport. Anthelmintic trials have been carried out on Lamu and the surrounding islands and over the last few years more than one-third of the total donkey population has come under the treatment regime set up by our charity. The difference in the general welfare of the donkeys on the islands is striking and the charity receives immense support from the local population. On one worming session over 176 bots were recovered from one donkey and there is an obvious problem in the area, not only from parasites but from trypanosomiasis, rabies and tetanus.

It would appear that twice-yearly treatment in Third World countries will extend the working life of the donkey by approximately five years.

Among efforts to improve the donkey's lot throughout the Third World and, with it, the lot of its impoverished owner, I have been given the opportunity to speak of my experiences in the practical field of parasitology at the World Association for the Advancement of Veterinary Parasitology Congresses held in Rio de Janeiro, Montreal, East Berlin and Cambridge. In Cambridge I was given the honour of chairing a workshop, and I feel the information gleaned from this will be of interest to all veterinarians.

Bahati, fully recovered, being returned to her owner.

Bahati and her foal.

With the consent of Elsevier Science B.V. a summary is reproduced here. The main objectives of the workshop were:-

1. To define the impact of parasitism on the welfare of donkeys throughout the world.
2. To report on recent and current projects in donkey parasitology.
3. To discuss strategies for the treatment/prophylaxis of parasitic infections in the donkey.
4. To outline priority areas for future study on donkey parasites.

A number of points were discussed including brief details of the trials carried out using different anthelmintics. Ivermectin was preferred due to its broad spectrum activity. The attitude of owners to teams dosing donkeys was queried. However, once the initial suspicion was allayed that (1) owners may be charged for the treatment, and (2) it was some ploy on behalf of the government to find donkey owners and tax them, the clinics were almost mobbed. In answer to a question as to why donkeys are not bred more, it was explained that poor health and parasite burdens prevented pregnancy. For example, since anthelmintic dosing began in Ethiopia, some stallions had become so fit and difficult to handle that, for the first time, requests for stallion castration were being received by the Veterinary University. There was no doubt the birth-rate would increase when dosing was carried out on a large scale. One delegate said he felt obliged to say that, in many Third World countries, donkeys were more important than children, as they supported the whole family.

Professor Jimmy Duncan emphasised the prevalence, biology and epidemiology of parasite species in donkeys. Comparisons were made with other equines and a full list of parasites found was presented.

HELMINTH PARASITES OF DONKEYS

STOMACH	*Habronema* spp
	Trichostrongylus axei
	Gasterophilus spp.
SMALL INTESTINE	*Parascaris equorum*
	Strongyloides westeri
	Anoplocephala spp.

LARGE INTESTINE	*Strongylus vulgaris,*
	S. edentatus
	S. equinus
	Triodontophorus spp
	Cyathostomes
	Oxyuris equi.
LUNGS	*Dictyocaulus arnfieldi*

Dr Morad Ragheb's paper dealt with studies on donkey parasite infections in the Middle East. Over the previous four years the speaker had been working on a project in the Nile Delta, funded by I.D.P.T. in co-operation with the General Organisation of Veterinary Services (G.O.V.S.) in Cairo. The gastrointestinal parasites found were similar to those described in the first paper. Several trials, each involving 100 donkeys, were conducted in different areas implemented by the mobile clinic run jointly by the I.D.P.T. and the G.O.V.S. Of all the donkeys and mules tested, none was free of parasites, and the average number of eggs per gramme faeces (epg) in donkeys from the outskirts of Cairo was 4,000 (see Appendix 6: Modified MacMaster Technique).

The workshop discussed differences in the dosage rate between horses and donkeys. The speaker said the horse rates could be used as a guideline but were not ideal. Glasgow University has been examining the pharmacokinetics of anthelmintics in horses and donkeys and differences have been observed - these data will be available later.

There was a long discussion on cyathostomes, and the apparent failure of ivermectin against larval stages. Alternative anthelmintic treatments were discussed, including the efficacy of benzimidazoles. It was reported from Zimbabwe that not many inhibited stages of cyathostomes occurred there.

Dr Sandy Love stressed the importance of strategic dosing based on worm egg counts and the importance of pasture management. He referred to the foundations of strategic anthelmintic treatments being parasite species, climatic factors, drug efficacy, dosing synchronisation and grazing management. He referred to studies in the UK where a small number of anthelmintic doses given at strategic time points reduced pasture strongyle larval contamination. Also, reduced dosing is necessary in extended dry weather when there is a minimal transmission of strongyle larvae but, during the rainy season, many larvae may be ingested so more treatments are necessary. Dr Love referred to studies in Greece and Ethiopia which had shown marked improvements in the well-being and fitness of the treated animals.

Dr Feseha Gebreab spoke on endo- and ectoparasitic infections of donkeys in Ethiopia. The working donkey population of Ethiopia was estimated at 3.9 million but their effective and essential use has been hampered by parasites, food deficiency and health hazards, while poor harnessing, causing saddle galls, also contributed to the short lifespan of the Ethiopian donkey. He reported *Babesia* in 60 of the 348 donkeys tested by blood smears with 51 harbouring *B.equi* and three *B.caballi.* Coproscopy of 216 donkeys and ovaculture in 12 donkeys with >5,000 epg revealed the following helminths in order of abundance and frequency: *Trichonema, Strongylus vulgaris, Strongylus edentatus, Strongylus equinus, Triodontophorus, Oesophagodontus, Trichostrongylus axei, Gyalocephalus* and *Poteriostomum.* Mean epg was 400. Post mortem examination of a single donkey also revealed *Gasterophilus nasalis, Gasterophlis intestinalis, Oxyuris equi, Parascaris equorum* and *Anoplocephala perfoliata.*

Professor Khalid Khallaayoune dealt with the parasites found in Morocco, where all donkeys were found to be infested with *Trichostrongylus axei* and *Habronema* spp. The heaviest infestations appeared to be in donkeys less than 5 years old and it was strongly recommended that an education programme be set up to advise on the control of helminth infestation of young foals and pregnant mares.

In the following debate, selection within parasites of donkeys and similarities between parasites of donkeys, ponies and horses were discussed. In the case of *Dictyocaulus arnfieldi*, a donkey could be heavily infested but show no signs, whilst a horse or pony would show clinical signs very early. Donkeys, therefore, were not always treated, whilst other equines were.

Trials in Ethiopia, funded by I.D.P.T., were discussed at some length. Of the three separate localities tested, all the donkeys in one village were treated with ivermectin, with fenbendazole in the next village and, in the third village, the donkeys received only a placebo. At the end of the two-year trial the ivermectin-treated donkeys were fit and strong, the fenbendazole donkeys had improved, but the villagers in the placebo area were distraught; they felt cheated that their donkeys were still thin and weak. The teams then had to return to the third village to dose regularly with ivermectin. The owners were only too well aware of the beneficial

Our team working in Lamu.

effects of treatment versus non-treatment. Questioned as to when was the best time for treatment in Ethiopia, the speaker replied that once at the end of the dry season and once at the end of the wet season were the most suitable, but as there were many climatic areas in Ethiopia, each could have different times.

Dr Lane Foil outlined the development of new methods for equine ectoparasite control. He reported that in North America the screw worm fly had been practically eliminated. Different insecticides were suggested for control of flies such as black flies and tabanids, while animals must be kept away from wooded areas. The tsetse fly remained a great problem, and Zimbabwe had tried various methods of control, including electrocution. More use should be made of holding animals in barns and shelters.

Discussing the future, all agreed that it was essential that regular worming was continued, and that the I.D.P.T. continued training and subsidising vets and universities to further study the problems facing donkeys worldwide. The Chairman hoped that the current study on histocompatibility being carried out at the University of Glasgow Veterinary School would enable more control of the movement of susceptible donkeys to areas of risk and so aid in future disease control. It was hoped that veterinarians and parasitologists would become more interested in the most over-worked and under-rated animal in the world.

Training of veterinarians, field managers and educational officers from throughout the world continues at Sidmouth. We try to fund as many training programmes as possible, to give help overseas where needed, and to fund non-intrusive research projects. I am co-operating with Professor Max Murray of the University of Glasgow Veterinary School on a paper relating to trypanosomiasis in the donkey.

Work done by Rosina C. Krecek and Lynda M. Gibbons shows us that little information is available for South Africa on the role of the donkey and the perceived importance of these animals to their owners. Recently a study was undertaken in the north-west province of South Africa to establish the socio-economic role and helminth parasitic levels of working donkeys (Wells and Krecek, *In Press*). The levels of worms in these donkeys were high; average egg counts 2,000 eggs per gram. Anthelmintics are not used in these areas because they are not available or affordable. Other problems, such as stock theft, have higher priority according to the farmers in the respective communities.

The Appendix includes various haematological, biochemical and physiological parameters pertaining to the donkey which have been obtained by the non-intrusive research carried out by veterinary surgeons at The Donkey Sanctuary.

Note of thanks

I would like to acknowledge the very great help we have received from the University of Glasgow Veterinary School in our work to control parasites overseas. My grateful thanks go to Professor Norman Wright, Dean of the Faculty, and Professors Jimmy Duncan, Max Murray and Stuart Reid, and Dr Sandy Love.

Reference

Wells, D., and Krecek, *R.C., In Press*, Findings of a socio-economic questionnaire implemented in communities using donkeys in Hammanstraal, South Africa, Animal Traction Network for Eastern and Southern Africa Workshop, Nairobi, Kenya (December 1995)

14
GENERAL DONKEY CARE
Rosalind De Wesselow

A DONKEY IS A DONKEY IS A DONKEY, to misquote. To the average member of the public this would no doubt be a satisfactory description - and with some justification. Although colour and size may vary, the image presented in 99 cases out of 100 is one of a quiet, amiable beast with friendly eyes and a long pair of ears. However, if the time has come when you are actually going to choose a donkey of your own, you should be clear in your mind as to the purpose for which you want him. I don't wish to be accused of sex discrimination but for the purposes of this article I shall refer to the donkey as 'he' (and by this I do not mean a stallion, but a gelding). The donkey's roles are many, and different types suit different roles best. Perhaps you may simply have wanted a donkey for years, in which case his age and appearance are not of importance, but you may want to acquire 'something to keep the grass down in the paddock', a ride for young children, an animal to drive between the shafts, or just a large pet. The donkey will fulfil all of these functions more than satisfactorily if selected for the part he is to play. I must stress one thing, however, before you read on - donkeys are sociable animals and are not suited to living on their own. A lonely donkey will bray and try to make contact with others in the neighbourhood and he may well mope. To quote (this time correctly) a friend of mine describing her beloved horse, 'After all, he is only human'; she said it without realizing the contradiction in her words, but although I laughed, I knew exactly what she meant.

Space is essential if you keep any equine. With even the most careful management, one acre is the absolute minimum on which to manage two donkeys. The area is needed not only for food (for which one acre is not adequate and you should offer straw all year round and supplement lack of grazing with hay in winter) but for exercise. Also you will find that donkeys tend to stale (urinate) in one area which they will not then graze, take over another patch for rolling and thereby very soon rub away the grass; the water-supply and its well-trodden approach will account for a few more square yards of unproductive ground, as will the gate or the part of the fence where they stand while you scratch them behind their ears. Add to this the area of their shelter, and you will find that in a small enclosure there is not much space left for the donkeys to graze and walk about and have the occasional frolic.

Donkeys live a long time - 30 years plus is quite normal for an animal that is well cared for - so bear this in mind when you are choosing and try to plan for his future when you are planning for your own. An animal that is already old is suitable for all the roles I have mentioned except for driving. He will, however, need a dental examination, as a donkey's molars tend to become pointed with age and the animal cannot grind properly. His teeth may need to be rasped occasionally by the vet to ensure that he can eat comfortably and digest properly but, if dental problems still persist and weight loss occurs, a little extra food may be necessary. An old donkey, like a foal, may also be a little more susceptible to chills after cold rain, but remember that no donkey is a hardy perennial - they are not native to these islands.

So far as riding is concerned, a young animal is not suitable, as he should not carry weight regularly until he is four years old. If you want a youngster and are offered a foal, it is important that he should not leave his mother before the age of 6 months at the very earliest. Personally I feel that even this is too young - 9 months to 1 year is far better. If he is a male, he should be castrated, as no stallion will make a suitable pet even if kept with a mare. An entire male, however friendly, may sometimes be unpredictable in his behaviour and is best kept by a 'professional'. Otherwise there is little to choose between mares and geldings and a combination of either will live happily together.

When you have chosen your donkey, arrange to have him transported to your home at a time when you are going to be there! Your actual presence at the unloading will help to create the right psychological effect so far as the new surroundings go. Make a little fuss of the new arrival, see that he is wearing a headcollar with a detachable leading rein, and take him to his new quarters. What you do then must depend on whether his field is already occupied by another animal, and you will have to use common sense. If there is already a resident donkey or donkeys, allow all parties to sniff each other across the gate before you introduce the newcomer into the field. The resident donkey should be more than ready to receive the stranger, but the excitement will very likely lead to a bit of a chase-around for a few minutes. The same will apply if the resident is a pony, but should your donkey be brought face to face with a horse, especially a young one, the introduction should be gradual. For a start, the horse may never have seen a donkey before and may be inclined to make the point by careering about and snorting. In this case, secure the donkey close to the field to graze or eat a little hay, while you stay around. If the horse is very excitable and it is possible to keep the two animals separate for 24 hours or so, it will be to the good. However, when you do introduce them, make sure that you hold the horse's head until the donkey has got fairly into the field and looked round, and make sure that no leading rein is left trailing from his headcollar. Once the animals have touched noses, it should be alright to let the horse loose. Many horses grow to be well nigh inseparable from 'their' donkeys, seeming to find a sense of security in their small even-tempered companions.

If the field is occupied by other animals, such as cows or bullocks, there will probably be far less excitement. However, with animals that are smaller than donkeys, such as goats, sheep or geese, it is as well to introduce the donkey into their field so that he is pre-occupied with the novelty of the place as well as with his new companions. If the opposite procedure is followed, and small animals are let into the donkey's own field, he may well chase them about for a while until familiarity is established. In any case, when putting a new donkey into new quarters, detach the leading rein but leave on the headcollar for a few days, as he may turn out to be shy or nervous, and it will be easier to catch him up if there is something on his head to get hold of. Don't leave a headcollar on permanently, as this may catch on things when the donkey is turned out.

This may be a good moment to make reference to dogs. Donkeys do not take kindly to strange dogs. Be sure your family pet is restrained from making himself at home in the donkey's field for the first day or two until they become well acquainted, or he will almost certainly be chased and a small dog can be badly hurt. Dog and donkey invariably become accustomed to each other and even become good friends, but strangers' dogs should

beware. This dog-following characteristic can be quite useful in seeing off straying dogs from your property!

So far as the field itself is concerned, there are other chapters in this book describing the ideal pasture and correct type of fencing. In this more general chapter let me say simply that donkeys require a sufficiency of not particularly high-quality grass. Sometimes they seem to be expected to live on air as, not infrequently, one sees them confined to a paddock eaten down to the earth. On the other hand deep lush pasture will quite certainly lead to disaster in the form of colic, laminitis or obesity. As well as liking grass, donkeys are very fond of browsing and enjoy tackling bramble patches and keeping hedges in trim. Be warned too, because he likes the bark of trees, so keep precious specimens securely fenced off. Also beware of planting poisonous shrubs too near his perimeter fence, as a donkey's neck and head stretched out horizontally reach quite a long way! So for his own safety's sake, if for no other reason, check up on what is within reach of the fence. Many evergreens are poisonous as well as some other things. While he relishes many weeds and wild flowers which may grow in his field, it is as well to keep thistles and docks under control by cutting or digging out. Thistles are, I think, overrated as a favourite food of donkeys

- they tend to eat only the top out of the plant, which then seems to react by spreading outwards, and a sizeable thistle patch can quickly form which will take over from grass. Docks are not eaten but will multiply if left. Ragwort should be pulled out and disposed of away from the field as it is more poisonous dead than living.

All donkeys need access to shelter. Contrary to what may be generally supposed, this is as necessary for the animal's comfort in the summer as for its well-being in winter. The reason for this is flies. Field animals can be tormented by flies - horse flies as well as the more common variety that cluster round their eyes, and not forgetting the occasional warble and bot flies which send them into panic. Flies are part of every warm sunny day, and only leave off their attentions in rain or dark. A shelter provides the necessary gloom that gives relief. I hate to see cattle bunched together in open fields enduring the onslaughts of flies, and far too many equines have to undergo the same thing. The normal pattern for my own animals in the summer is to stay out at night and come to stand in their shelters before mid-morning, where they remain until the end of the afternoon. The other essential reason for a shelter is as a refuge from rain. Cold, frost and even snow do not seem to worry donkeys unduly, but a heavy penetrating downpour is something for which they are quite unadapted. A soaking may well pave the way to a chill, bronchitis or pneumonia. You can hardly be responsible for seeing that the donkey is always brought indoors if it is raining, but provide him with a field shelter and he will go under cover himself.

The shelter should have a half door so that it can, if necessary, be closed and yet admit fresh air, always important even with a sickly animal. If the shelter is required solely as a summer or rain shelter and not as a feeding place, the floor need not be hard standing, although this is always desirable. If, however, you intend to use it for feeding as well, very necessary in wet wintry weather, the animal will be spending far more time in there and mucking out will need to be a regular routine. In this case the shed should have a concrete floor. Incidentally, this will benefit the donkey's feet, as these are not really suited to stand on turf the whole time, and a hard surface helps to wear the hooves down a little.

If you are going to take over an old shed that has been used by cattle, remember that various troubles such as lice can be picked up by donkeys from the wooden door posts, etc., on which previous animals have rubbed.

A coat of stockholm tar, or something similar but not containing the chemicals used to treat woodworm, should be applied, preferably a little before the donkey moves in. If you are going to build a new shed, see that it is sited at a convenient spot, because the bedding will need to be transported to the manure heap or wherever else you wish to take it. The destination, wherever it is, must not be in the same field as the animals, as this will encourage the spread of internal parasites. The other thing to bear in mind is that the straw and haystore should be as near as possible to the feeding place. Straw is the most common bedding used, and should be on offer as feed at all times, but there are alternatives. I suppose it should go without saying that a store must be capable of being securely fastened against inquisitive noses! Lastly, while on the subject of shelters, it is a good idea to have a cupboard either in the hay store or in the shed itself (above donkey level) in which you can keep a few necessities such as hoof pick, any ointment required, curry comb, etc.

In the winter, if the weather is dry and fine it is not necessary to feed donkeys indoors and when possible I prefer to feed hay outside. Indoors or out, hay should not be spread about on the ground as a matter of routine as this leads to much wastage; inevitably it gets walked on and it will not then be accepted as food. The use of nets and racks is not recommended as the donkey's natural feeding position is with the head down, and a corner manger or feed bin is preferred.

Access to drinking water is most important, and donkeys drink more than you might probably suppose. Water is heavy to carry and personally I think that a proper cattle trough installed by a qualified plumber more than makes up for what you spend on it. It never runs dry and it is easy to clean out. If you are unable to provide this, make sure that the container to be used is suitable, e.g. not made of lead or - at the opposite extreme - plastic, which is so easily knocked over. At least provide yourself with a hose-pipe that can run from an appropriate tap to the container, and leave it ready for use outside the fence. Do not site the trough or container under trees or it will become full of fallen leaves in autumn.

Before your donkey arrives try to find out whether he has had tetanus and flu inoculations and, if in doubt, ask your veterinary surgeon to remedy this as soon as possible. Ideally, the donkey should be wormed before he is introduced into his new domain, to avoid contamination of his own pasture. It will be a good thing in any case to put yourself in touch with a local vet so that he knows the set-up should he ever have to come in a hurry or at night. It is also important to make contact with a farrier. This contact should really be made before you acquire the animal, as his services are essential. The horn of a donkey's foot grows surprisingly quickly and, as most farriers are very busy, it is unwise to wait until the hooves need paring before getting in touch with one. If you explain that you would like to be taken on, on a regular six- to eight-weekly basis, it will make it easier all round. It is a good plan to pick out your donkey's feet every day, both to remove anything that may be troubling him, as well as to familiarise him with the handling of his feet.

Donkeys love being groomed and daily attention will give great pleasure. I find their chief joy seems to be when I scratch them gently with my fingers inside their ears - their necks stretch out, their eyes half close and I almost believe they purr! I suppose it is probably the only part of their body which they cannot reach with their teeth or rub against something. By the way, one of the delights of keeping more than one donkey is to watch them grooming each other. Two will stand side by side, facing different ways, and steadily groom each other with their teeth for 10 or 20 minutes at a time.

Do ensure that your donkeys are checked daily either by you or by somebody who knows how to recognise trouble, otherwise one could have an accident and remain in pain or even die without your being any the wiser. This may not sound very likely but it can happen. Colic, for instance, as well as being very painful, can lead to a twisted gut which can cause an agonising death, and colic can be brought on by a surfeit of lush grass, a chill or inappropriate titbits passed over the fence by a stranger. Some picnic leftovers, such as food containing meat or dairy products, not to speak of the wrappers, can be lethal to an equine. If your field is easily accessible to the public, I think it is a good idea to display a notice asking people not to feed the animals and explaining why. Make no mistake, people do love donkeys and derive great pleasure from stroking and petting them; most donkeys have a fan club beyond the immediate family that owns them. A little-thought-of danger is a children's swing hung from a branch within a paddock. Natural inquisitiveness combined with an urge to scratch his neck can lead to an equine pushing its head between the ropes. Subsequently, when turning away, the ropes can get twisted and the animal's panic can swiftly make a lethal noose.

Sometimes circumstances may alter and one of two things happen - either your donkey reaches the end his life or for some reason you are unable to continue keeping him. In the first instance, if your vet feels that nothing further can be done to make him more comfortable and happy, don't send your old friend off to meet his end in strange and frightening surroundings. Your vet will do the deed and suggest somebody who will take the remains, or you may know of a 'professional' who will come to your home and do both. The companion should not, if possible, be present when the vet is putting the other one down, but afterwards it is important to leave the body for a short time. If the donkey can actually see that his friend is dead, he will understand and grieve without the pining that the shock and mystery of a sudden disappearance will bring on.

In the second instance, the responsibility is yours to see that he is happily placed. Once a donkey is in the hands of a dealer it is immediately at risk of one sort or another. For this reason, never send an animal to be sold at a market or fair where its ultimate destiny may be the Continental meat trade. If you have advertised it as for sale, always check carefully the identity and circumstances of anyone offering to buy, e.g., whether they have sufficient grazing, etc. We have to remember how dependent animals are upon us and use all our efforts not to let them down.

ROSALIND DE WESSELOW was born in Brussels of an English father and Irish mother; she later lived in the Lake District and was educated at Eastbourne.

She worked in the Ministry of Defence in London for nine years before marrying in 1961. After a short further spell in London, she moved to West Sussex where she has lived ever since.

In 1962 Rosalind de Wesselow started keeping donkeys and built up to a stud of about 20 animals. However, on finding how many donkeys there were about, she decided not to add any more to their number and stopped breeding them. At present she has four elderly mares.

Her interests are various and include literature, the arts, travel and the welfare of children and animals.

Rosalind de Wesselow is a Trustee of the Donkey Sanctuary and the International Donkey Protection Trust.

15

BREEDING AND CARE OF THE YOUNG

Priscilla Kirby, Updated by Valerie Mathews

WHY BREED AT ALL? The only acceptable answer is: to improve the breed.

However, it is a fact that as in the horse and pony world, many donkeys are bred for the wrong reasons, with the breeder feeling only a passing responsibility for the life he arranged, or allowed to be created.

It is a sad fact that the Donkey Sanctuary has taken into care over 7,000 donkeys. The Sanctuary does a quite magnificent job in rescuing uncared for donkeys, educating owners and raising standards in many areas, but it should not be there in a breeder's mind as a last resort when deciding whether to breed - that is not the purpose of the Sanctuary.

A mare owner, whether of one donkey or several, may wish to breed in order to perpetuate that line. Each owner has to decide on the standard of the mare. Some may be good enough to breed either fillies or future stallions; but from some mares only a filly foal is looked for. If, from such a mare, a colt is born that is neither of top class standard or of a size suitable for riding or driving, then the breeder should consider very carefully the future of that foal when weaned. Pet homes for non-useful animals do exist, but their permanency is less predictable than for other donkeys. If the breeder is not prepared to geld and keep such a donkey until a permanent home appears then, in my opinion, it may be kinder to have the donkey put down than to allow it an uncertain future.

Having said all that, there is nothing so delightful and rewarding as the young donkey, and any year in which I cannot justify a foal is that much bleaker.

Studs

A stud is basically a name for a breeding centre for equines. One or more stallions will be present, and the stud owner's mares and youngstock will be on the premises. Some studs are private with no visiting mares accepted, but in general, stud owners are quite happy to accept visiting mares to be put in foal. The stallion owner will charge a stud fee; this could better be described as a service fee, as the mare's owner pays for the stallion's service, not necessarily for the resulting foal. Most stallions are advertised at stud and their fee will be quoted, for example:

Bright Knight - Stud Fee £50.00 (N.F.F.R.) plus livery

Livery is the charge for keeping the mare and includes food, grazing and also a percentage of overheads such as fencing, insurance, shelters and adequate supervision. N.F.F.R. means 'no foal-free return service' and not as one mare owner asked me - 'Does that mean no fun, free return?'

How to choose a stud

Both the stallion and the stud at which he stands should be carefully considered. The stallion's and mare's pedigree and conformation faults should be compared. Other members of both families, such as the stallion's dam, and his progeny from other mares, are important to show which genetic features are obvious in each generation.

Other factors then come into the picture. Usually 'Murphy's Law' means that the mare owner lives in Sussex, the ideal donkey stallion for that mare is in the North of Scotland, and the mare owner's ideal stud will be equally far away.

The stud has become less difficult to choose as a list of studs is now available from the Donkey Breed Society upon application to its Secretary or Stud Book Registrar. However, mare owners should always visit a stud prior to sending their mares. Such visits should be by appointment with the stud owner. Most stud and stallion owners are only too pleased to show visitors around, and discuss all aspects of the mare's visit.

A young stallion's reputation may well be based on his achievements in the show ring and on his own pedigree. However, after two or three years at stud such factors, whilst still important, should be considered together with the progeny that the young stallion is now producing. A stallion in the end will be remembered for his offspring. A stallion could produce up to forty foals in one year, so the impact of a popular stallion on a breed can be remarkable.

Whilst show-ring results can be very helpful in sorting out the stallion's

A foal at the Donkey Sanctuary.

obvious breed points, there are many excellent stallions who either do not show at all, or who live in areas where showing is not easily achieved. Never follow fashion for fashion's sake; take the time to have a good look round.

Keeping a stallion

The entire donkey, like many other entire animals, can be extremely dangerous to have around, and serious thought should be given to the problems that may have to be faced before deciding to keep one.

Is it necessary? A stud owner with suitable facilities and experience may need a new bloodline to cover the daughter of existing or possibly related stallions. Unless an owner has the facilities necessary, then starting a stud can be a traumatic experience. Several studs have been started by a mare owner's wish to keep a colt foal entire. Assuming the colt is of top class standard and will therefore be an asset to the breed, the decision to stand him at home should be taken with care. Would it be wiser to keep part or total ownership and let him stand at stud at a large stud with readymade facilities, and perhaps more experience of handling stallions?

Equally, handling and working with stallions is a way of life. They are totally different in their outlook on life, they tend to be quicker thinkers, far livelier to handle, more rewarding to train, and will become very much part of the family.

Dangers

It must be remembered that when a stallion is running with a herd in the wild, during mating he will hold the mare's neck with his teeth. Equally, when he is protecting his mares or proving his status amongst other mares, his only weapons are his feet and teeth. Therefore, even in domesticity these same weapons can be turned against anything and anyone who is in the wrong place at the wrong time. Cats and dogs, and other small animals such as small calves or sheep may be attacked either in play or anger. Equally, humans can and have been attacked when a lack of anticipation has provoked a stress or risk situation. Just occasionally there is also a colt or stallion that will be dangerous through design rather than bad management. One girl of about 18 was disfigured for life when a stallion got over-excited at a show, the handler tripped up and the stallion went down on top of her and scraped her face. Another stud owner miscalculated a stress situation and was attacked by her young stallion, receiving very severe injuries with scars on her arms, legs and body that will be there for life.

Factors that provoke a risk situation

1. Mares and fillies in season, and strange mares about.
2. Other stallions and colts about.
3. Inadequate facilities, fencing, stables, etc.
4. Human failure. Lack of anticipation.

Do not

1. Lead one stallion past another without adequate preparation, i.e. shut the top door of the stable or tie the second stallion up.
2. Lead a mare past a stallion without preparation.
3. Leave dogs or other small animals in with a stallion.
4. Turn your back on a stallion when working in a stable or yard, especially during the covering season.
5. Isolate your stallion - give him company.
6. Allow small children to be around a stallion unless constantly supervised, and never in a stress situation.

On the other side, the owner must also have a suitable temperament. The owner of a stallion must be a quick thinker, enjoy the challenge of the entire male, never have any fear of the stallion, have a highly tuned natural anticipation for trouble, a great deal of native common sense and be physically capable of dealing with all likely situations.

A stallion should not be kept isolated and caged up, at the same time his ability to get to where and whom he wants is quite amazing. Suitable planning of all the facilities on the stud is required.

Most colts will grow up with geldings quite happily and may not need to be separated until they start work, usually at four years old. Some adult stallions spend their winter months with a gelding friend, well away from any mares or youngstock - others need to be kept away from geldings from an early age. Other stallions will happily live with one or more mares in the winter.

Personally I keep my colts with geldings as long as possible and thereafter they mainly live without other donkeys. We have ponies and cattle, and the stallions are very happy running out with them in the fields or in the winter, sharing their yards. As most of my donkey mares are served in the spring they are usually too heavy in foal to stand the frivolous rompings of the stallions during the winter months. Occasionally we have had a difficult mare to get in foal, and by keeping her with the stallion she has finally been successful.

In order to do his job well the stallion must be fit and healthy. In addition to normal wormings and vaccination programmes, exercise should be regular. A fat stallion is not healthy. A stallion exercise paddock need not be very large, as most stallions will spend a large part of their time pacing up and down the fence nearest to their mares. Our stallions are exercised in a variety of ways in addition to their time in a paddock. Most are trained to drive, and this is good in several ways: it increases the donkey's fitness, gives him plenty to think about and adds to the bond between owner and stallion. We also lead the younger colts and stallions in hand and drive them on long reins, teach them to lunge and lead out on a lead rein when riding our horses.

Covering the mare

Compared with some horses and ponies, most donkeys are extremely obvious when they are 'in use' (i.e. ready to stand for the stallion). It is inadvisable to allow a donkey mare to be covered until she is in her fourth year, as it is generally accepted that a donkey is not mature until that age. However, the stud owner should try to get as much information as possible from the mare owner regarding previous breeding habits, such as length of season. Most donkey mares will be in use for 5-7 days so serving them on the 3rd and 5th days should be sufficient. If necessary a further visit to the stallion on the 7th day can be added.

Preparation

The covering of mares should take place at the same time each day. The stallion then is keen to visit his mares, and will also realise that when he is taken from his stable/yard/field at other times of the day it is not for the same purpose. Covering should take place in a small secure area or yard, ideally with solid-sided walls, so that there is no danger of either escape or injury to the animals involved.

We bring the mare to the covering yard first and she is tied up to a ring with a quick release knot. An assistant stays at her side. The stud groom will have ensured the mare's vulva has been washed. He will then go and fetch the stallion. The stallion should be totally controllable, and therefore should wear a bridle with the lead rein attached to the bit. Voice control and the stallion's obedience to commands should mean that very little pressure is needed on the bit. However, it is essential to have that measure of control in case of unexpected problems. Our stallions work in a cavesson which gives total control, but does not affect their mouths for driving. Stallions tend to be livelier at the beginning of the year, and with a new mare. Some have very clear colour preferences and others will make plain which mares they like or which they just tolerate.

We use a jute stable rug with an added neck piece; this is placed on the mare before the stallion mounts her. Most stallions can be taught not to bite the mare's neck, but if the stallion does follow his perfectly normal instincts and holds the mare, then a jute covering ensures no mark on the mare. The mare's tail should be clean and bandaged to protect the stallion.

Hygiene procedures vary from stud to stud, and the stud owner should consult in detail on this subject with his veterinary surgeon. Hygiene throughout a stud is a top priority and must be part of everyday routine.

The stallion should be first introduced to the mare over a solid partition; most donkey mares in use will show by champing (opening and shutting their mouths and laying their ears back), urinating, holding their tails up and 'winking' with their vulvas. The stallion is not a machine and requires a certain amount of 'foreplay'. Each stallion takes a different length of time before he is ready to serve the mare. We usually allow the stallions to mount the mare once or twice prior to serving, and most stallions will be ready to serve in 5-10 minutes from meeting the mare. Some, especially young stallions, require longer and may tax the owner's and the mare's patience.

Mares who breed regularly are usually no trouble at serving. Donkeys seem to be far more highly sexed than most ponies, and they love being in foal. Maiden mares and fillies can be a different matter. They may be roaring in season at home with another mare, and then become very coy when a stallion appears. Great care should be taken by the stud owner not to rush the maiden mare; however, an extra assistant can be helpful during service of a maiden.

Great care should be taken to see that the mare does not kick the stallion as he dismounts, as this can cause severe damage. Working stallions, if shod, should not cover mares unless boots are fitted on their front feet. Equally mares should never be shod behind when sent to stud, and kicking boots should be used if necessary.

The in-foal mare

Care of the in-foal mare starts before sending her to stud. Like the stallion, the mare should be in fit condition, free from parasites, correctly vaccinated and with feet in good order. A mare not in such condition will be less likely to get in foal and less likely to carry a foal to term. If born, a foal from such a mare would start life in less than good condition. Mares who have to travel to stud are more likely to stay in foal if they are used to travelling. A bad traveller may get in foal and then reabsorb or slip the foal through the stress of returning home. If no regular travelling can be provided, it may be wiser to leave the mare until she is well in foal, perhaps, as much as 12 weeks.

Before visiting the stallion, the stud owner will have given the mare owner a nomination form which will include details of pedigree, age, colour, height, whether maiden/barren/or with foal at foot; details of worming and vaccinations, and previous breeding record. This is a very important part of the process, as it gives the stallion owner vital information regarding the correct care and handling of the mare.

When the mare returns from stud, fitness and health should be maintained throughout pregnancy. Do not feed the mare for two just because she is in foal. However, her feeding habits should be carefully monitored. Knowledge of the mare owner's soil types and structure will decide which minerals and trace elements should be fed to the mare during pregnancy; a vitamin supplement is also essential.

On collecting the mare from stud, the mare owner should pay the stud owner's account which will include any veterinary bills incurred. This account is due before the mare may be removed. If payment is made in cash or by cheque with cheque card, then probably the service certificate will be handed over with the mare. However, it is more usual for the service certificate to be forwarded at a later date. The stud owner has the right to refuse to accept any mare without giving a reason.

Assuming foaling is to take place in about the March - May period it should be remembered that the mare will be very heavily in foal at just the time of year when ground conditions are at their worst. During this period ploughing through deep mud or hard rutted frosted ground to reach shelter is not ideal. If possible keep the mare on a sound even surface with a sensible amount of steady exercise. The mare's feet should be carefully tended throughout.

Gestation

Very variable in the donkey. We have had healthy live foals ranging from 10½ -14½ months from last service. Stockmanship is what counts. The mare owner's knowledge of each individual mare and mares in general is the best guide.

Foaling

This should be considered as the period from when the mare commences 'bagging up' (when the udder starts to swell) to when the foal is born, up and feeding..

This is somewhat longer than some might consider, but there is much to be done and prepared during that time. The mare's udder starts swelling some three weeks or so prior to foaling - though one maiden mare in fact started bagging up over seven weeks before she finally foaled.

During this period careful consideration should be given to where the mare will foal and where she and the foal will be afterwards. If possible, I prefer to have a mare stabled at night and out in a small secure paddock during the day. The stable should be at least 12 foot square, airy with no draughts, well drained, and should be disinfected before use. Infra red heat available in the box is useful for winter or spring foals. The bed in the stable should be deep clean straw, and should be put down several hours prior to foaling so that any dust from the straw will have settled. Our foaling box has a ring in the wall in case the mare needs to be tied up at any time. However, there is no manger or bucket holder or hay rack. Any hay will be fed in small quantities on the floor, food in a removable bowl, and water in a small plastic bucket which is removed at the start of foaling. Many owners can miss the act of foaling, but I think I have been present at the birth of all but three of my foals. Two foals arrived during the day, and the third was born to a new mare who was not bagged up, and so I had no idea she was in foal.

About 72 hours before foaling, the mare's teats will become distended and she may run a little milk. Her pelvic muscles slacken and the bones around the top of the tail become moveable. When foaling is close, the mare may be restless and will stop eating.

Usually the act of foaling is quite quick, about 30-60 minutes from the beginning of the contractions and, with very few exceptions, donkeys are more than capable of coping on their own. The normal presentation is forelegs followed by the head. If this is not the case or there appears to be too slow progress, then call a vet immediately. Inexperienced owners can cause a lot of harm by trying to assist the mare. There are many excellent books with illustrations on all stages of foaling, but it is impossible to deal with such a complicated subject safely in a few short paragraphs. For the inexperienced owner, so far as possible, resist the urge to meddle. If present

The bag appears.

A gentle pull as the mare strains.

at the birth, keep out of the way, still and quiet. It is better to call the vet unnecessarily than to leave it too late. When the foal is born, make sure the nose is clear of the bag. Do not help the foal to break the umbilical cord, as the blood flow between mare and foal is completed after birth. After a few minutes' rest, either the mare or the foal will start to move and the cord will then break naturally. The foal's navel should then be sprayed with an antiseptic spray.

The mare has not finished yet; she must still pass the placenta or afterbirth. However, this may take up to an hour. During this period the mare will usually turn round and begin cleaning the foal by licking it all over. This establishes a bond between mare and foal, and is a very important stage. Try not to interfere at this stage, especially with a young mare. If a mare doesn't attempt to clean the foal up then a quick rub down with a clean towel can stimulate the foal. A sprinkling of salt on the foal's back may encourage the mare to commence licking.

When the foal tries to get up it will fall over several times, but each attempt is assisting in the natural strengthening of the muscles in the legs. Provided the foal is not in danger of injuring itself, then leave well alone. When the foal has got the hang of walking, it should start to search for the mare's udder. This next hour or so is the hardest for the owner. Most mares and foals get everything sorted out without help.

A few maiden mares may not like the idea of the foal suckling, usually because they are so fascinated by the foal that they keep turning round with it. Often all that is needed is to hold the mare's head for a minute or two and all will be well. Very occasionally a young mare will actually reject a foal, in which case contact a vet immediately.

If the foal is weak and unable to stand, then it is essential to get some food into it. Ideally, if the mare's milk can be used, then milk her and feed about 2oz to the foal. If the mare's milk is not available then mix a teaspoon of glucose in 2oz of water and feed at blood temperature, then call the vet. There are several reasons for weak foals or lack of milk, and expert help should always be sought for anything out of the ordinary. Bottles and teats must, of course, be sterile.

The mare's colostrum is most important to the foal and the sooner the foal starts feeding the better. The antibodies in this milk protect the foal over the first days of life. It is essential that foals should receive the colostrum within two hours of birth.

Make sure that the foal's head is freed; the bag is full of amniotic fluid.

The foal should be allowed to slide out slowly.

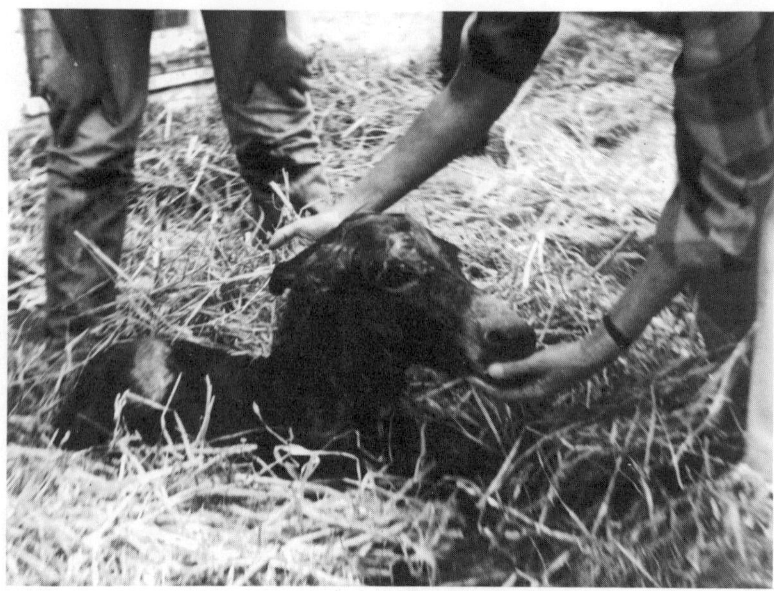

Check that the foal is all right, and that there is no mucus blocking any passages.

The mare resting before passing the placenta. A vet should be called if this has not appeared after one hour.

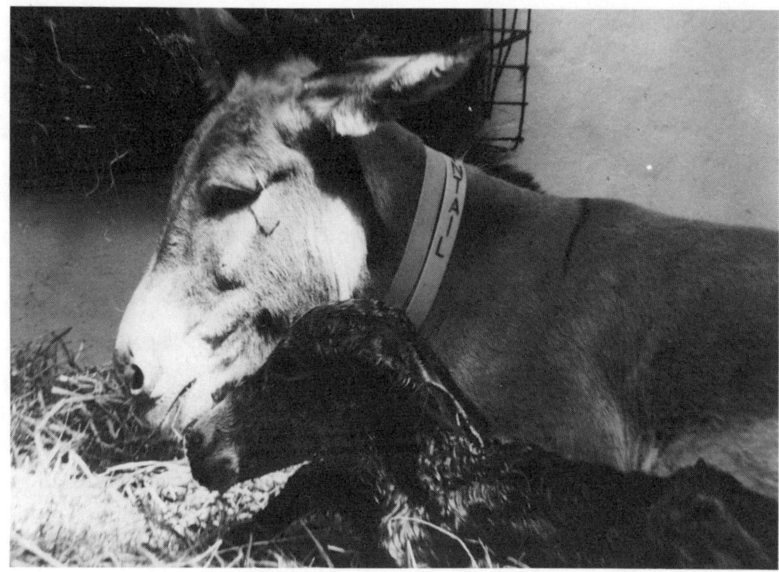

Close contact and licking the foal helps to start the milk flowing.

I always try to have an experienced mare foaling first each year, and from her I take about 4oz, or more if possible, of colostrum and freeze it. This is just a standby in case of shortage of milk or other problems later in the year.

Assuming a normal foaling, the foal will be given an anti-tetanus injection the next morning. The foal will then be vaccinated against tetanus when old enough. At this time, the vet will check the mare and foal fully, and will also check the afterbirth to be sure it is complete. Once checked this should be burnt.

Rearing foals - birth to six months

Foals very quickly adjust to their new world and after a few hours will be moving quite fast around their box. Weather permitting, both mare and foal may go out in a small paddock the next morning, but ideally with no other stock in the paddock. We use a teatowel wrapped loosely round the neck to lead the foal with a hand on the rump; it will then walk alongside its mother to and from the fields.

Small donkeys, like children, can become quickly ill, and any listlessness in a foal should be immediately checked. If the foal's temperature is raised above 102°F, then call the vet. Foals can stop eating and if this occurs not only the foal but the mare should also be checked. Her udder will tell you if the foal has suckled recently, and if not, check to see if there is undue heat in the udder. Again call the vet. Never wait to see if the foal improves later in the day.

A young foal's environment should be as clean as possible to avoid the possibility of any infection entering through the navel.

The foal will require fairly lengthy periods of sleep and therefore the weather must be watched. Unless it is summer, it is wiser to have a short period of exercise in the paddock interspersed with longer periods in the stable. A foal's coat does not keep rain out, and if the foal gets soaked it may well become seriously ill, catching a chill or even pneumonia. This lack of protection against the weather lasts until the baby coat is shed and the new coat is through. For this reason, all our mares with foals are stabled at night, and all youngstock are stabled during their first winter. Another

The donkey's sharp hoof is protected by a rubbery substance which peels within hours of birth.

cause of pneumonia can be from dust or bacteria in the hay and straw in a poorly aired stable.

Shortly after birth the foal will pass the meconium, a dark brown substance. If it has not passed this, the foal will probably be seen straining unsuccessfully and again the vet should be called.

The next problem with the foal will probably coincide with the mare coming into season some 7-14 days after birth. The mare's milk changes consistency, and the foal has a tendency to scour. If the foal is listless again check the temperature and call the vet.

There is very little justification for covering a mare on her foal heat (5 or 6 days after the birth) or first season and indeed it is very rare for me to ever put a mare with foal at foot in foal again that year. I prefer to leave foals on their mothers until natural weaning takes place, between 7-12 months. However if the foal is an entire colt, care should be taken. One colt foal we had, managed to get a two-year-old filly in foal when he was only 32 weeks old. We know exactly the timing as he was moved to a different paddock the next week and gelded! Donkeys of both sexes are remarkably precocious and great care should be exercised to avoid unwanted problems.

During the early months the foal has much to learn. Firstly, that humans are good, and that they should be obeyed. This basic fact can be got through to a small foal quite easily and kindly during the first weeks. The foal should get as much mental stimulation and education as possible. It is so simple to ensure a trouble-free future of leading, riding or driving by teaching the young foal to walk over every possible different surface, including 'Slow' signs on the road, and even the dreaded drain! The foal should learn to be tied up regularly, be groomed, have its feet picked up, rasped and tapped. Within a week or two of birth the foal will be pushing in to inspect its mother's short feed, and soon will enjoy a bucket of his own. A worming programme should be started at four weeks old, and this should be adhered to strictly.

During the early months a foal can be introduced to the horse box or trailer. Place the box in a small paddock and close the shelter up. The mare will probably go straight in to explore anyway, and if the foal is led in and out two or three times, he will then usually follow his mother in and out. We then leave hay and straw in the box and leave them to use it as a stable for a day or two in the daytime, under careful supervision. Then one day

A DBS Champion stallion.

the foal and mare are shut in and taken for a short drive, returned to the paddock and released again. Time spent in this way pays dividends later on.

If, through circumstances, it proves necessary to rear the foal yourself then, as when bottle rearing any young animals, one has to go further in taking on the mother role than just supplying nourishment. Also to be considered are companionship, discipline and weather forecasting. For companionship the loan of another donkey is obviously the most suitable answer but if this is not possible then a goat, or even a sheep, can give companionship to a young donkey.

Hand rearing foals

See Appendix 9

Donkey Breed Society Stud Book

The Stud Book was started in 1969 to provide a standard for the breeding of donkeys. Reggie Summerhays had laid down the breed guidelines and, with the magnificent help of many very experienced horse and pony judges, a system of inspections was started.

In the first two years some 2,000 donkeys were inspected, with less than half passing for entry. At this time loads of 300 donkeys at a time were being imported from Ireland and sent to dealers all over the country.

Many of today's studs are based on those donkeys bought from dealers' fields or in markets. It was obvious that much inbreeding had taken place before the donkeys left Ireland and on the boat anything could happen, so the sooner a record was started the better.

The aim was, and still is, to maintain and improve the standard of the breed.

Entry into the Stud Book is by inspection only for both stallions and mares at four years or over. The Society also maintains a General Register for all donkeys.

VALERIE MATHEWS has owned and bred donkeys for over 30 years and has been a member of The Donkey Breed Society since 1968. She was Chairman of the Society in 1987, and was a member of its Welfare Committee for some years and is currently Chairman of its Stud Book Committee. Valerie has always been interested in the welfare of the donkey and has been a Voluntary Welfare Officer for the Donkey Sanctuary since 1980. With her husband she maintains a Holding Base for the Sanctuary in South Wales and assists in the transport of donkeys within a wide area.

16

GROOMING, HANDLING, RIDING AND DRIVING

Annie Chapman BHSI(t)

DONKEYS LEARN BY GRADUAL, PROGRESSIVE REPETITION. Take into consideration the donkey's age (ideally between 4 and 20 years), build, conformation, temperament, confidence in traffic and physical fitness.

Grooming

Grooming gets the donkey used to being handled and helps to gain his confidence. After fitting a headcollar and leadrope, tie your donkey up using a quick release knot, preferably to a piece of string that will snap in an emergency. Until your donkey is used to being tied up do not leave him unattended, an assistant should stand at his head during the first few grooming sessions.

Pick out the feet, using a hoof pick, making sure that the frog and white line areas are clean. If you pick out the feet in the same order the donkey quickly learns the sequence.

Starting with a dandy brush, brush the coat in the direction of hair growth from the poll on the near side and working towards the tail. Feel the body as you brush, looking for lumps, bites or sore places. The object is to remove all caked mud and dirt. Use a body brush for sensitive areas like the face, legs, belly and the tail. Take extra care where tack will be positioned as any dirt will cause rubs. A plastic curry comb is used to clean the body brush and can be used on the coat in the same way as the dandy brush. A rubber curry comb is useful when the donkey's coat is moulting. Use it in a circular motion to remove any loose hair from the coat.

Wipe the corners of your donkey's eyes using damp pieces of cotton wool. If 'matter' is not removed this attracts flies and can become sore. The nose and dock areas should also be cleaned as necessary. If you are

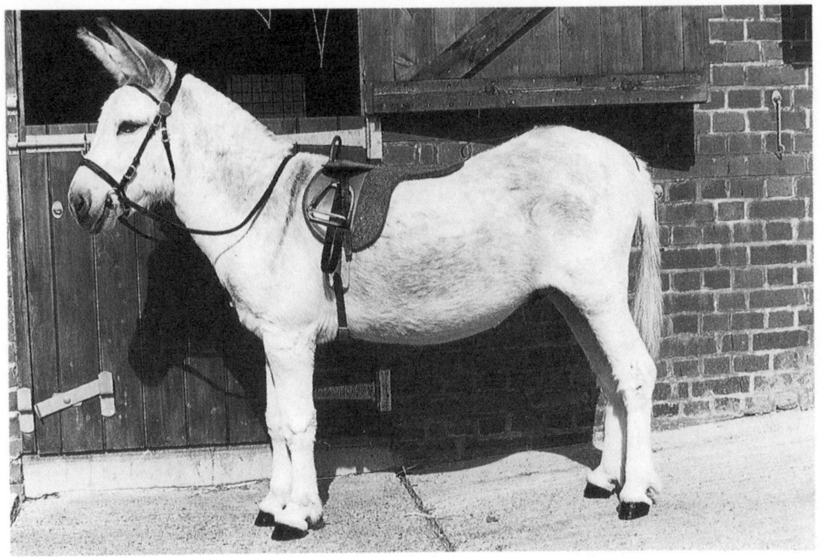

Ready to ride.

going to a show then you can oil the hooves.

The riding bridle

A standard pony bridle will not fit most donkeys, you will need a longer (full size) headpiece and browband. Use a straight bar rubber or synthetic snaffle bit or a mouthing bit. I find that a jointed bit hangs low in the mouth and encourages the donkey to put his tongue over the bit. This evasion quickly becomes a habit which reduces control.

Fitting: Work from the near side (the donkey's left). Undo the noseband of the headcollar and put the reins over the donkey's head, so that they rest around his neck. Hold the headpiece in your right hand and the bit across the palm of your left hand with your thumb free. Put your right arm over the donkey's neck so that you are able to restrain him and hold the bridle up at the same time. Slide your left thumb into the corner of the donkey's mouth and, as he opens his mouth, lift the bit into position. Keeping the bit up in the mouth by holding the headpiece up with your right hand, now insert his ears between the browband and the headpiece by bringing them forward. Take care not to bend them backwards as this is uncomfortable for the donkey. Once the ears are through, slip the headpiece into position behind the ears and make sure that the browband is wide enough to lie comfortably at the base of the ears.

The fit of the bridle should be checked by someone with experience, as your donkey will not behave well if he is uncomfortable. The throat lash should be loose enough to allow a hand's width between it and the jaw. The noseband should allow two fingers' width. The bit should just wrinkle the corners of the mouth.

In-hand training

Attach the clip of the lead rein to the offside ring of the bit then pass the lead rein through the near side bit ring so that the lead rein acts on the chin groove and the bit is not pulled through the mouth. Take him for walks

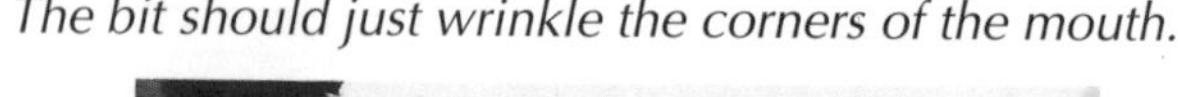

The bit should just wrinkle the corners of the mouth.

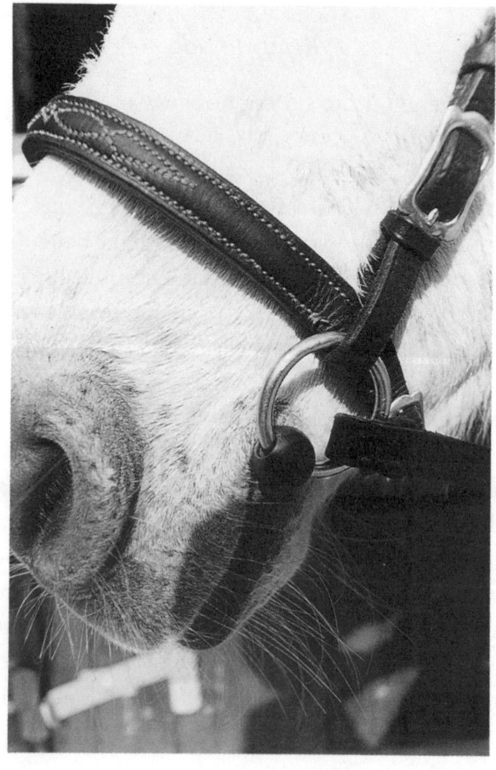

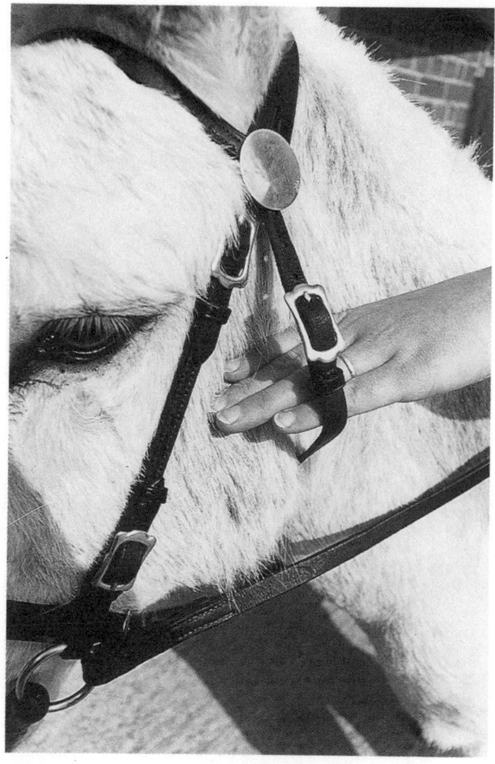

The throat lash should be loose enough to allow a hand's width between it and the jaw.

down a quiet lane. Teach him to 'walk on' and 'halt' from your voice aid. When halted he should stand with equal weight on all four feet. Proceed to 'trot on' and encourage him to trot freely beside you without you having to pull him, or he you, along. You should remain on the near side, level with his shoulder whenever possible. Slow down gently, do not go straight from a trot to a complete standstill. When manoeuvring remember to turn the donkey away from you to avoid being stepped on. Give plenty of verbal praise when he behaves well. If you plan to show him in hand then he must learn to walk and trot freely, to halt square and to stand still when being examined by the judge.

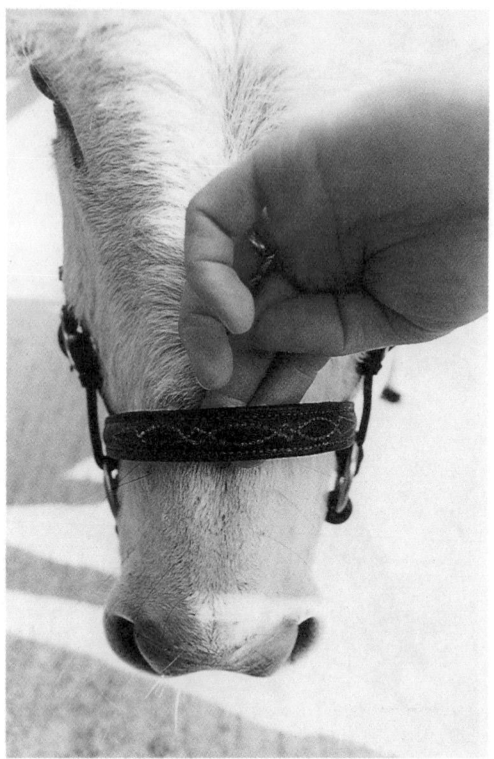

The nose band should allow two fingers.

The saddle

The saddle (a felt pad is ideal or a synthetic donkey saddle is a practical alternative) should be placed on the withers and gently slid back into position so that the hair on the donkey's back lies flat. The girth should be fastened close to the elbow and tightened gradually. You should be able to slide your hand comfortably in between the girth and the donkey's side. Before the rider mounts, pull the donkey's front legs forward one at a time so that the hair under the girth lies flat. Check the girth once the rider has mounted. The girth straps should be secure and the holes not worn. Fleecy girth sleeves help to prevent rubbing. I recommend a crupper as this stops the saddle from sliding forward. To fit the crupper stand close to the rump on the near side facing the tail. Slide the crupper over the tail and up to the base of the dock, making sure that all the dock hairs lie smoothly. Lay the

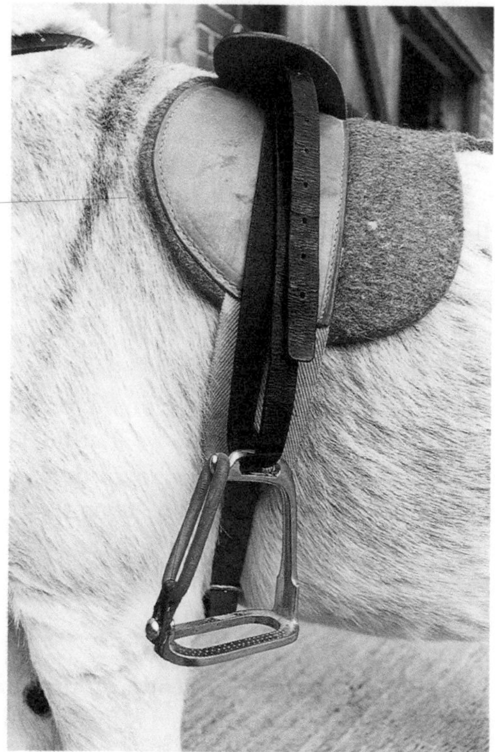

A safety stirrup iron.

strap along the donkey's spine and fasten through the 'D' ring on the back of the saddle. You should be able to get a hand's width comfortably between the crupper strap and the donkey's spine.

A leather saddle, if used, should be checked to ensure that the tree (saddle frame) is sound and that there is no pressure on the donkey's spine or withers.

Stirrup irons and stirrup leathers

If your felt saddle does not have proper safety bars for the stirrup leathers, then make sure that you use safety stirrup irons so that your rider's foot cannot get stuck. If there are safety bars then ordinary stirrup irons can be used. Make sure that the safety catches on the bars are down during riding. Allow the donkey to become accustomed to the stirrup irons banging against his sides. Lead him about in walk and trot until he is quite happy, before you start putting any weight on his back.

Riding

Your rider should weigh less than 50kg (8 stone) and have a well fitted jockey skull cap which conforms to BSI standards and riding boots with flat soles and a low heel. Initially, enlist the help of a child who has riding experience. Keep hold of the child at all times and have an assistant to lead the donkey around in an enclosed area. Go around in both directions. Always praise the donkey when he behaves well and try to remain calm if he becomes upset by the new proceedings. Never allow children to ride on the road unaccompanied.

Holding the reins for riding

Place three fingers around the reins and the thumb on top, with the slack of the rein going up through the hand and out at the thumb. The little finger rests under the reins and is the closest to the donkey's mouth. There should be a visual straight line from the bit, along the rein, through the hand to the rider's elbow. Elbows should be bent and should rest easily at the rider's sides.

Position in the saddle

The rider should sit up straight in the centre of the saddle with equal weight on both seat bones. The knees should be bent so that the lower leg is under the body with the heel lower than the toe and the stirrup iron on the ball of the foot. There should be a visual straight line from the rider's ear, through the shoulder and hip to the heel. A guide to the correct stirrup length is when the rider's foot is out of the stirrup with the leg hanging down, the bottom of the stirrup iron should be level with the rider's ankle bone. Make sure that both stirrups are the same length and that the stirrup leathers are lying correctly.

Aids (signals)

Basic aids for your child to learn are:

Walk on: by taking up a light rein contact and gently squeezing the donkey with both lower legs. To start with this leg aid should be accompanied by a voice aid ('walk on'). The donkey will quickly learn the leg aid and then the voice aid will not be necessary.

Halt: by sitting up and dropping the weight deeper into the saddle and then gradually increasing the rein pressure until the donkey stops. Again this should be accompanied by the voice aid ('halt').

Trot on: this signal is similar to the walk on aid but, as the donkey is already walking, he then knows to speed up to a trot. To bring him back to walk use the deep seat and gentle rein pressure as for halting but make sure that he walks forward and does not come straight to a halt from a trot.

Turning: I prefer to teach children to use an open rein when turning, this means that the child is not encouraged to pull on the donkey's mouth. To turn left the left rein should be moved away from the donkey's neck, with the thumb leading, allowing the donkey's head to turn in the required direction. A contact with the donkey's mouth should be maintained. Squeeze with both lower legs with the outside leg positioned slightly further back than the inside leg, this helps the donkey to bring his body around on the turn. To turn in the other direction the aids should be reversed. If you have problems please seek professional advice.

Driving

Unlike the riding bridle, the driving bridle has winkers (blinkers). The most common bit for driving is called a Liverpool bit. The noseband on a driving bridle needs to be tighter than for riding to prevent the cheek pieces bulging and the donkey seeing behind or under the winkers (blinkers). The sight of the cart rolling behind him could cause him to panic and bolt.

Start by long-reining: this is driving without the cart! You walk (or run) behind your donkey but use the aids with your voice and reins as if you were in a cart. Initially just use the bridle, pad and crupper. Start off in a field or enclosed space and then progress to a quiet lane.

Use voice aids: walk on and halt, then walk on again. It is best not to long-rein with someone leading the donkey as the donkey will listen to the leader and not the long-reiner. However, to make sure that he stands still when you say halt, have someone ready to go to his head and hold him still if necessary. When he is obedient in walk you can proceed to trot. Give him lots of verbal encouragement and praise when he goes forward and stays in a straight line. After a few lessons you can then long-rein him with the collar and breeching fitted, with the traces trailing on the ground on each side of him so that he gets used to the noise and the feel of the traces

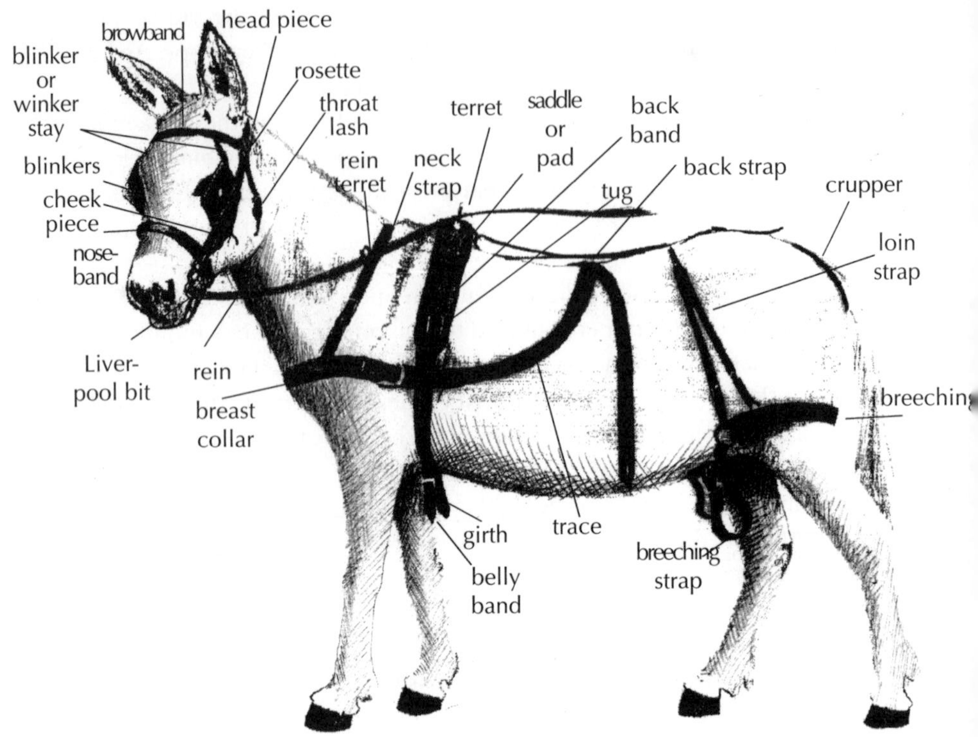

The harness complete.

against his sides. Your assistant should hold the traces and gradually take the strain on them so that the donkey learns to pull forward without jerking. Then get your assistant to hold the breeching so that the donkey becomes used to the effect of travelling downhill with the weight behind him, and to stopping the vehicle.

Teach him to back, with your helper pushing him while you say 'back' using pressure on the reins. When teaching him to turn make sure that you swing out to allow room for a cart to turn behind him; his front legs should cross over as he turns in a small area. In later training, when the donkey is in the shafts, your assistant can pull the outside shaft around to help him turn. The donkey will learn to push into the inside shaft to bring the vehicle around.

Holding the reins for driving

Practise holding the reins correctly in your left hand. With the left rein resting over the index finger and the right rein between the second and third fingers, grip both reins with the lower fingers. Make sure that both reins are the same length. Your donkey will not drive in straight lines if you are not holding your reins level. Get someone experienced to show you as holding the reins for driving is different from riding. Your right hand is free to assist when turning, to hold the whip and to give signals. The whip should rest loosely in the right hand with your thumb up the shaft. Angle the whip across your body over your left hand. When using the whip it should only touch the donkey between the pad and the collar. When shortening your reins hold both reins with the right hand behind the left hand, slide the left hand towards the bit and then release the right hand.

Obtaining a cart and harness

The cart will either have a swingle tree or two fixed trace hooks. A swingle tree is a moving attachment on the centre of the front of the cart which has a hook at each end where the traces are attached. The swingle moves as the donkey pulls, so that there is less direct pressure on the breast collar which is the most suitable collar for donkeys.

In order to find a cart that is the correct size you should know the height of your donkey measuring from the ground to halfway up his ribs (where the shafts will rest) and from the front of his chest to his tail. The front of the shafts should be level with his chest and you will need enough room behind his tail to make sure that his hocks will not hit the cart when he is trotting downhill.

If you hold the shafts at the required height you should be able to see if the cart will ride level: the floor should be parallel with the ground.

To test the balance

Ask someone to sit in the cart, while you hold the shafts at the correct height; there should be very slight weight on the shafts. The seat of the cart can usually be moved to alter the balance.

The average donkey can pull a vehicle weighing up to approximately 128kg (20 stone) plus a medium sized adult or two children on a fairly level road at trotting speed which can be maintained for 2-3 miles. At walking speed a total of 3 cwt can be pulled.

Fitting the harness

The breast collar buckles around the neck. A breast collar can easily be fitted too low. It should be fitted two inches above the point of the shoulder, taking care not to impede the windpipe. The traces attach to each side of the breast collar and should be twisted up about the buckle until you are ready to 'put to', so that they do not drag on the ground.

The pad or saddle has a 'D' in the centre at the back. It should be positioned approximately one hand's breadth behind the withers. (I have found that donkeys need the saddle further forward than ponies because of their different conformation). The back band or strap is attached to this and then to the crupper and breeching strap, which fit around the dock and hindquarters respectively. The tension on the back band should be one hand's breadth at the buckle. There is a stitched slot on the back band through which the loin strap passes and then fastens to the buckles on each side of the breeching. The loin strap holds the breeching up on the donkey's rump. Make sure that the breeching is not too low as it will pull the donkey's hind legs under him when he has to hold the weight of the cart when stopping. When the traces are tight the breeching should have a hand's width between it and the rump. On each side of the breeching are breeching straps, these buckle to the breeching Ds on the shafts using a figure of eight loop. It is most important to check that the breeching straps are not worn thin.

Once the crupper, breeching and breeching straps are in place then fasten the girth on the pad, first passing it through the loop from the breast plate (if used). Check the tightness of the girth as for a saddle (the girth does not have to be as tight as for riding). Slip the belly band strap into the keeper or point hole to prevent it dragging or banging against the leg.

Thread the reins through the pad and collar terrets with the buckles to the outside, fold the long end of the reins and tuck them under the back strap on the OFF SIDE to keep them tidy and out of the way.

Put on the bridle taking care with the ears; a bridle that unbuckles at the headpiece is useful. Check the fitting of the winkers (blinkers) - the eyes should be central and the winker strap not too tight or too loose. Fasten the throat lash, allowing one hand's width at the jaw, then the noseband should fasten firmly to keep the winkers steady. Fasten the curb chain by twisting anti-clockwise until flat and attaching to the hook on the near side. The curb chain should come into contact with the jaw when the bit is at 45 degrees to the mouth (for showing this should be a double link curb chain without a lip strap loop). Lastly attach your reins to the bit. Start with 'rough cheek'; this is when the reins run through the bit ring and around the top slot. You are now ready to 'put to'.

Putting to

To avoid the donkey being startled lead him to the vicinity of the cart and get him used to it. Make him face a wall or fence so that he cannot rush away from the cart. Choose level ground so that the cart does not roll away! Have an assistant to stand in front of the donkey facing him, holding the cheek pieces on each side of his face.

Always bring the vehicle up to the donkey with the shafts raised well above the rump, lower gently into position and slip the shafts into the tugs. Never back the donkey into the shafts. Un-loop and thread the traces inside the belly band and hook up to the swingle tree or trace hooks on both sides. Always attach the traces first so that if the donkey tries to move out of the shafts he is attached to the cart and will not get caught up. Fasten the breeching straps on to each side of the shafts. A short strap should be put around the shaft once, including the trace within the strap. With a long strap make a figure of eight around the shaft, with the traces within one loop only.

Fasten and adjust the belly band (this holds the tugs down). Check the tugs and shafts for correct height and balance; there should be some movement. When you are sitting in the cart the shafts should 'float' in the tugs if the cart is balanced correctly. You will also notice the buckle on the tugs moving slightly; there will be no weight on the donkey's back. Double check all harness for safety, comfort and fit. Check the balance of the cart.

Your kit

You will need a driving whip, gloves, an approved jockey skull cap, a blanket for your knees and some sturdy shoes. Make sure that you have plenty of assistants.

Once the vehicle is attached then gently rock it backwards and forwards so that he gets the feel of it. To start with lead from the bridle as well as having someone holding the reins from outside the cart. Once he is confident then you can get into the cart, still having a person at the donkey's head.

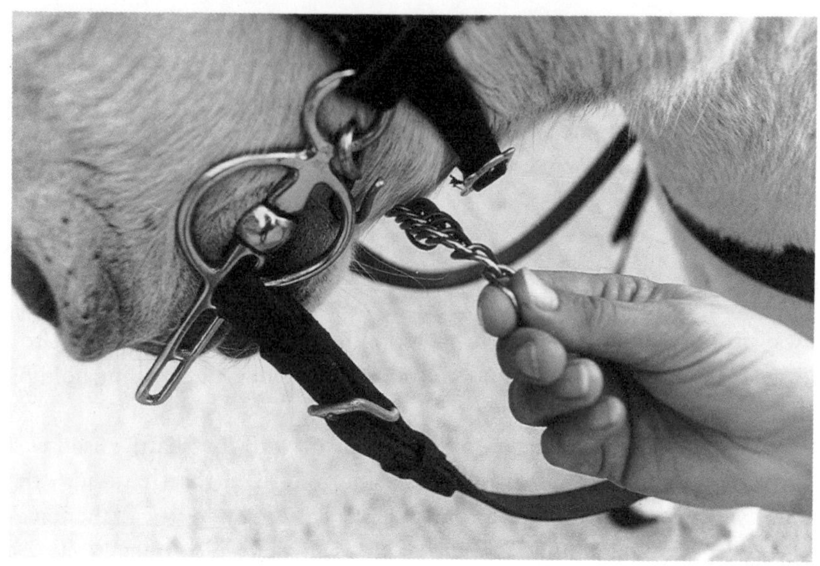

Fastening the curb chain. Reins fitted to the top bar.

A Liverpool bit with reins fitted 'rough cheek'.

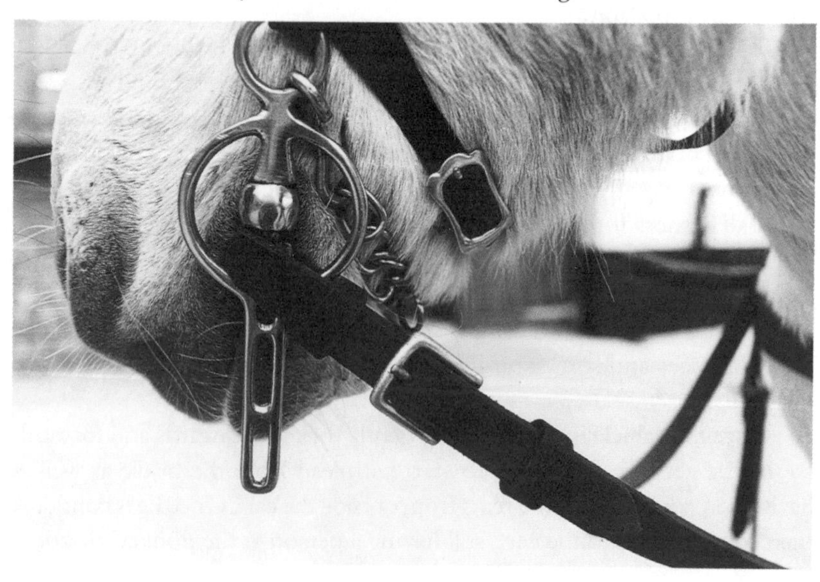

With a long strap make a figure of eight around the shaft, with the traces within one loop only.

Getting into the cart

Stand beside the off side of the vehicle, making sure that the reins are flat. Take the reins in your right hand with the near side rein on top and the middle finger separating them. Loop the long end of the reins over your little finger or your arm so that you do not catch your feet in the trailing end. Mount into the cart and sit down on the off side of the seat, transfer the reins into your left hand. Always face forwards when getting in or out of the cart so that you can control the donkey with the reins if he tries to move before you are safely aboard.

Your assistant should remain at your donkey's head until you are ready. Devise a signal with your assistant so that you can nod when you are ready to move off ... if you speak the donkey will anticipate.

The driver is called a whip. The whip should sit up straight and rest his feet flat on the floor, some carts will have a foot rest. His left hand should be carried in the centre of his body just above the navel keeping a bend in the elbow.

When you first start to drive without someone leading the donkey from the ground make sure that an assistant is ready to catch hold of the donkey's head when you halt, as you won't be able to jump out without frightening him. Use the same aids as you used in his early training 'walk on' and 'halt' to start and stop. Do not trot for the first few trips and make sure that you are on level ground as hills make everything much more complicated.

If the donkey becomes worried then go back to the previous stage for a few sessions. If you intend to drive on the roads regularly then you should consider having shoes fitted to your donkey. Consult your farrier for advice.

When you have finished your drive make sure that you remove the cart and harness safely by reversing the harnessing and putting to procedures.

Remember you must build up the fitness of your donkey and it takes time to harden his skin in the areas where the harness can rub. If your donkey sweats then consider clipping him as this will help him to stay cool and his coat will be easier to keep clean which, in turn, prevents galling.

After you have removed the tack from your donkey, wash any sweat marks away, pick out his feet and then let him into the paddock so that he can have a roll and walk about with his companion to cool off. Do not let him have a long drink until he has cooled off (just a few mouthfuls). Feed in accordance with work and bodyweight but remember that he wants to be fit not fat. Store your harness in a dry place. Take good care of it by cleaning it regularly and replacing any worn straps.

Safety

It is a good idea to take emergency supplies and spares whenever you decide to go driving. Some suggestions are: a headcollar and leadrope, a knife, a hole punch, a leather strap, a length of rope, string or baler twine, a splice (a short leather strap with a buckle at each end), a spare trace, money for the telephone (or your mobile phone!), a note pad and pen, a hoof pick, a foot pump and a puncture repair kit. Never drive without an assistant.

Remember that it takes time to become proficient and safe with your donkey cart on the roads. The Donkey Sanctuary can arrange courses on preparing for driving.

Reference: *The Professional Handbook of the Donkey,* 2nd edition, 'Driving and Tack Required' by Vivian Ellis

ANN KATHERINE CHAPMAN (known as Annie, Donkey Sanctuary Training Centre Co-ordinator). Annie completed her British Horse Society B.H.S.A.I., B.H.S.II., B.H.S.I.(t) qualifications in 1983 and obtained her British Driving Society preliminary certificate in 1996 after previously having completed a shorthand, typing and book-keeping course.

She was previously employed as a Horse Riding Instructor and subsequently began work at the Donkey Sanctuary in 1991 in the Accounts Department. Within six months Annie moved to the Welfare Department where she soon became involved with the development of training courses in donkey care now provided by the Sanctuary for prospective rehab homes, current donkey owners and for animal welfare employees in other organisations, including the R.S.P.C.A. (See Appendix 10 for further details of courses.)

17
PASTURE MANAGEMENT FOR DONKEYS

John Fry

WHEN WE LIST AND WORK OUT THE VALUE of all the assets associated with our donkeys, the land comes near to the top. Yet do we treat it with the same loving tender care that we give to our animals, their tack, stabling, transport? All require regular attention and maintenance if they are going to give of their best and produce to their full potential. The ideal pasture should not only provide food, but also an exercise area for as long a period during the year as possible. Naturally it must be safely fenced and watered. The aim is to provide conditions which encourage the most productive grasses - Ryegrass, Timothy, Cocksfoot, Meadow Fesque - not weeds and non-productive grasses. Palatability is often a reflection of the way the pasture is managed rather than the type of grass originally sown. Drainage is probably the most important single factor in the provision and maintenance of grass fields for donkeys. Signs of poor drainage are usually obvious - surface water or water-loving weeds (for example, rushes, tussock grass and buttercups). Always aim to maintain a good soil structure.

Grass growth is often reduced because of structural damage which can result in water logging, poor root development and poor growth. Some types of soil are more likely to suffer damage, which is usually caused by grazing too many animals per acre during wet weather. Soil structure can often be improved cheaply by breaking up the subsoil to allow better drainage (subsoiling and pan busting) so long as a suitable drainage system is present.

It is impossible to answer the question, 'How many donkeys can I keep on an acre?' because the answer varies according to:

- Soil type and fertility
- Length of the grazing season
- Rainfall climate
- Area of land available
- Number of separate paddocks
- Worm control

As a guide, good grassland properly drained and fertilised has the capability of providing grazing and some hay for approximately 3 donkeys per acre. But remember that as donkeys are not usually kept under ideal conditions for maximum productivity, these rates are often difficult to achieve. Grass production depends on maintaining a uniform ground cover of useful grasses which are regularly, but not too severely, grazed. Over-grazing tends to encourage weeds, whereas under-grazing produces low quality, coarse and rank grasses.

Because grass growth is uneven throughout the year and donkey numbers are constant, it is beneficial to have an arrangement with a local farmer to bring sheep into the fields at times of grass surplus, or to make hay/haylage for the next winter. 'Grazing', especially with sheep in the winter, is ideal. Not only will they ingest donkey-hosted worm larvae and therefore reduce the pasture worm burden, but they will also graze much of the grass rejected by donkeys.

Harrowing in late February/March when the land is dry enough is useful for dragging out any dead grass and moss, to encourage young fresh growth. Unfortunately, unless it is done with a heavy spiked or chain harrow, it is worthless - others merely make pretty patterns. However, it will help to dissipate the manure and to some extent reduce the worm burden. Remember droppings should be removed in less than 24 hours. Removal after this period will, of course, still help to reduce the worm burden, but will not be as effective. Rolling should be used only as part of the procedure for improving poached or damaged pasture. Be very careful - it can often do more harm than good, and may damage soil structure, as referred to above. If the pasture is to be cut for hay/haylage, there is justification in rolling down any stones to reduce damage to harvesting machinery.

The following is aimed at those looking after a large group of donkeys. The main requirements are suitable fencing, the erection of summer shelter sites and the laying of a track to facilitate the movement of large groups of donkeys.

Pasture land at the Donkey Sanctuary.

Grazing

The technique described in this section can be used on small grazing plots as well as on a large scale. At turnout, the donkeys go into a field that has had slightly less fertiliser than those set aside for hay and they are strip-grazed behind an electric fence. By using this fencing system, the risk of laminitis is reduced. The other advantages of this grazing system are that the donkeys have fresh grass in front of them every day, and they do not defecate and trample on good grass. All the donkeys in the Sanctuary are weighed every month so that we can keep a careful check on their weight loss or gain. This is important for successful large-scale donkey management. Soil should be kept fertile and it is essential to have it analysed every 4-5 years.

Application of lime, phosphate and potash should then be made according to the results of the analysis. Beware of expensive 'trace element' fertilisers. If donkeys are found to be deficient in trace elements, it is usually more effective to supplement the animals' feed, rather than try to make up the deficiency in the soil. Unbiased specialist advice is required before this is attempted. Nitrogen is undoubtedly the key to grass growth, but grass will not respond unless the quantities of lime, phosphate and potash are also correct. Nitrogen should be applied as and when required, and generally 3-6 weeks before growth is needed, but be aware that the raised protein level in the grass will increase the risk of laminitis.

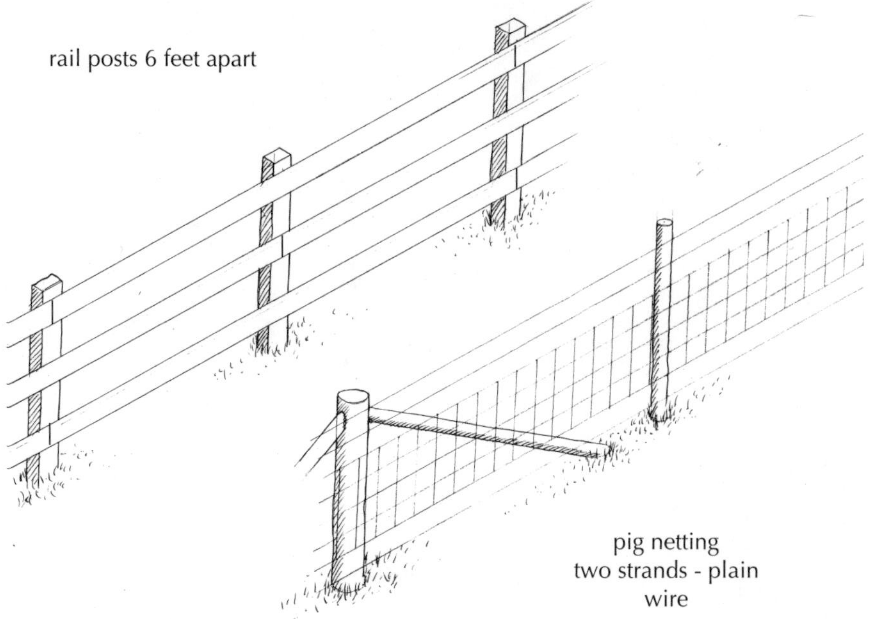

A large by-product of housing donkeys for 6 months is manure. This is stored in a large compound where it is left to break down for a year to eliminate parasite eggs and larvae. This also helps with the control of donkey worms. After that time, this rich plant food is ready for use. It is then spread on the fields that will be used for making hay the following year/season. The dirty water produced on the concrete run out areas must be collected and stored and only spread when ground conditions allow. The Environment Agency safeguards the purity of rivers and ground water supplies and polices facilities for storage and disposal of animal waste. Imported farmyard manure can be useful to maintain the humus level in the soil and will add some useful phosphate and potash.

The land should not be grazed until 6 weeks after spreading. Be especially careful if poultry manure is used as it is high in nitrogen and can cause photosensitivity (sensitivity to the sun).

The next large event on the farm is hay-making. Rotation of hay fields is an important factor of pasture management. A field that is grazed one year will, if possible, be made to hay the next and vice versa. Fields that are reserved for hay receive a larger dressing of fertiliser as soon after the

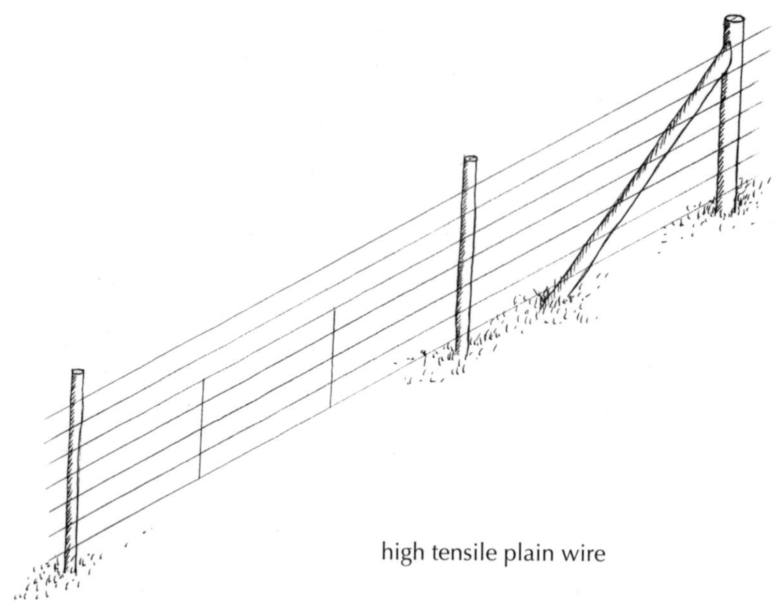

winter as ground conditions and temperature will allow. The rotation of hay fields will help to control the worm burden on the grazing area and reduce the weeds that seed early, because they will be cut before they shed their seeds. The most effective way to control weeds is to do everything possible to encourage grass growth - check the following factors:

- Correct stocking rate
- Avoid poaching and panning (creation of mud)
- Correct drainage and ditching
- Alternate hay and grazing
- Practise winter grazing sheep
- Chemical control or
- Re-seed as a last resort

If a hormone weedkiller is required to deal with more persistent weeds, e.g. docks, always remember that it works best when the weeds are actively growing, more of the weedkiller will be absorbed into young fresh growth. Treating old and established growth, especially just after seeding, will not be effective. Do not forget that poisonous weeds are more likely to be eaten after treatment. Ragwort is particularly poisonous and it is a requirement of the law that it be pulled and destroyed (Weeds Act 1959).

Reference: *The Professional Handbook of the Donkey*, 2nd Edition, 'Pasture Management for Donkeys' by Clive Scott.

JOHN FRY has been employed in agriculture all his life. He is from a farming family and in 1962/3 he attended Bicton College of Agriculture where he gained a National Certificate in Agriculture and the College Certificate.

John worked for six years as a farm foreman on a mixed farm and then moved to the Donkey Sanctuary, where he has worked since 1974. He started work with the Sanctuary as a manager at Slade House Farm and is now General Farm Manager of all the Sanctuary's farms. He is also farm manager of one of the Sanctuary's two farms in Dorset, with over 600 donkeys in his care.

Outside of the Donkey Sanctuary his interests include the promotion of care of the countryside.

18
POISONOUS PLANTS
Andrew Trawford

Bracken (*Pteridium aquilinum*)
Bracken is widespread in Britain, and is found on light, acid soils in a variety of habitats, but is especially prevalent in hill areas. Growing bracken is not particularly palatable, and would probably not be eaten at all if there were plenty of fresh grass available. The whole plant contains several toxic substances, some of which remain after cutting and drying. The effects of poisoning from bracken are cumulative, therefore some weeks may pass before the poisons begin to have an effect on the animal. Of the toxic substances in bracken thiaminase is the most important in equines. Thiaminase is an enzyme capable of destroying thiamine (vitamin B_1) which induces thiamine deficiency in horses. The main clinical signs are incoordination, very pronounced heart beat after mild exercise and, as the disease progresses, severe muscular tremors. These are followed by convulsions, opisthotonos (backward flexing of the neck) and death. Thiamine deficiency can be treated with daily injections of thiamine (vitamin B_1). Some horses die suddenly without warning as a result of acute heart failure. Haemorrhaging occurs in cattle and sheep.

The rhizomes (roots) are five times more poisonous than the fronds. The most common period of poisoning is from August to October when the fronds are turning brown.

Box (*Buxus sempervirens*)
Box is an evergreen shrub or tree. Its distribution is limited to a few areas of southern England, where it is locally abundant on chalk or limestone in beech woods and scrub. Box is cultivated widely as an ornamental or hedging plant. All parts of the plant are poisonous. The poisoning is due

to steroidal alkaloids. A fatal dose for a horse is reported to be 750g of leaves. Symptoms include vomiting, abdominal pain, diarrhoea, inco-ordination, convulsions and coma. Death from respiratory failure may occur rapidly. Treatment is symptomatic.

Ragwort (Common Ragwort - *Senecio Jacobaea)*

Ragwort is poisonous both dead and alive. It is a yellow flowering weed. Ragwort was designated as an injurious weed in the Weeds Act, 1959. Ragwort is very poisonous for cattle and horses, but other stock seem to have a greater tolerance. There is a general belief that grazing with sheep assists in controlling the plants. The toxicity is caused by pyrrolizidine alkaloids (for example senecionine, jaconine, jacobine). There is an acute form, where the animals die in a few days, but generally consumption over a period of weeks causes slow but progressive damage to, and fibrosis of, the liver. Clinical signs are similar in cattle and horses. Initially there are digestive system disturbances, which may include colic and diarrhoea (sometimes with blood) but more often there is constipation and straining. Some animals may be jaundiced, and all become emaciated. Horses in particular show nervous signs and aimless wandering (walking disease, sleepy staggers). An early sign in horses may be a tendency for sensitivity to sunlight in unpigmented skin, particularly on the face, a white blaze for example. Blindness, paralysis, pressing of the head against solid objects, weakness and coma may be seen terminally. As destruction of the liver is irreversible, recovery of an animal is impossible once outward signs appear and treatment is hopeless. Animals seldom recover from ragwort poisoning.

Ploughing is possibly the most effective method of control, as spraying with herbicides is expensive. Approximately 3kg fresh weight of the plant is thought to be enough to kill a mature cow.

Yew *(Taxus baccata)*

Yew is considered by some to be the most toxic plant in Britain. The leaves are extremely poisonous, the berries less so. The poisonous substance is the taxin(e), a complex mixture of alkaloids that is absorbed rapidly from the digestive tract and interferes with the action of the heart. The toxicity of yew is not decreased by wilting or drying. Yew is most toxic in winter. The lethal dose has been estimated as 0.5-2kg for horses. The clinical signs reported in cattle and horses are similar. They include muscular

Bracken.

Box (variegated).

Ragwort.

Yew.

trembling, unco-ordinated movements, coldness, rapid then weak pulse, and sometimes excitability preceding stupor and collapse, during which breathing may be accompanied by groaning. In others sudden collapse is the only sign. In many cases animals die only a few hours after eating yew, so signs are never seen. Treatment is symptomatic.

N.B. There are few documented cases of plant poisoning in the donkey. The text has therefore cited the parameters for other livestock, especially the horse, in order that the necessary data for diagnosis and treatment may be extrapolated.

Note of thanks

To Catherine Morriss for her work on the section of poisonous plants.

References

ADAS, *Ragwort*, Ministry of Agriculture Fisheries and Food, London (1990)

Angus, K.W., *Plant Poisons on the Farm*, The Moredun Foundation, News Sheet Vol. 2, No 5, Edinburgh (1994)

British Horse Society, *Poisonous Plants and Trees*, The BHS Welfare Committee (1985)

Cooper, M. R., and Johnson, A. W., *Poisonous Plants in Britain and their effects on Animals and Man*, Ministry of Agriculture Fisheries and Food, London. Ref. Book No. 161 (1984)

19
THE DONKEY SANCTUARY AND ITS SISTER CHARITIES

Elisabeth D. Svendsen

PEOPLE ARE ALWAYS ASKING ME 'Why donkeys?' It's a hard question to answer until one thinks of the average lifespan and conditions for donkeys throughout the world, the abuse and cruelty they suffer, their stoic humility in accepting all meted out to them and their ability to continue working to help mankind until they drop. Since my early childhood donkeys have always fascinated me and, even now, after 28 years of rescuing donkeys and having encountered literally thousands of them, I still feel emotion when I cradle the head of a newly arrived, frightened donkey, with worried eyes and an air of resignation that the ill-treatment it has been receiving is going to continue. The joy of my job is seeing that donkey regain its health and begin to enjoy the donkey paradise so richly earned, and which it is guaranteed for the rest of its natural life.

'But how did it begin?' everyone asks me. It began with one little donkey called Naughty Face, and she was really responsible for the start of the Sanctuary in 1969.

Since Naughty Face's arrival the Donkey Sanctuary has become an organisation with over 7,000 donkeys taken into care in the UK, and has led to the setting up of an international charity caring for donkeys throughout the world, as well as indoor riding centres where disadvantaged children can learn new skills and to love the gentle, humble donkeys. Altogether 196 staff are employed, and veterinarians throughout the world have received free information of vital importance to the well-being of donkeys. Want to know more? Then read on!

The arrival of Naughty Face at the hotel we owned in Ottery St Mary brought joy to me, but also brought complaints from the residents! Her mournful brays as she paced up and down in her lonely paddock were very

Naughty Face.

unwelcome at 4 in the morning and, realising that she was lonely, I bought Angelina to keep her company. In my ignorance I did not realise that both were in foal but, to my delight, two lovely babies were born some six months later.

Eager to learn more, I joined the Donkey Breed Society and soon I was appointed Area Representative for the South-West as, with my usual enthusiastic zest, I learned quickly!

By this time I had my own stallion, St Paddy of Kennetbury, and had become a reasonably successful breeder. I say 'reasonably' because although I had no problem in arranging the production of super foals, I could never bear to part with them!

One of my jobs as area representative was to help and advise members on the purchase of donkeys, and one of these occasions was to change my life and help literally millions of donkeys worldwide.

At a horse sale in Exeter livestock market, I was looking for a donkey suitable for a young family when I suddenly saw several donkeys crammed in an outside sheep pen. I could not believe their condition - they were pathetically thin, had sores and lice, and could barely lift their heads. I looked into their sad, haunted eyes and felt their fear and pain. One donkey in particular affected me - her coat hung in great mats, she was emaciated and her feet were long and twisted. Appalled, I asked the man standing by the pen how much she cost. He didn't even look at her - 'Forty-five pounds,' he said. It was a terrible price for a donkey in such a condition and I took a few minutes to think about it. By the time I turned back to say, 'I'll take her' it was too late. She was being forced up into a lorry along with the other six donkeys in the pen, her tail twisted cruelly behind her. She had been sold to work on a beach, along with the rest of her group, and I was distraught that I had been unable to help.

Not long afterwards a visitor to the hotel rang to tell me of a donkey which had collapsed on a local beach. I jumped in my car and rushed to the beach, where the hotel guest was waiting anxiously. She told me that a man had just put the donkey in his wagon and was driving away. I followed and after a few miles it arrived at a rough field, being met by a man, who was obviously the owner. He was very aggressive when I approached and asked if I could buy the poor donkey, but after a bitter argument he sold her to me - for £40! I carried her home in my horse box and Lucky Lady, as we named her, lay on a straw bed, being fed by a glucose drip for two days before she attempted to lift her head, which I cradled in my arms. Her recovery was slow but satisfying, and I knew I must devote my life to rescuing rather than breeding donkeys!

The news soon spread, and I looked after donkeys in terrible trouble. Gyppo's legs had been cut to ribbons as the result of a car dealer putting heavy chains on her and forcing her to climb piles of wrecked cars to drag sections out for re-use. Tiny Titch had been so badly beaten that sacking was embedded in his shattered backbone, and So Shy had most of her teeth smashed from constant beating. All came into my care to recover quietly.

One day the BBC telephoned, and came to do an interview. The cameraman was wearing a long fur coat (it was the fashion in the early 70s) and whilst Bob Forbes, the interviewer, coaxed me into an interview, one of the stallions became confused by the figure bending over the camera. At the height of the interview, St Paddy finally decided the coat was a visiting mare and he did his best to perform the required service! The BBC left me in peace for some years after that!

On June 20th, 1974, I was left a legacy! It was 204 donkeys from a Miss Philpin who had run a sanctuary in Reading. My life really changed then, and we had to leave the hotel and buy a farm near Sidmouth where I could live and look after my growing donkey family!

My previous business experience proved invaluable in obtaining funding, doing interviews and arranging charity matters, all with the help of the Charity Commission. The small charity I had registered was amalgamated with Miss Philpin's, and a reliable team of Trustees was appointed.

I had qualified as a Froebel teacher and I longed to put my love of children and donkeys together, so in 1975 the work of the Slade Centre began, taking donkeys to schools for children with special needs in the local area. The response of the children was amazing. They loved the donkeys and the donkeys loved them. The children learned new skills not previously thought possible, and even autistic children would shout with delight as they rode the gentle donkeys!

After planning problems were sorted out I began raising sufficient funds to build an indoor riding centre, as the children were devastated when our team was unable to visit during the winter months. Even one day is a long time to children, and five months without donkey rides is a lifetime! Eventually we had enough money and the Slade Centre was built.

The next problem I had to face was the steady inflow of donkeys with their problems and needs, so another farm had to be purchased to house them. It seemed impossible that there were so many donkeys in need, but I was determined not to turn any away.

I was very concerned about donkeys overseas. Although I had never travelled much I was aware that donkeys were not treated well in many countries. So I went to look for myself, and what I saw convinced me of the need to set up the International Donkey Protection Trust. It is unbelievable to me that donkeys have always been so badly treated - they are humble, willing and patient animals and have been overworked and ill-treated by man all through history! Studying donkeys in Tunisia I found few donkeys aged over 15 years, although I knew I had donkeys over 40 years old in the Sanctuary. Taking a small laboratory kit out with me, I soon found parasites to be the main problem. Not only did the worms eventually eat their way out of the donkey's gut, causing embolisms which brought on early death, but they reduced the value of what little food the donkey was able to forage, and that led to emaciation and saddle galls.

I was given the opportunity to speak at a World Veterinary Parasitology

Congress and, although I am not a vet, the audience was very kind to me. I started by asking if any of them knew what the average temperature of a donkey should be, but no one could answer. I then asked who thought it to be the same as a horse's temperature, and almost everyone put up their hands! When I told them the donkey's temperature is almost 2° less than the horse I had their attention! Up until then the donkey, if treated at all, had been treated on the assumption that it was a small horse! Using the knowledge and experience of our veterinary department, and with contributions from experts in their fields, we produced the first edition of *The Professional Handbook of the Donkey*, which is now used as teaching material at almost every Veterinary University in the world and is provided free of charge to vets upon request. We have studied all the parameters relating to the donkey based on the thousands of donkeys taken into our care, always using non-intrusive research techniques, and some tables are included in the appendix.

We currently have an extremely well equipped donkey hospital, with an operating theatre, recovery areas, X-ray and ultrasound facilities and laboratory, run by qualified veterinarians and nurses. We have eight farms in the UK, as well as two farms in Ireland, all run by individual managers and trained staff. There is also a well organised Welfare Department which organises rehabilitation homes for pairs of donkeys. Offers to give donkeys a new home are followed up by visits to check that conditions are suitable, and prospective owners attend one of our training courses to receive instruction on donkey care and management. Provided everything is in order, the new owners can then take in their lodgers! Our Regional Welfare Officers and 68 voluntary officers follow up reports of cruelty and neglect in the UK and Ireland. They also liaise with local councils in those areas where donkeys are being used for gain (e.g. beach donkeys), so that we can keep a tight control on operators not providing suitable working conditions for the donkeys. We have recently introduced a painless hoof branding scheme for beach donkeys, which enables us to keep a greater control on the donkeys being used. Along with the British Horse Society Riding Establishments Act Committee Section we can now influence councils to refuse the issue of licences where the donkey does not receive fair treatment.

Occasionally problems do occur despite our best efforts, and a report of donkeys in trouble in the Blackpool area brought consternation to us all. Normally we have nothing but praise for the way Blackpool beach donkeys are looked after by their owners and monitored by the Council, but in 1992 one particular operator/dealer started to cause us great concern with regard to his wintering facilities for the donkeys. Following visits from our Welfare Officers the situation improved but on follow-up visits there was a gradual deterioration to the point where urgent intervention was needed. In co-operation with the RSPCA action was taken.

It started with one donkey seen on the beach on June 11th which the RSPCA asked us to take into care. By later that afternoon this had increased to sixteen donkeys, as the vet insisted that the whole group be taken off the beach.

Our Chief Welfare Officer spoke to the RSPCA officer and said he would like to be there when the RSPCA went to visit the owner's stables, where the rest of his donkeys were kept. Arriving first at the stables, our Welfare Officer found a dealer loading donkeys onto a wagon and advised him that they should not be moved. However, the dealer drove off with the eight donkeys already loaded, followed by our Welfare Officer who telephoned the RSPCA en route. When the RSPCA arrived the wagon was stopped and on checking the donkeys it was found that they were all in poor condition and needed to be taken into care.

After returning to the stable yard and checking the remaining donkeys it was decided that, due to their condition, they should all be removed. The police were called to break into the premises and to everyone's surprise three more donkeys were found locked in a small room with boarded windows. All 35 donkeys were taken into a temporary home in Garstang.

It was June 17th, 1992, before I was able to see the donkeys for myself, accompanied by June Evers, Paul Svendsen and our Senior Veterinary Surgeon. We had been at Glasgow University where I had received my honorary doctorate and while there we heard the news that the group, with the exception of two donkeys who were too ill to travel, were to be moved to our Buxton holding base. There they would stay under the loving care of Ray and Julie Mutter, our manager and his wife, until they were fit for the final stage of the journey to Devon. We were able to change our itinerary to be present when the donkeys arrived. I just cannot describe my feelings when I saw these donkeys; I have often seen donkeys in a terrible condition - but to see so many in such poor condition, with injuries and overgrown hooves, but also so terrified of humans, was indeed distressing.

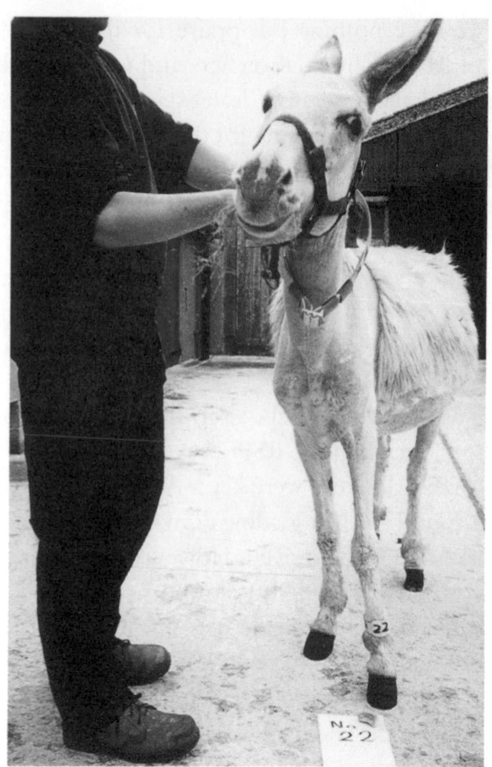

Sara BP before.

Everybody helped and one by one the donkeys received loving attention, were given a good feed and then allowed to rest and enjoy the comfort of stables deeply bedded with straw.

Three weeks later, after intensive care, veterinary and farriery treatment, and when the donkeys were fit to travel, we started to bring them to the Sanctuary in Devon. The two donkeys who had been kept in Garstang were at last pronounced well enough to travel and they too were moved to Devon.

As the prosecution was pending against the owner we could not reveal too much information at that time. For security reasons we split the donkeys into smaller groups around Slade House Farm in case any attempt was made to take them back to Blackpool.

As the donkeys arrived here without names, they were named after

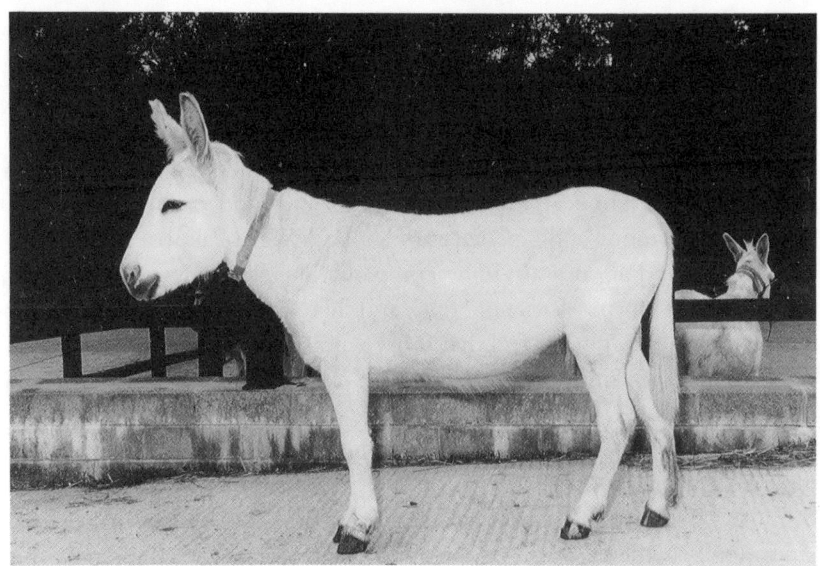

Sara BP after.

members of our staff. Two of the donkeys were in foal and, thanks to their rescue, produced and reared two delightful little foals. A little colt we named Mal was born to Ellen, and Penny gave birth to Fiona. Unfortunately, due to the terrible time experienced by the mares during their pregnancies, both foals needed special care, and little Mal had to spend some time in our donkey hospital. However, the future for all the donkeys is now secure as, at the trial held in September 1993, the owner pleaded guilty, and the donkeys were relinquished to the Sanctuary. We had dreaded the thought of having to send them back and would have done everything in our power to stop them being returned to such an uncaring owner.

Sadly, there are times when we feel a donkey no longer has a good quality of life. This is generally with the very old or extremely sick, and normally occurs when the animal has lost all interest in his surroundings and has a tendency to lay down more frequently than usual. All decisions are taken jointly by a member of the senior veterinary staff and one of the executives of the charity and the donkey is put quietly to sleep in his own stable. If the donkey has an inseparable companion, as is often the case, the companion is left for at least half an hour with his recumbent friend, and in this way he accepts that his friend has gone and so pines less. When this is not done, the surviving friend can become so distressed by constantly searching for his companion that he can develop hyperlipaemia and may also die.

Naughty Face certainly has a lot to answer for. The Donkey Sanctuary is now the 55th largest charity in the UK (Charities Aid Foundation figures) and we fight hard to keep our administration and fund-raising costs to the minimum, currently at 8.4 pence in the pound. We are almost totally non-commercial and are not a trading company. The Sanctuary is open every day of the year from 9 a.m. until dusk and there is no charge to visitors for admission or parking as I feel that those who support us have the right to see how we are using their funding. The whole emphasis here is on the donkey and its needs.

In addition to our daily work we also have an Adoption Scheme which involves the public in the work of the Slade Centre and the Elisabeth Svendsen Trust for Children and Donkeys, and the educational School Adoption Scheme has brought the opportunity for school children to visit the Sanctuary and receive practical training, as well as providing educational aids for the school.

The majority of our funding comes from direct donations from the public. We never cold mail, i.e. send out letters of appeal to individuals from lists provided by agencies, and we are totally opposed to telephone appeals, feeling it to be an intrusion on people's privacy.

Legacies, and particularly residuary bequests are a vital part of our finance, and the names of all those who have remembered us in their wills are inscribed on the Memory Wall at the Sanctuary. A memorial service is held each year, when families and friends can join with us to remember their loved ones. The service is held on the Feast Day of St Francis of Assisi (4th October) in our giant marquee, and we are joined by several of our donkeys, who particularly enjoy singing along with the hymns!

The work ahead is enormous. After their arrival at the Sanctuary all stallions are castrated when fit, as we have a non-breeding policy. However, many poor mares arrive in foal, and the foals are, of course, given the same promise of care for life as their mothers. That life could well be 50 years, which means that I'm going to be obliged to live donkeys' years to complete my work!

Of course, I could not have built up the charities without the immense loyalty of all my staff, many of whom have been with me from the very early days. I am known as 'Mother' to both staff and donkeys and, despite having so many employees, I feel that I know them all personally.

We were recently interviewing for a new surveyor, and an interviewee asked our Personnel Manager the question, 'What is your staff turnover?' Richard Barnes replied, 'We don't really have a staff turnover, apart from maternity leave, and the mothers nearly always come back when the little ones are old enough!'

Brian Bagwell worked with me for many years as Deputy Administrator, until he took early retirement. Brian's place has been jointly taken by Mal Squance, who was previously my personal assistant, and my son, Paul Svendsen. With Richard Barnes as Assistant Administrator, we have a wonderful team of qualified senior staff, so both the Trustees and myself are happy that the future for our donkeys is assured well into the 21st century!

20

DONKEY THERAPY FOR CHILDREN WITH SPECIAL NEEDS: the Slade Centre and the Elisabeth Svendsen Trust for Children and Donkeys

Julie Courtney

THE USE OF DONKEYS as riding therapy for children with special needs was the brainchild of our Founder and Honorary Administrator, Dr Elisabeth Svendsen, MBE. Being a qualified teacher and a long-time member of the Donkey Breed Society, she decided to bring her two great loves together and in 1978, after a difficult three-year period negotiating planning permission, Dr Svendsen was able to raise the funds needed to create a purpose-built riding centre here at the Donkey Sanctuary in Sidmouth. In 1994 Dr Svendsen opened a second centre in Sutton Park, Sutton Coldfield near Birmingham with the great help of the Elise Pilkington Trust.

The work carried out at these centres using donkeys is widely recognised for its therapeutic benefits to children with physical and mental disabilities. Contact with the donkeys through riding tuition improves balance and develops weak muscles. Through this interaction vocabulary is stimulated and self-esteem and confidence are boosted for all children whatever their disability.

The centres are open every weekday throughout the year. Schools visit on a regular rota basis during term time. During the school holidays 'drop-in' sessions are held each day of the week, 10.00 a.m. until 3.30 p.m., when parents of children with special needs can bring their families for the day (with a picnic) or a shorter visit. One Saturday morning a month (10.00 a.m. until noon) there is a Saturday Club, again for parents to bring

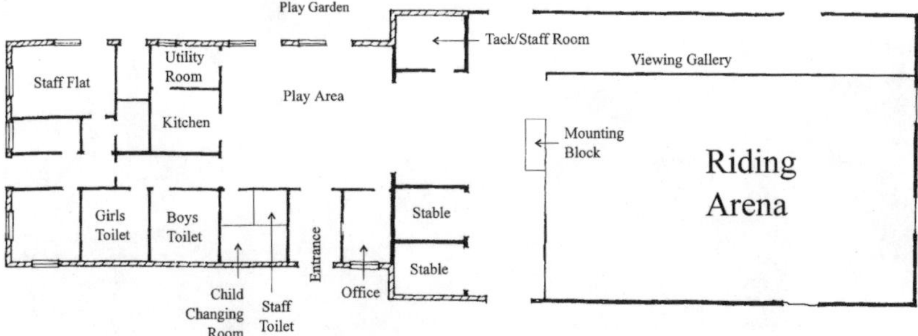

Outline map of the Elisabeth Svendsen Trust for Children and Donkeys Riding Centre.

the whole family. During the summer months mobile teams operate from the centres, using a lorry, to take donkeys, a cart and staff to visit schools in the areas that cannot manage to visit the centres.

The donkeys are all chosen from the Donkey Sanctuary and great care is taken in their selection. They must be healthy, placid, biddable and above all, they must enjoy human company. A good number for a working team of donkeys is 12 to 15, preferably with a few of the team being larger donkeys, i.e. 11 hands (the average height being 10 hands). Usually 6 donkeys per day are worked and we have found this to be ideal; each donkey does enough to remain fit and interested and not so much as to get tired and bored.

Before any new donkeys are used with the children they undergo a selection and training process which starts with a visual assessment by the centre's staff. Then they move into the centre's group, spending a few days with a suitable donkey 'friend' before meeting the rest of the group. They are then introduced to the routine of the working donkeys, being handled, groomed, having their feet attended to, being tacked up and then led (without a rider) in the group and being taken through all the exercises that are used in the lessons. Only after they are quite happy with our routine are they ridden by the children.

The closeness of these calm, gentle donkeys is of great benefit to these children in many ways, from riding and driving, to touching, cuddling

Riding arena.

and talking to them. The donkey will accept any kind of attention and seems to understand the needs of the children.

The centres are built very much on the same lines:

- A reception/play area where the children can play whilst waiting for their ride (with a large selection of soft play toy shapes, creative, sensory and manual skill toys) or have lessons with their teachers.
- A kitchen where a cooked lunch or a snack can be prepared for the children. This is a great help in developing the social skill of eating together in a smaller group than the children are used to at school.
- The suggested riding arena is 70' by 40' and is floored with 5" of waxed sand and polyester fibre on geotextile membrane on hardcore. There are overhead gas heaters and extractor fans.

Internal adjacent grooming stalls accommodate the donkeys during the day between riding sessions.

The viewing gallery is used by children waiting for their ride, or by interested members of the public who can watch the riding sessions.

Riding sessions vary in length. School groups attend for any period up to 4 hours and during that time each child will have at least one session of riding or driving, more usually two sessions.

All rides are given under qualified supervision and vary greatly with the needs of the children. For some it may be that a quiet walk of 10 minutes is plenty, while others may spend some of their time stroking and touching the donkey. The aim is to provide pleasure and to maximise the children's abilities.

The children are encouraged to be independent and confidence is given by a lesson structured around the correct riding principles, including selecting a riding hat, taking their turn to ride and mounting. It must be said here that some children may not be strong enough to ride with a hat. They may be too small to wear one or may absolutely reject the hat and, in all these cases, their teachers must give permission for the exercises to go ahead without a hat. The exercises within the ride can include changes of rein, inclines and turns across the arena and changes of leading file. Riding figures and shapes in the arena and the use of pictures, letters, numbers and symbols around the arena builds up not only the children's riding skills, but also their recognition of letters, numbers, colours and shapes (they are learning with fun).

The children are encouraged to talk to the donkeys, to greet and thank them, to recognise them and to use their names. Where possible they write, draw or vocalise what they did and saw in their lesson.

Not only ride exercises can be used, but variations of riding games too, such as:

Musical mats or hoops: The children ride around the arena and dismount and run for a mat/hoop when the whistle blows, or the arm drops ...(response, co-ordination and awareness work alongside counting and colour perception).

Scavengers: A team game with the child and donkey at one end of the arena and, at the other end, a bucket or cone with items in or on it, i.e. hoop, bean bag, ball or any coloured item. The children have to dismount, run to collect the specific item and then bring it back to the donkey, mount and trot to the other end of the arena. Many variations of the game can be devised ...(counting, colour, shape recognition and memory development).

Round the world: The children are encouraged to turn themselves around completely whilst sitting on the saddle by sitting to the side, sitting facing the donkey's tail, sitting to the other side and then back facing the donkey's head ...(confidence building and a complete change of the normal routine).

The children can also be encouraged to ride the donkey whilst facing its tail....great fun and a very good muscle strengthening motion.

Some children can be encouraged, while supported, to stand on the

Riding inside the Elisabeth Svendsen Trust centre.

donkey's saddle, or (with the saddle removed), to lie back flat along the donkey's back (balance and co-ordination) and some have been known to do this whilst the donkey is moving. Obviously a great amount of awareness and support from adults is needed in the exercise but the child's sense of achievement is obvious ... a huge smile!

The use of cones or poles in the arena to give the rider a course to ride around or step/jump over (with or sometimes without the help of the leader) is a very interesting and stretching exercise (co-ordination and confidence).

Follow the leader: Taking it in turns to be the leader, moving the donkey and rider to the front by using a sound e.g. beep, beep.

Copy cat games: Copying the Instructor or another rider's movements, actions or sounds whilst seated on the donkey. This can be done either stationary or moving.

Trotting: The exercises and games are normally carried out at a donkey 'walk' pace. However, most of the children enjoy a period of trotting within their session. Some children who are unable to join in any of the above games/exercises because of their disability can really enjoy a period of

Riding outside the Slade Centre.

trotting in their ride. Some who have been thought not to speak have been heard asking for 'more'!

Great care is taken that all children have a fair chance and that the games are encouraging for all and relevant to their needs. For instance, children with poor balance and co-ordination benefit from races and exercises that involve turns and changes of pace.

When the weather is suitable rides can take place outside using the grounds of the centre. This gives the children an opportunity to put into practice the riding skills learnt in the arena and to use observation for the sights and sounds around them and to be relaxed in the company of the donkeys.

Each centre's staff consists of a Supervisor or Principal in charge of the centre who organises the visits and co-ordinates the schools and works closely with:

A qualified riding Instructor; two or three qualified grooms; a handyman/driver/donkey leader; an assistant who helps with the children and/or leading the donkeys; a secretary who also helps where necessary; a cook (part-time) and a cleaner (part-time).

Recommended qualifications for the above staff should include NVQ

Care, Basic Food Hygiene, up-to-date First Aid training and certification, PSV and/or County Council driving test of competence, secretarial qualifications, B.H.S.I. and/or B.H.S.A.I.

Our centres have voluntary helpers without whom we could not operate. A good working team of approximately 20 people help on a regular basis supporting the children, or leading the donkeys. All voluntary helpers attend a donkey awareness course at the Donkey Sanctuary or at the Riding Centre.

Notes for voluntary helpers

If the Instructor can be thought of as the zip fastener in the garment of riding for special needs, the voluntary helpers are the fabric of that garment. They give strength, cohesion, colour and consistency to the lesson and act as on-the-spot eyes, ears and back-up to the Instructor. They are first-line givers of encouragement, assistance and discipline within the lesson. In short they are invaluable - without them the class could not function.

I have often been asked, 'What makes a good helper?' and the first, most important quality is a realistic wish to help in all aspects of the riding, not just with the donkeys, or the children or with any one part of the lesson but, as the need arises, with anything that is currently top priority.

On a broader note, let me outline to you what happens during an average lesson. Apart from the Instructor, helpers lead the donkeys, assist the children riding, either one or two per child, and helpers may be needed to collect the children and fit their hats ready for the next session. All these people will need to liaise with the Instructor, teachers and, most of all, with each other. Each person, however, must not, on any account, neglect his allocated job and must be aware of the lesson as a whole and awake to any of the Instructor's commands. The format of the lesson will depend on the children's abilities and needs and the priority of the Instructor, but the aim is to combine pleasure, education and increase dexterity through the use of the donkey. This means, in plain language, that there has to be riding, teaching using school figures, e.g. changes of rein, circles and serpentines, ride formations, individual exercises and exercises as a ride to give mental and physical stimulation and control. There is usually a game to finish the lesson which should underline the lesson learnt. Enjoyment and education can only progress if they go hand-in-hand.

Now, enough of generalisation, on to the nitty-gritty, starting at the front and working backwards. Each donkey needs a leader who should have a basic knowledge of donkey behaviour so as to appreciate the donkey's likes, dislikes, moods and foibles and so use them to their best advantage. Helpers should be able to lead the donkey from both sides as needed, be attentive to the commands of the Instructor but also be aware of the child and the other helpers. They must be able to maintain a pace that keeps the ride together, neither hurrying or dawdling and must give the children the opportunity, when appropriate and with discretion, to guide and control the donkey themselves. Most of all, they are the leaders of their own particular donkey and are responsible for that donkey's behaviour. The leader must be in control of the donkey, not the other way around! Donkeys, like children, are happiest with sympathetically administered discipline and failure to control them is dangerous for all concerned.

As well as a leader, there must also be a helper for each child. It is normal for helpers to assist the child onto the donkey having first checked that the girth is tightened. (It is a wise precaution to check the girth from time to time as the saddle may settle during the course of the ride.) Assisting the child onto the donkey may mean anything from standing close enough to supervise and give a helping hand if necessary, to lifting a child from his chair and placing him onto the donkey's back. The basic rule is: to assist as little as possible (the more the children do for themselves the better) but always be aware of the children's limitations and of their safety.

The 'getting-on' process is one of the most difficult and complicated things the child will be asked to do. The amount of assistance will vary with each child and the helper's approach has to be extremely flexible because each child must be seen as an individual and be treated as such. Again, there must be close liaison between helper, Instructor and teachers so that the right degree of assistance and encouragement can be given. On a personal level a helper should only undertake what he feels he can cope with. If a child is too heavy or difficult, get help, don't put yourself or the child at risk - you are both too valuable!

Once the child is on the donkey, life doesn't get any easier. Decide with the Instructor on the stirrup length, if stirrups are to be used. Check that the child is comfortable and sitting appropriately. Note I do not say sitting correctly, as a child may not be able to, but comfort and balance are important. If the child is riding on a blanket pad great attention must be paid to balance. The helper must give the child every assistance to ride the

Donkey tacked up: note western saddle.

donkey properly within his limits. If you are in doubt on any point, ask the Instructor and ask immediately - before the problem becomes a crisis!

During the ride it is easier to walk on the opposite side of the donkey to the leader so as to avoid stepping on each other. If there are two helpers with the child then the leader has to walk well up to the donkey's head to avoid impeding the helper.

As the leader is responsible for the donkey, so the helper is responsible for the child. The minimum assistance should be given, ranging from walking next to the child to total support. Total support is as strenuous as it sounds, with one hand around the child's back or under his arm and the other on the child's thigh. As well as physical support the child may need encouragement and reassurance, especially if he is new to riding. Again the amount of assistance needed will vary with each child so, once more, the rule is, if in doubt, ask. We want to see achievement, but not at the expense of happiness. It is, therefore, vitally important that the helper should be able to relate to the child and have an understanding of, and sympathy for, his problems whilst maintaining discipline and encouragement throughout the lesson. We find this is a two-way flow with the helpers who put the most in getting the most gratification out of both the children and the day. Yes, it is hard work, yes, it is strenuous and yes, you do feel shattered but it is all worth it - believe me, I know!

This is a very short and very general résumé of the role of helper. Much is down to common sense and cannot be put into the rigid confines of the written word.

I would just like to conclude by saying that a good helper must be firm but flexible, kind but committed, and, above all, be a member of a team all working together for the benefit and happiness of both children and donkeys. (Jos Biggs, B.H.S.I., Slade Centre, Sidmouth)

The riding equipment used includes a fully adjustable headcollar (to which reins are attached), a bridle with a nylon snaffle bit (to which the leadrope is attached) and a Western saddle over a padded numnah. We have found this to be the most suitable, both for the comfort and control of the donkey and the safety and stimulation of the child.

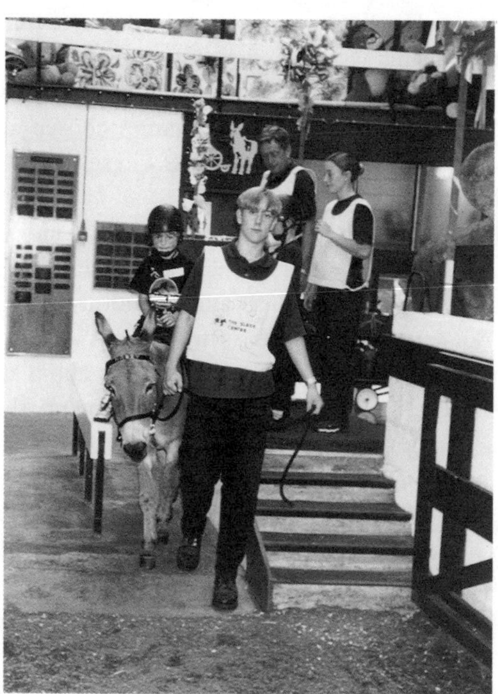

The mounting block.

Where possible all children mount using a mounting block with as little adult help as possible.

Eight stone is the weight limit for a child to ride a donkey. Heavier children, or young adults, progress to riding in a cart and learning to drive a donkey. During driving the child is either closely supervised by an accompanying tutor and 'false' reins are used, or the donkey is led. Many of the children become very proficient and are well able to control the donkey and cart, and then trips around the grounds and courses laid out in the centre's fields are used. Children of whatever ability enjoy the driving experience. Children with very little mobility and who are unable to support themselves at all can enjoy a trip in the cart supported by their carer.

The driving equipment consists of a breast collar harness and a choice of exercise type cart, or a specialised trap with rear access via a ramp (designed to take a wheelchair and its occupant). The reins are only attached to the bit when appropriate.

Our aims are to give an improved quality of life to those who come through our doors. To achieve this we need a dedicated, co-ordinated and above all flexible team. We take everything possible into consideration, from the choice of donkeys to the teaming of particular children into certain groups. The types of rides and games chosen are co-ordinated with the lessons that the schools are currently teaching or the physiotherapist's exercises.

Because each young person is treated in such an individual manner, it is impossible to make hard and fast rules, so general guidelines, common sense and good liaison with teachers and physiotherapists are essential.

Our age range covers toddlers through to young adults, but our expectations must be realistic. With ingenuity just about any situation can be used constructively, from grooming and tacking up, through to riding off the leading rein or driving a slalom course (all very closely supervised, but with the child feeling in control).

Although each ride must have a certain discipline and structure, care must be taken not to be repetitive, so that all aspects of riding and driving remain stimulating and genuine improvements can be made, at various levels.

When deciding what form a lesson or ride should take consideration is given to each person's likes and strong points and then these are balanced against his own aims for progress, so that the session will be both enjoyable and rewarding.

Children riding in the arena.

Each day through the term has a schedule which details which donkeys are to be used in which sessions, whether riding or driving, who shall be the leader and who the supporter. Staff, helpers and teachers are involved in the construction of this plan and after the sessions an informal discussion is held on the success of the day, so that we can progressively build for the next session.

The Aims Chart is a great help. These can be changed and updated as required and a different level can be expected from each child as the sessions progress. Each child has an Aims Chart and Report once a school year.

All children with special needs can enjoy and benefit from their therapy time with the donkeys.

Children with severe learning difficulties can be the victims of congenital brain damage, autism, pre-natal rubella, accidents or abuse. Usually there is a lack of speech, little comprehension and often bizarre behaviour - self mutilation, head banging, rocking and outbursts of violence - most of which becomes far less evident when the child is taken to the donkey. There is a therapeutic benefit and satisfaction gained from being near, touching and riding a donkey.

Children with challenging behaviour are noticeably calmed by their contact with the donkey. Just stroking the donkey can be sufficient for some children, although as time goes by almost every child will ride happily, with a degree of control and awareness not encountered in the play area situation. The donkeys hardly seem to notice any noise or disruption and if by chance they do get handled roughly (something that we try to avoid) then they take that in their strides too.

All work with these children has to be accomplished with total patience, taking the pace and the level from the child, not the helper. Progress may often seem non-existent until records are consulted or a case or session discussion is held and then it may be seen that improvements have been made.

Children with moderate learning difficulties can have emotional and behavioural problems or speech and nervous disorders. They too can gain a tremendous amount from donkey riding and association with the donkey.

All the children, no matter what the problem, are encouraged to greet the donkeys, touch and cuddle them and during the children's riding sessions the helpers will be gently encouraging them. It is very satisfying to report back improvements in speech, awareness, enthusiasm, balance or general

Slade Centre Achievement Chart

RIDING THE DONKEYS ***AIMS TO WORK TOWARDS***

Enthusiasm to Ride/Patience
Choose Hat/Wear Hat
Greet Donkey
Get on Donkey
Sit
Sit up Straight
Awareness of Surroundings
Holding the Reins/Pommel
Stop the Donkey (Using Words)
Start the Donkey (Using Words)
Thank the Donkey
Know the Donkey's Name
Thank the Helper
Know the Helper's Name
Take off Hat
Return Hat to Hat Cart

DO YOU KNOW THE:

Donkey	**Outside:**	Trees	**Arena:**	Colours
Ear		Flowers		Symbols
Eye		Birds		Letters
Saddle		Car		Numbers
Reins		Dog		
Cart		Chicken		
Collar				

Comments:

Riding Instructor: Jos Biggs BHSI ....

Principal: Julie Courtney ....

Aims chart.

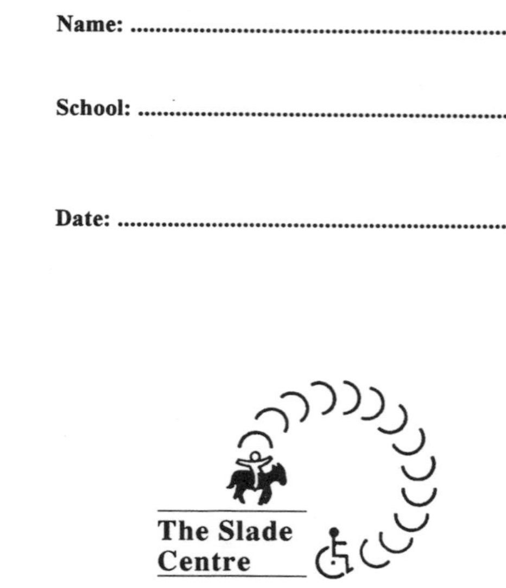

WHAT CAN I DO AT THE DONKEYS?

Name: ....

School: ....

Date: ....

The Slade Centre

Registered Charity Number 270551

BENEFITS OF VISITING SLADE CENTRE

1) Social Interaction within a more informal setting than the classroom.

2) Sense of achievement - verbal and non verbal.

3) Motivation to use language in a setting where pressure is not primarily perceived to be on language skills.

4) Benefits of the physio aspect of balance and co-ordination and muscle strengthening.

5) Awareness of need to care for animals who need patience and understanding.

6) Withdrawal rooms for individual language work.

7) Integration with other schools.

8) The opportunity to use communication skills in selecting their choices from the lunch menu, also preparing & clearing the tables.

Benefits chart.

good behaviour. Children who are intensely anti-social to other children, and who tend to always play alone, appear more relaxed and happy once they are riding - the motion soothes them and, with the helpers giving them plenty of positive attention, they will often respond very well.

There are many variables and degrees of Down's syndrome from those termed 'high grade' with well developed basic academic skills to those who never speak, often suffer from deafness and may have further disabilities.

Both groups benefit greatly from riding. The high grade child will be able to ride very well and learn the correct way to put on the hat, mount, hold the reins and control the donkey. Being able to achieve these things means a great deal to them and their parents. Behaviour, speech, vocabulary and balance are all improved whilst riding and during contact with the donkeys. The older student can be taught to drive a donkey.

The child who is more severely handicapped with Down's syndrome can often be aggressive, violent and abusive. These children can control their behaviour far better when riding the donkey than when they are in the play area.

Children with a hearing impairment (of whatever strength) find enormous benefit from their riding sessions. They are taught to be aware of the Instructor and to watch for the next instruction. Their confidence, posture, balance and language can all improve, especially when the children are encouraged at school to vocalise as much as possible and integrate with hearing friends. The donkeys are very forgiving of their hearing aids that sometimes 'whistle', but most children ride without them. These children show great interest in their riding sessions and are able to adapt to any exercise that they are asked to do. As one parent said, 'They are only deaf'!

For children with little or no sight, obviously smell, touch and sounds are very important. They must understand what donkeys are, meeting them and touching them all over before the children are allowed, or may wish, to mount and ride. They soon become confident and are able to ride, balance, follow a game and do exercises as requested.

Children with severe physical deformities who are confined to a wheelchair can sometimes gain more than most from the act of riding. They fully appreciate that, when mounted, they can at last achieve some degree of physical equality. They are at once elevated to a normal height, and, instead of always looking up to others, they are at eye level. This brings a feeling of confidence and general well-being. The majority of these children just love to canter, the faster and longer the better.

Children vary so greatly in their abilities that it is very difficult to generalise concerning the standards and quality of riding that can be achieved. We work closely with teachers and physiotherapists, and just to look into the child's eyes will tell you how much they are loving their ride. Parents will also say that behaviour and co-operation of stiff little limbs is improved on a 'donkey' morning!

It would be hard to list the many and varied problems, syndromes, mental, physical and special needs (with all that this term encompasses) that children have brought to the donkeys but, without exception, every child has benefited and can continue to do so.

I would like to thank all the people who have helped me write this chapter.

JULIE COURTNEY, Principal, the Slade Centre based at the Donkey Sanctuary, Sidmouth, Devon.

Previous Occupation - Assistant Administrator, the Donkey Sanctuary.

I joined Dr Svendsen as her secretary in October 1974. In those days my work with the Donkey Sanctuary consisted of typing, mucking out, talking to supporters, in fact anything connected to running a sanctuary for donkeys! My knowledge grew as the Donkey Sanctuary grew and I became Assistant Administrator. This was a great honour and responsibility. I knew a little bit about everything and then, as now, loved all aspects of the work.

The use of donkey therapy for children with special needs has always interested me, so when the Principal of the Slade Centre retired in 1992 I offered myself for the position with my experience of working with the donkeys for many years, my love of children, my firm commitment to keep the high standards of riding therapy and to ensure the children had fun at the centre. Formal training? No, I have none as such but I have a great dedication to the donkeys and loyalty to the Donkey Sanctuary and the Slade Centre and I love the work.

21a
HISTORY OF THE DONKEY BREED SOCIETY

Bill Tetlow

THE DONKEY SHOW SOCIETY, as the Donkey Breed Society was originally known, was formed in 1967. Its founder was the Hon Robin Borwick who, in 1964, wrote a book called *People with Long Ears* - a must for every donkey aficionado. This book did a great deal to revitalise the interest in donkeys but it was three years before he fulfilled a lifetime ambition by forming the Donkey Show Society.

Acting on advice from Glenda Spooner, he co-opted Susan Greenaway as Secretary, Robert Camac as legal advisor and one of the most respected figures in the equine world, Reggie Summerhays, as its President and, along with a group of enthusiastic owners, they set out to encourage the good breeding and improvement of the status of the donkey.

These were the foundations on which the Society was built and which stand it in good stead to the present day - to encourage the use of the donkey, to promote its well-being and protection as well as its general welfare.

In 1968 the name was changed to The Donkey Breed Society as it was thought to be closer to the aims of the members. Although the title may suggest its primary interest is to 'breeders' or for 'breeding' this is not the case and the Society is open to all donkey lovers whether or not they breed or even own donkeys. There has, on two occasions, been an attempt by some of the members to change the name of the Society by deleting the word Breed from the title but this has always been heavily defeated at the A.G.M.

For centuries the donkey has been the victim of neglect and one of the areas affected has been in the breeding of donkeys. In-breeding and lack of care in the selection of breeding stock in the past left the donkey with many conformation faults. To redress this the Stud Book was set up in 1969.

The object of the Stud Book was to encourage members to be selective in the donkeys they chose to breed from, as improving the conformation of the donkey would help its well-being in later life. Many of the donkeys taken into the Donkey Sanctuary without this privileged upbringing often have conformation faults which necessitate specialist care when they get older.

Since 1969 the Stud Book has recorded the parentage of well over 3,000 animals. With the approach of the EU a special section has been opened for foreign donkeys and, more recently, a General Register has been added to keep track of as many donkeys in the UK as possible and their offspring, whether or not they are eligible to be entered in the Stud Book.

The showing of donkeys was encouraged right from the start of the Society as this was always considered to be the shop window as to what could be achieved.

As well as ordinary agricultural shows, certain shows are designated as DBS Championship status shows. To win one of these is quite an achievement because competition is fierce and collecting the ticket at the AGM on behalf of one's donkey is a feather in any owner's cap.

In 1970 the first national DBS Championship Show was held and now donkeys from all over the UK compete every year for the coveted DBS British Championship Award.

In 1970 we saw another milestone for the Society as that was the year it became a registered charity with the ability to raise funds to aid donkeys in many ways.

Donkeys are particularly good with children, inspiring confidence, especially in the nervous child. In 1971 the Junior Section of the DBS was set up to encourage the interest of young people in donkeys, their care and management.

This has been a great success. Juniors are encouraged to take tests in various aspects of donkey management and care for which they receive awards working towards the gold award. There are also tests in riding, driving, road safety, as well as projects which can be incorporated into school work. One of the highlights of the Juniors' year is the camps that are run around the country, one of these being held at the Donkey

Sanctuary. The current membership of 180 juniors thoroughly enjoy these activities.

The Junior Section is the lifeblood of the Society and several former Juniors are now active members in the senior section. Others have gone on to make their livings in the equine world - one of them being the assistant to one of the country's leading racehorse trainers.

Donkeys can do more than just stand around in fields or go to shows. One of the main interests of many owners is driving. In 1973 the Driving Section of the DBS came into being and, over the years, has introduced and encouraged many members of all ages to this aspect of the donkey's repertoire. Progressively donkeys are driven in pairs, tandems, uniforms and teams. Donkeys are particularly suitable for disabled drivers who have confidence in the animal's calm disposition. Over the years standards have risen dramatically and the drivers have an enviable safety record. Driving is great fun whether it be competing at shows or just going for a jaunt round the country lanes. Donkeys used for driving tend to be fitter and healthier, so, as well as being a great source of pleasure for the owner, it is beneficial for the animal.

Judging donkeys is a skilled task so a training scheme was set up by the society in 1973 and continues today to produce many fine judges. A royal accolade was achieved in 1979 when one of the Society's seminars was held in the Royal Mews of Buckingham Palace.

Our Founder President died in 1976 leaving us many fond and proud memories. The role was taken over by Mrs Stella Walker, author of *Enamoured of an Ass* who continued until 1992 when Mrs Ursula Roberts was elected President. In memory of our first President, the Summerhays Memorial Award Scheme for Brood Mares was established.

In 1985 the Society was registered as a Private Company Limited by Guarantee. An Activities Committee was set up in 1987 to encourage an enjoyment of donkeys by people of all ages through the promotion and organisation of activities which demonstrate the full range and attributes of the donkey.

Aims of the Society

Being a member of the Donkey Breed Society gives you the opportunity to meet other like-minded people who have the best interests and the welfare of the donkey at heart. It is not necessary to own a donkey to become a member. We aim to be a welcoming Society, providing a full range of activities of interest to all members from the youngest to the oldest, whether donkey owners or not.

Whilst the Society aims to improve the quality and the conformation of donkeys by promoting careful and selective breeding, it also seeks to encourage a fuller and more active life for those donkeys which are either much loved family pets or simply companions for animals.

The showing classes at both major and minor shows allow the general public to see donkeys at their best. However, many alternative events are organised countrywide to cater for the enjoyment of those who do not wish to show or who just do not have donkeys of show quality. These events include donkey walks, picnics and treasure hunts.

Increased interest has been shown in driving the donkey to a wide variety of vehicles. This can be of particular importance to senior members who are unable, through size and weight, to ride the donkey, yet wish to continue the enjoyment of mutually gained skills. There is a strongly active section within the Society representing the interests of drivers and those who work their donkeys. Animals with a varied and interesting life are undoubtedly happier, as indeed are their human keepers. We know just how versatile the donkey can be and the Society aims to encourage further this aspect by creating more and varied events in which members can take part, either of a competitive nature or for their own enjoyment.

Our Society has a special place for those of the younger generation who can join as Junior members. Showing and driving classes are open to Junior members, but the Society rules that no Junior may handle a colt or stallion at a show. For Juniors there are ridden classes as well as lead reining ones. There is a programme of education for Juniors culminating in proficiency tests which are often taken at residential camps held at various locations throughout the year.

Our aim is to cover the whole country with a network of Area Representatives. These are the people who, invariably, are the first point of contact for interested members of the public, and it is they who organise the various events throughout the year to cater for the totally committed enthusiast as well as the member who just enjoys the social side of things.

The Society aims to promote the donkey to the general public in any realistic way it can, but it will not stand by and see the donkey being ridiculed or mistreated in any way whatsoever. The donkey is an animal of great

Lisa Joynes, DBS Junior, winning first prize at the Great Yorkshire Show with Donkey Sanctuary rehab Emmy.

gentleness and is very affectionate but, unfortunately, it is one that has suffered and in some places continues to suffer, from mankind's inhumanity. The Society aims to educate people in the care and welfare of the donkey so that both human and donkey alike will enjoy the comfort and pleasure which can flow from the shared relationship.

Showing donkeys - a personal view

One would think that after showing donkeys for over twenty years, and averaging between 16 and 18 shows a season with a certain amount of success, one would be qualified to write an article on the above, but, since only three years ago I was described by one of the DBS founder members as a newcomer, I approach the task with a great deal of trepidation.

Showing donkeys is one of the most rewarding and pleasurable of pastimes but before embarking upon it may I pass on a few tips to help a would-be competitor avoid making all the mistakes that I made.

Before starting your showing career, go to shows, watch the classes and learn what is expected of you and your donkey. If you have any questions, ask the competitors, but always remember to wait until the showing is finished. You will never win any popularity contests if you get under the feet of someone who is trying to get an animal ready for showing and is already running late for their class. Donkey people are very friendly and are always willing to pass on tips and information if asked at the right time. Once you know what is expected of you the next step, in the safety of your own paddock, is to find out if your donkey shares your enthusiasm.

Training a donkey takes time and should never be rushed. Begin by leading him round the paddock, slowly building his confidence. Remember, when training, little and often is by far the best method. Get your donkey used to spoken commands - 'walk', 'trot', and 'stand' are the only words that should be used. If at a later date you should aspire to driving your donkey then the word 'back' will be added to his commands but no more or you will only confuse him.

Reward your donkey for obeying a command by patting him. An occasional tit-bit is alright but do not make a habit of it or he will expect it all the time. It is not much fun being halfway through a class and remembering that you have left your polo mints in the car, while a belligerent donkey refuses to take another step until he receives his reward for the last 'trot on' he has just completed. Always remember the golden rule - rewards are for work that has been done, not work that might be done.

Walking round and round a paddock may not be boring to you but it will be to an intelligent donkey so, once you have gained his confidence and he is obeying commands, it is time to take him for walks. It is advisable at first to take someone with you just in case something frightens the donkey and you need help. Taking your donkey for walks is not only an excellent way of making training more fun for you and your donkey but it also introduces him to sights and sounds that he will never meet in the safety of his paddock. It will also prepare him for the hundred and one different things that he will meet at the modern agricultural show.

When your donkey will walk, trot and stand on command, and is not frightened by cars, tractors, double decker buses, motor bikes, cows, sheep or the local pony club in full cavalry charge, he is ready for the next and most important step in his education.

It is not unknown for a new competitor, after spending weeks on training, hours on grooming and polishing tack, to fail to turn up at a show because the donkey refused to get into the trailer. Having a team of

1992 British Supreme Champion Happy Valley Kulio, owned by Mrs Jane Price of Totnes, Devon.

brawny men on hand to load the donkey at home is not the answer because not only will the donkey arrive at the show sweated up and definitely not in the right frame of mind to be shown but he will also be even harder to load for the journey home. Nor will you impress your new donkey friends if they have to be coerced into heaving a reluctant donkey into a trailer.

Your donkey should be used to being loaded, taken for a drive and unloaded, long before you attempt to take him to a show. Like every other part of training it is all about confidence and showing him that the trailer is not something to be afraid of. One way of achieving this is to leave the trailer in the paddock with him and put his food in there. It is best if you start by placing the food halfway up the ramp and then, over a period of days, slowly move it further up the ramp and into the trailer. In my experience it is the ramp which appears to frighten donkeys most and once they have conquered this fear it is usually plain sailing. When he has begun to go in and out of the trailer of his own free will, make it part of his every day training on the lead rein. Once he does this easily then he is ready for his first trip on the road.

If driving a car with a trailer on the back is a new experience for you then do not attempt to take your donkey out for a drive until you have logged up a few hours going solo. If your donkey's first journey is with a driver who bounces him all over the place, he will not want to get back in the trailer and all your training will be set back weeks.

So now you are almost ready to make a start and you have to decide which show to enter for your debut. I began my showing career at the Adlington Donkey Show in Cheshire. This was a 'donkeys only' show and an ideal place to start, based on the proviso that if you are going to make a fool of yourself it is best to do it amongst sympathetic friends. Sadly, the Adlington show no longer runs but there are other similar shows and I would always recommend this type of show for starters.

Once you have entered the show, the planning has to begin and remember preparation is everything. If the weather is warm enough the

day before the show you may bathe your donkey but even if the weather is hot he will still need a rug on so that he does not catch a chill. Make sure that everything you are likely to need is loaded, e.g. brushes, hoof oil, hoof picks, bridles and lead reins, etc. Then check that you have all the paperwork you might have received such as schedules, entry numbers, etc. Finally, check what time your class is, set your alarm and get a good night's sleep, remembering that you need to arrive at the show at least an hour before your class time.

So everything is taken care of as far as your donkey is concerned. He is beautifully schooled, perfectly groomed and his tack is immaculate, now we need to spend a little time on the handler. It is no good having your donkey looking like a million dollars if you turn up looking like a refugee from the local charity shop. You do not need to spend a fortune on fancy clothes and in fact you may well get what you require from the aforementioned charity establishment if you buy carefully.

For ladies a hat is a must, but remember you are showing a donkey not leading the winner in at Royal Ascot. Wear a sensible jacket, tweed always looks well and most ladies who show donkeys wear trousers but of course a skirt is just as acceptable. Your shoes are most important, firstly they must be comfortable and, secondly, you must be able to run in them in both wet and dry conditions. Whilst not essential for a man, a hat does look smart. A brown bowler or a trilby looks good, or a flat cap with a matching jacket looks really well. Plain coloured trousers and sensible shoes make up the outfit. Always remember the important one in the ring is the donkey and you should not wear anything that will draw the judge's attention away from him.

After the time spent making your donkey look good and teaching him to behave impeccably, we need to make sure that your ring manners do not let your donkey down. No matter how boorish your behaviour may be at the check out in the supermarket on a Friday evening do not try repeating it in the show-ring on a Saturday afternoon. Donkey judges do not understand about customer care and you will be destined to spend the day languishing at the bottom of the line up. Always be polite and always do what the ring steward asks of you without dissent. If the judge asks a question answer politely and concisely, do not enter into any form of dialogue. Your donkey's sire might have been British Supreme Champion but you must never, ever, inform the judge of that. All that the judge requires to know is the age of your donkey and, if in a stallion and gelding class, which category he falls into. If it is a mare class you may be asked if your mare is in foal. At this time honesty is always the best policy. Just because your mare has a bulging waistline, owing to too much spring grass, do not say she is in foal. You may fool the judge but not your fellow competitors and you will soon find that you are not very popular at the Après Donkey.

Après Donkey is the best fun of all and takes place after the showing is over. When the donkeys have had their tack removed, have been given a drink and a full hay net and you have changed into something comfortable, you are ready for the fun to begin.

Preparation is minimal. All you need is a picnic, several bottles of wine and a teetotal driver. The Après Donkey is better at certain shows than others. Nottingham County, the Great Yorkshire, the New Forest and Poynton are 3 star shows, the Supreme Championship is a 4 star show and the Royal Highland a 5 star show.

I must point out that the advice in this chapter is based on the principle do as I say, not as I do. Unfortunately the author has the somewhat dubious reputation of turning up late for shows, having to borrow hoof oil because it has been left behind and on one occasion even arrived at a driving show having forgotten the cart! Showing if approached with the right frame of mind is tremendous fun both for you and for your donkey.

MR WILLIAM TETLOW was born in Halifax in West Yorkshire. Educated at Clare Hall School and Halifax and Bradford Technical Colleges specialising in business studies. Self-employed in farming since leaving school until joining the Sanctuary in 1991 as the Regional Welfare Officer for the North of England and Scotland. Became a donkey owner in 1976 and joined the Donkey Breed Society. Served on the council of that organisation as Publicity Officer from 1986 until 1988 and as Vice Chairman from 1995 until 1997.

21b
DONKEY SHOWING
by a Judge

Rosemary Clarke

As a breeder and exhibitor of donkeys for the last 27 years, I have heard the statement, 'We don't want to show' more times than I care to remember. As a judge for the last twelve years I know only too well that, inevitably, that is just what will happen. The world of the average family donkey is full of exhibition and taking part in the school nativity play, the Palm Sunday parade, the play school visit. Each of these generates admiration. Some would see it as a far cry from the Donkey Breed Society Supreme Show but, in between the two, there is the local show. 'Nothing too competitive' says a defensive owner, but the lure of a rosette is there for all to see and, having won a green one, it would be very nice to win the red one and so it goes on ...

Show classes are full of exhibitors who already know what to do and the following thoughts have been compiled to enable even the newest donkey owner and exhibitor to appear in the ring with a working knowledge of what is required for both themselves and their donkey.

Dress for the competitor

From the judges' point of view this should not be allowed to affect the end result in anything but a condition and turnout class. It is worth remembering however that you are as much a part of the overall picture as your donkey and to detract from him because you are wearing dirty jeans and trainers would be really sad. The name of the game here is to be smart, and as well groomed as your donkey, without being ostentatious.

Dress for your donkey

The correct attire for your donkey is determined in part by the traditions and hierarchy of the old equestrian order, in part by the Breed Society for safety reasons and in part by the restrictions of one's own budget. Coloured nylon headcollars have a valuable part to play in every day donkey management but no place in the show ring. A leather headcollar or bridle will give a neat and tidy impression. Both can be embellished with brass if your donkey is a male, but should be kept plain for a mare. For the sake of safety it is essential that all entire males are shown in bridles with bits attached.

In hand classes

You will find that in most classes the judge will adopt a position in the centre of the ring, while the ring steward will move around directing the movement and placement of each donkey. The judge will view each exhibit carefully as it enters the ring. Do not imagine at this stage that the judge's attention is lacking if he does not watch you personally right the way round the ring. It is normal practice to view each exhibit at the walk down one side of the ring only before the steward asks each to trot individually round the ring. Do not allow your donkey's attention to wander or attempt to engage another competitor in conversation, both will detract from your hoped-for good impression. It is important that your donkey has learned to walk out well, first or last, and to trot out alone when required. If it is reluctant to do either a judge will soon have doubts as to the correctness or conformation. Overuse of canes and schooling whips, whether from behind or across the shoulder, detract from your exhibit and such behaviour inevitably causes a donkey to present itself in a crab like manner that may cost you a place or two. A judge can only make his decision on what is going on now, not on what you say happened yesterday.

Once the entire class has been lined up for individual inspection it is essential that you remain alert and keep your donkey standing with legs and feet nicely spaced. Most judges tend to take frequent looks up and down their line, so don't allow your donkey to fall asleep. Attention will be drawn to you for the best of reasons if you look efficient rather than sloppy and could well mean moving up one or two placings.

Each exhibit will then be given a thorough inspection from all sides. This will include checking the teeth for correct alignment, as parrot mouth is a serious defect, and checking feet for freedom from seedy toe and cracks. This is a show class so even though the perfect animal is yet to be born, we are still seeking as near to perfection in conformation, manners and movement as can be found on the day. You should stand facing your donkey's head, trying not to block the judge's view of your exhibit, and be ready to move smartly off for an individual walk and trot when asked. Again this movement must be accomplished as efficiently as possible. Walk away from the judge in a straight line, turn with the donkey on your inside, trot straight back towards the judge and carry on past. This enables the judge to check that your donkey moves correctly in a straight and true fashion.

Having inspected each donkey individually, the judge will now ask the steward to call the class to order and parade them round the ring in a clockwise direction for final assessment and placing. Keep your eye on the steward, many a place has been lost because they couldn't catch the attention of an inattentive exhibitor and many an exhibitor has taken advantage and assumed a place higher than they deserved. If you are fortunate enough to have won, congratulations. If this was not to be your day, keèp smiling, preserve your dignity and that of your donkey. There is always another day. Do not treat the judge to a tirade of abuse and comment about what your donkey won last week. Such conduct only serves to lower the image of donkey exhibitors in the eyes of the public and after all, we all know secretly that our own donkey is the best.

If your donkey does not find favour with judges in the breed classes, which are assessed entirely on conformation, try entering condition and turnout classes where presentation is all important, or pet donkey classes where a good temperament and generous nature are the criteria.

Junior classes

These tend to be divided into two categories - Ridden and Young Handlers. Both demand a greater degree of obedience from the donkey and a demonstration of skill by the child. The judge is not assessing the donkey from a conformation point of view, but as an accessory to the child. If that accessory performs the requested movements efficiently, it improves the chances of a higher placing within the class, so some home training pays dividends.

In riding classes the donkey as a leading rein mount is perfect, but it should walk and trot freely on a long rein and be obedient to the handler's voice. The stop, start, won't trot syndrome is agony for a young jockey and will soon put him off totally.

The older child must fit the donkey, so height and weight will soon determine whether or not he looks in proportion to his mount. At nine years of age the leading rein rider must be able to perform solo, and now the beautifully behaved, butter wouldn't melt in its mouth donkey who was a sure candidate for the Nobel Peace Prize invariably takes on a total change of character. Won't steer, can't trot, must get back to its friend in the trailer park and knows exactly where the ring exit is! Judges are human. They don't expect miracles - are well aware that children are easily upset or embarrassed and are usually fairly good at assessing the situation, but again practice at home can pay dividends.

For Young Handlers classes the child must be able to walk and trot the donkey, both individually and in company, lift up the donkey's feet and stand the exhibit out square.

Criticism is often levied at the turnout of juniors in donkey classes compared to the equivalent pony classes. A neat and tidy appearance will always pay dividends. There is no need for full hunting apparel. Jodhpurs, a tweed jacket, shirt and tie and correctly fitted hat to the latest British safety standard, will present just the right degree of formality.

Driving classes

Donkey driving has gained in popularity over the last few years and driving demonstrations are frequently a major ring attraction at shows and other events. Driving classes are categorised according to the type of vehicle driven, either as a Private Driving class for vehicles of traditional design or an Open Driving class for exercise vehicles and any that are not acceptable as Private Driving Vehicles. Private driving classes are judged on presentation as well as the manner in which the donkey drives, which means that the vehicle and harness must be correct, fit well and be polished to perfection. An Open Driving class, on the other hand, is judged only on the donkey's performance as a driving animal as, providing the vehicle fits and the harness is safe, no marks are awarded for cleanliness or appearance.

In driving classes you will be judged first on presentation, when the picture you present to the judge is very important. The vehicle should fit the donkey and be well balanced so that it does not hamper the donkey's performance in any way.

After the donkeys have been pulled into line, the safety and fit of the harness is checked and the overall appearance of the turnout assessed, with the general appearance and tidiness of the whip being taken into account.

Following this inspection each turnout will be invited to give an individual show. A simple circle on the right and left reins at the trot, a rein back of four paces and a quiet walk forward to finish is all that will be required.

Formal driving classes often make up only a small proportion of those that can be entered. Great fun can be had learning dressage tests and doing obstacle courses and, if your vehicle and harness leave a little to be desired, how about entering a Best Whip class where the skill of the driver is the only criterion. Donkeys really do love to work and a well driven, well trained donkey is a joy to judge.

I hope that these few paragraphs have gone a small way to answer some of the queries for first time exhibitors. There is much more to showing than just the breed classes, but above all it should be a pleasurable exercise for both donkey and handler.

The thrill of a red rosette never diminishes but the first that your donkey receives will always be extra special, so good luck.

ROSEMARY CLARKE Born in Oxford in 1945. Educated in Oxford and at Maidstone Grammar School. A member of the Donkey Breed Society Judges' Panel for the last ten years, Chairman of their Shows' and Judges' Committee for three of the last four years. Married to the Senior Partner in a large family business, with three children.

22

LEGISLATION

Bert Duncan

IT IS MY INTENTION in this chapter to give a brief summary of the more important animal protection legislation that applies in England, Wales and Scotland. These Acts apply to any animal and is therefore relevant to donkey owners and keepers. For more detailed information, references should be made to the various statutes and orders mentioned.

Cruelty

The principal Acts for the protection of animals are known as the Protection of Animals Act 1911 (England and Wales) and 1912 (Scotland) which have been amended on a number of occasions.

Within the meaning of the Protection of Animals Acts the infliction of substantial unnecessary suffering and any unreasonable omission on the part of the person responsible for the welfare of an animal which results in such suffering constitutes an offence.

The following actions constitute cruelty in law punishable by imprisonment or fine. The Courts have the power to order disqualification and confiscation of any animal which has been subjected to cruelty.

THE PROTECTION OF ANIMALS ACT 1911

Offences of cruelty:

Section 1 If any person :

a) shall cruelly beat, kick, ill-treat, over-ride, over-drive, over-load, torture, infuriate or terrify any animal, or shall cause or procure or, being the owner, permit any animal to be so used, or shall, by wantonly or unreasonably doing or omitting to do any act, or causing or procuring the commission or omission of any act, cause any unnecessary suffering or, being the owner, permit any unnecessary suffering to be so caused to any animal; or

b) shall convey or carry, or cause or procure or, being the owner permit to be conveyed or carried, any animal in such manner or position as to cause that animal any unnecessary suffering; or

c) shall cause, procure or assist at the fighting or baiting of any animal; or shall keep, use, manage, or act or assist in the management of, any premises or place for the purpose, or partly for the purpose, of fighting or baiting any animal, or shall permit any premises or place to be so kept, managed or used, or shall receive or cause or procure any person to receive money for the admission of any person to such premises or place; or

d) shall wilfully, without any reasonable cause or excuse, administer, or cause or procure, or being the owner, permit such administration of, any poisonous or injurious drug or substance to any animal, or shall wilfully, without any reasonable cause or excuse, cause any such substance to be taken by an animal; or

e) shall subject, or cause or procure, or being the owner, permit to be subjected, any animal to any operation which is performed without due care and humanity; or

f) shall tether any horse, ass or mule under such conditions or in such manner as to cause that animal unnecessary suffering

such person shall be guilty of an offence of cruelty within the meaning of this Act, and shall be liable upon summary conviction to imprisonment for a term not exceeding six months or to a fine not exceeding £5,000, or both.

Section 2

For the purpose of this section, an owner shall be deemed to have permitted cruelty within the meaning of this Act, if he failed to exercise reasonable care and supervision in respect of the protection of that animal.

Provided that, where an owner is convicted of permitting cruelty within the meaning of this Act by reason only of his having failed to exercise such care and supervision, he shall not be liable to imprisonment without the option of a fine.

THE PROTECTION OF CRUEL TETHERING ACT 1988

This is an amendment to the 1911 Protection of Animals Act, which deals with cruel tethering under Section 1 (f).

Section 11. 1911 Act

Dealing with diseased or injured animals found by the police

This section provides a police constable with the power to summon a veterinary surgeon and remove any diseased or injured animal without the owner's consent or have that animal humanely destroyed without the owner's consent. Any expense incurred whilst carrying out such a removal or destruction is to be recovered from the owner. For the purpose of this section 'animal' means any horse, mule, ass, bull, sheep, goat or pig.

THE WELFARE OF ANIMALS DURING TRANSPORT ORDER 1994

This order came into force in January 1995 and makes general provisions for the protection of animals in transit.

Article 2 Exemption

This order shall not apply to transport of pet animals unless in the course of business or trade.

Article 3 General protection

No person shall cause or permit an animal to be transported in a way which causes or is likely to cause injury or unnecessary suffering.

No person shall permit the transport of an animal that is unfit by reason of it being a new born, diseased, infirm, ill, injured, or fatigued or having given birth within the preceding forty eight hours or being likely to give birth during transport or for any other reason.

Provision allows for an equine animal to be transported to the nearest available place for veterinary treatment or to the nearest available place of slaughter if the animal is not likely to be subject to unnecessary suffering by reason of its unfitness, but such an animal may not be dragged or pushed by any means or lifted by a mechanical device, unless this is done in the presence of and under the supervision of a veterinary surgeon who is arranging for it to be transported with all practicable speed to a place for veterinary treatment.

Article 4 Loading and unloading

The Order makes further provisions for loading and unloading on a vessel, aircraft or vehicle. No person shall load any animal into or unload any animal out of a vessel, aircraft or vehicle in a way which causes or is likely to cause, injury or unnecessary suffering to the animal. It is also the duty of any person in charge of an animal to prevent injury from:-

a) inadequate or insecure fittings in that part of the vessel, aircraft or vehicle in which the animal is being carried.

b) undue exposure to action of the weather or sea.

c) an inadequate supply of fresh air and from exposure to temperature, humidity or air pressure or from undue exposure to noise or vibration.

Article 5 Feeding and watering intervals

Equines (horses and donkeys) to be provided with food and water before the start of a journey and at suitable intervals during the journey. The interval between the occasions when rest, food and water are provided should not exceed fifteen hours for horses and donkeys.

Article 6 General duties of persons in charge of animal transport undertakings

Article 6 states that every person in charge of animal transport which is in the course of business or trade shall ensure that the animals are entrusted only to persons possessing the knowledge necessary to administer appropriate care to the animals in transit.

Article 7 Journey plans

Journey plans apply to equine animals only if the journey is likely to exceed fifteen hours. In such a case the person in charge of any animal transport which transports animals for trade or business shall draw up a journey plan. This plan must show rest, feeding and watering stops, the place of departure and destination and show the journey hours from start to finish.

Article 8 Animal transport certificate

This article applies to all journeys which are not required to have a journey plan under article seven. A person in charge of any animal transport undertaking for trade or business shall ensure that during the journey the consignment is accompanied by an animal transport certificate.

Article 9 Exceptions to this order

Where domestic donkeys are transported:-

a) for a distance of 50 kilometres or less, to, from or within land used for agriculture in a vehicle owned by the owner/occupier of that land and the vehicle has an internal length of not more than 3.1 metres then the following provisions shall not apply:-

The use of partitions to protect animals from the motion of the vehicle. Provisions of barriers or straps. Provisions of internal ramps or lifting gear. Protective overhead cover, however, must be provided, as must an animal transport certificate.

THE WELFARE OF HORSES AT MARKET (AND OTHER PLACES OF SALES) ORDER 1990

This Order came into force in 1991. 'Horse' means a horse, pony, ass, hinny or mule.

This order makes provisions for the welfare of horses in markets. In a market it is an offence to permit an unfit horse to be exposed for sale, to cause or permit any injury or unnecessary suffering to a horse, to bring or cause to be brought there a foal unless it is at the foot of a dam or to expose it for sale separately, to handle horses in a particular way or to use excessive force to control any horse. The use of sticks, crops, whips, goads, or certain other instruments is also prohibited.

The market operator must ensure that horses are properly penned and that there is accommodation for unfit horses. They must make separate penning for others and provide lighting and bedding. Duties are placed on the owner or his agent or person in charge of a horse to ensure that it is adequately fed and watered.

DONKEYS USED FOR COMMERCIAL PURPOSES
THE RIDING ESTABLISHMENTS ACTS 1964 AND 1970

These Acts give protection to the donkeys used for commercial purposes by beach and donkey derby operators. A licence is issued by a Local Authority to persons carrying on a business of keeping horses (including donkeys) to let out on hire for riding, or being used in providing instruction on riding for payment or both. The licence holder must have an insurance against liability for injuries sustained by hirers. The licence is renewable annually.

HORSES (PROTECTIVE HEAD GEAR FOR YOUNG RIDERS) ACT 1990

An Act to secure the wearing of protective head gear by children whilst riding horses and donkeys. The Act makes it an offence for any person to cause or permit a child under the age of fourteen years to ride on a road unless the child is wearing protective head gear.

Other Acts and Orders within the headings which give protection to animals including the donkey are:

CODE OF PRACTICE FOR THE OPERATION OF BEACH DONKEYS

1. The hours of work in respect of donkeys shall not exceed the following:

   From 9.00 a.m. to 12.30 p.m. and 1.30 p.m. to 5.30 p.m. (The maximum work period without a one hour break should be 4 hours).
2. At 12.30 p.m. each day all saddles must be loosened and all donkeys fed and watered.
3. No sticks or whips shall be used on any donkey and the kicking of a donkey is strictly prohibited.
4. No person over the age of sixteen years, or over the weight of eight stones (50kg) shall be permitted to ride any donkey.
5. When the tide, or other circumstances do not permit the donkeys to be on the sands, the donkeys will not operate in any other place without written permission from the local authority.
6. Donkeys must not be ridden or driven so as to expose the rider or any other users of the foreshore to any danger.
7. Proprietors will be held responsible for keeping the sands where their donkeys are standing in a clean and sanitary condition.
8. No donkeys must be taken on the sands unless they are in a clean and tidy condition and no harness used on such donkeys which is not considered by the responsible officers to be properly fitted and safe.
9. Paramount consideration must be given to the condition of donkeys who must be maintained in a good state of health. In the case of a donkey let out for hire or for carrying for hire, the donkey must be suitable for the purpose.
10. No donkey under the age of four may be used for the purpose of riding.

11. The feet of all donkeys must be regularly and properly trimmed and if shod their shoes must be professionally fitted and in good condition.
12. No person under the age of sixteen should be responsible for donkeys at any time.
13. The name of the person in charge of the donkeys should be clearly displayed.
14. All donkeys must have a certificate of fitness to work from a qualified veterinary surgeon and should either be freeze-branded or hoof-branded by an independent agency appointed by the council to identify each licensed donkey.
15. Any animal welfare officer approved by the local authority or any police constable is authorised and appointed to supervise the licensed donkeys plying for hire on the foreshore and to enforce the regulations laid down by the Council.

THE PERFORMING ANIMALS ACT 1925

This Act controls the training and exhibition of any performing animals. A Certificate of Registration is needed. This certificate is obtained from the local authority.

PROTECTION OF ANIMALS ACT 1934

This Act prohibits any public performance in which unbroken horses are thrown or struggled with or stimulated to buck as in certain rodeos.

THE DOCKING AND NICKING OF HORSES ACT 1949

This Act prohibits the docking of horses' tails or their nicking, unless a Veterinary Surgeon has certified that the operation is necessary.

ABANDONMENT OF ANIMALS ACT 1960

This Act makes it an offence of cruelty 'if any person, being the owner or having charge or control of any animals shall, without reasonable cause or excuse abandon it, whether permanently or not, in circumstances likely to cause it unnecessary suffering, or cause or procure or, being the owner, permit it to be abandoned'.

THE ANIMALS (CRUEL POISONS) ACT 1962

This Act prohibits the killing of any mammal by means of cruel poisons.

THE PROTECTION OF ANIMALS (ANAESTHETICS) ACTS 1954 and 1964

This prevents the infliction of unnecessary suffering on animals during operations.

THE TRANSIT OF ANIMALS (ROAD OR RAIL) ORDER 1975

This Act relates to carriage of animals by road and rail. 'Animals' covers cattle, sheep, swine, goats, horses (donkeys). The Order refers to the vehicle construction and also the protection of the animals during loading and unloading and also gives the amount of space required by each animal during carriage in a road vehicle or in a receptacle which is being transported on a road vehicle.

This order is one which will be replaced by the new EU rules on the Welfare of Animals during Transport within the near future.

CINEMATOGRAPH FILMS ACT 1937 AND VIDEO RECORDINGS ACT 1984

These Acts prohibit the taking and showing of films or videos which depict, amongst other things, mutilation and torture or any acts of violence to humans or animals.

DONKEYS STRAYING ON THE HIGHWAY - ANIMALS ACT 1971

If any donkey is found straying on or at the side of any highway except where the highway passes over common land, for example National Parks where certain people have grazing rights, the owner or keeper of that straying donkey is liable to be prosecuted and fined. The owner may also be responsible for reasonable expenses incurred in the removing of the donkey or donkeys from the highway.

Any person may remove a straying donkey from the highway but it is that person's responsibility to ensure that the donkey or donkeys are properly fed and watered.

I would advise that if a straying donkey was found on a highway that it should, where possible, be restrained and moved to a place of safety and the local Police advised immediately.

HIGHWAYS ACT 1980

Section 155 also makes it an offence to allow a horse, including asses and mules, to stray on or at the side of a highway.

Tethering

In principle tethering is opposed as a method of keeping equines on a permanent basis when there is no regular daily exercise.

From time to time it may be necessary to tether your donkey and if tethering is temporary, or regular daily exercise is provided, then the following Code of Practice is recommended for equines kept at grass.

CODE OF PRACTICE FOR TETHERING HORSES, PONIES, DONKEYS, AND ALL EQUINES.

1. Choosing the site

a) Well grassed, especially if grass is going to be the sole source of food, and free from poisonous plants, shrubs and trees e.g. ragwort, laurel and yew.

b) Reasonably flat.

c) An area of shade must be available - essential during summer.

d) The area of tether must not cross a public footpath or be close to a public highway, especially where there is fast moving traffic.

e) The ground must not be waterlogged.

f) There must be no large objects within the area of tether, eg. tree stumps or bushes which the tether can get tangled around.

g) Size of site must depend on:

i) The amount of grass available.

ii) The frequency that the donkey will be moved - minimum size 20 feet radius.

2. Type of tether

a) A leather headcollar or wide leather neck band fitted with a swivel.

b) Must be firmly staked.

c) Metal chain of appropriate weight for the animals to be tethered.

d) Attached at stake with 360 degree swivel fitting at ground level, allowing donkey to cover a complete circle without tangling tether.

3. Age and condition of donkey

a) Donkeys less than two years old must not normally be tethered.

b) Mares in season must not be tethered near stallions or vice versa.

4. Clean water

Must be available at all times in a trough or container that is securely placed and not easily upset by the animal.

5. Food

Must be given in all cases where grazing is not adequate.

6. Frequency of inspection

Donkeys and tether must be inspected at least twice in 24 hours.

7. Changing the site

Frequency must depend upon the type of ground, amount of grazing, size of donkey; but site should be changed every 24 hours if grass is the sole source of food.

8. Weather

Donkeys must not be tethered in extreme weather conditions, such as heatwave, frost, snow, driving wind and rain etc.

Special note

Companion Animal Welfare Council

This was instigated by Dr Elisabeth Svendsen and Lord Soulsby, to advise ministers on legislation necessary for companion animals. Members of a Steering Committee attended a meeting in the House of Lords in July 1995. This Advisory Council should help in clarifying new legislation in the future.

Role of the Donkey Sanctuary

In conclusion, there are many occasions when seeing donkeys, whether in fields, in stables or on the beach, you may think that there is cause to obtain experienced advice as to whether or not what you are seeing is cruel. If you would like to contact the Donkey Sanctuary, Welfare Department, Sidmouth, Devon, EX10 0NU telephone Sidmouth 578222, they will be pleased to help and advise. The Welfare Officers of the Donkey Sanctuary inspect beach donkeys on a regular basis and liaise with Councils on licences being issued.

Note

Copies of legislation can be obtained from HMSO or their agents.

All quoted legislation is as at the time of writing, August 1996. The new

EU Rules on the Welfare of Animals during transport have to be implemented in all member states by 31st December 1997. This of course will effect our UK Animal Transit Legislation. It is intended that the new EU Rules on Transport of Animals will be one single order covering all aspects of Animal Welfare during transport. I have no further information from the Ministry of Agriculture Fisheries and Food at the time of writing.

MR BERT DUNCAN was born in Dundee, Scotland in 1935 and educated in Dundee. After National Service in the RAF he spent 36 years working for animal welfare. He served as a Chief Inspector of the RSPCA and Superintendent of the SPCA in Scotland prior to joining the Donkey Sanctuary in 1983. In 1997 he retired from the Donkey Sanctuary as Deputy Chief Welfare Officer and National Co-ordinator of Friends of the Donkey Sanctuary but continues to assist on a consultancy basis.

A - Z of Donkey Health

Abscess: a pus-filled cavity that can occur anywhere in the body, though the commonest sites in a donkey are the skin or the foot (see lameness). It may be necessary to administer antibiotics, therefore veterinary advice should always be sought (see chapters 2, 4, 5 & 12).

Allergy: a specific sensitivity to a foreign substance that causes the body to react either peripherally or systematically. The three main peripheral symptoms are itching, inflammation and oedema. Systematically anaphylactic shock may result (see also Sweet itch, Urticaria, COPD, Photosensitisation and chapter 4).

Alopecia: means loss of hair, but must be differentiated from hair loss as a result of the donkey rubbing or biting itself because of irritation, e.g. Lice infestation, Sweet itch, Ringworm, Mange. Alopecia may be the result of a hormonal imbalance, a dietary deficiency, metabolic diseases or selenium poisoning (see chapter 2).

Anaemia: is a blood parameter rather than a disease and is a reduction in the number of red cells in the circulatory system.
This may be caused by:-
(a) Blood loss - can be the result of acute haemorrhage (obvious if external but not if the bleeding is internal), or it may be due to severe parasitism, both endo and ectoparasites can cause chronic blood loss (see also chapters 4, 12 &13).
(b) Haemolysis (destruction of red blood cells by the body) - normally occurs within the body, but if excessive, can lead to anaemia and jaundice. Possible causes of this are certain types of poisoning (e.g. bracken, see chapter 18), auto-immune disease or certain infections not found in the UK, e.g. equine infectious anaemia.
(c) Aplastic anaemia (inability of the bone marrow to produce sufficient numbers of red blood cells) - can result from chronic infections, iron deficiency, neoplasia or certain plant and drug toxicities. Veterinary advice should be sought.
In all cases the donkey will be weak and depressed with pale mucous

membranes (see chapter 4).

Aneurysm: is a dilatation of an artery (sometimes a vein) following weakening of its wall and resulting in a pulsating sac which is liable to rupture. Aneurysms can occur in the abdomen, chest and brain, and may result from a congenital weakness of the blood-vessel, from disease of its lining cells or from injury. The cause is generally a sudden and violent muscular effort.

The term 'verminous aneurysm' was in the past used to describe the massive reaction to migrating *Strongylus vulgaris* larvae, found in the mesenteric arteries. This can lead to obstruction of blood vessels by dislodged blood clots, and consequent colic. If there is sufficient damage, the artery may rupture and the donkey may bleed to death. Verminous aneurysm is a misnomer for verminous arteritis of horses caused by immature strongyle worms (see chapter 4).

Anorexia: is the condition where a donkey will not eat. Appetite is an important indicator of a donkey's health and refusal to eat can be one of the first signs that they are unwell (though a good appetite is sometimes maintained in sick donkeys). Sudden onset may be due to colic, fever, pain, especially in the mouth or feet, or a sudden change in environment or feed. Some donkeys do have food preferences and if a particular food is refused, the donkey may be willing to eat an alternative. Any donkey off its feed should be examined by a vet. If the condition persists, a state of hyperlipaemia can occur, particularly in overweight donkeys, which will often prove fatal if not treated early enough (see chapters 2, 4, 6 & 12).

Anthelmintic: substances given to donkeys to treat parasitic worms. They include ivermectins, benzimidazole and pyrantel derivatives. Methods of dosing include drenching, injection or in the feed (see chapter 4 - Resistance to anthelmintics).

Anthrax: a bacterial disease causing sudden death (see chapter 12).

Arthritis: is quite common in older donkeys, but can also be seen in younger donkeys and causes include acute or chronic trauma to joints, rheumatism, a mineral deficiency and fluorosis (chronic fluorine poisoning). There may be a generalised stiffness when first getting up but this often improves with gentle exercise. Anti-inflammatory pain killers are often prescribed.

Botulism: a form of food poisoning, often fatal, caused by *Clostridium botulinum* toxins, which produce paralysis. Botulism has been reported in donkeys as well as horses, most recently as a result of feeding contaminated big bale silage. Signs are quite vague but there is extreme dullness, inability to swallow and therefore copious drooling of saliva from the mouth and muscular weakness leading to paralysis. The condition is nearly always fatal and is notoriously difficult to confirm by laboratory examination (see chapter 6).

Bracken poisoning: long term ingestion of bracken (particularly in its green state) can lead to poisoning. This plant is usually only eaten if the pasture is poor. The plant has an enzyme thiaminase which destroys thiamine in the donkey and this affects the brain leading to staggering, inco-ordination, weakness, emaciation and anaemia. Treatment with large doses of intravenous thiamine is required, as well as removal of the cause, though symptoms can occur long after the donkey is removed from the bracken. Horsetails have the same effect as bracken (see chapter 18).

Broken wind: see COPD.

Bruised soles: the soles of the feet can be bruised by traumatic injury such as walking over very stony ground when the soles are thin or flat and sometimes occurs if the feet have been trimmed back too far. When the surface of the sole is scraped away a red discolouration, or bruise, can be seen. The condition improves as the horn of the sole grows and the bruising subsides. It may be necessary to provide protection of the soles in severe cases by bandaging the foot with some gamgee padding for a week or so. The padding should be checked and changed regularly to prevent the sole becoming infected and soft. The application of a gentian violet and tetracycline spray is often used to harden the horn and prevent infection.

Castration: this surgical operation involves the removal of the testicles from a stallion (Jack) donkey. The operation is usually performed under general anaesthesia although it is sometimes possible to use sedation and local anaesthesia. It can be performed once the testicles have descended though it is usually preferable to wait until at least six months of age to give a general anaesthetic. The operation can be carried out at any time of the year if suitable facilities for surgery and post-operative care are available, but most vets prefer to carry out the operation during spring or autumn when it is not too cold or wet and when there are less flies to aggravate the castration wound. Castration wounds are normally left open to allow drainage. Sometimes there is swelling around the wound which may extend to the sheath. The donkey should be encouraged to exercise in order to minimise the swelling (see chapters 3, 4 & 13).

Cataract: an opacity of the crystalline lens of the eye and usually occurs in both eyes simultaneously. It is usually seen in old donkeys and is a senile change, but can occur at almost any time of life or as a sequel to trauma, infection or inflammation of the eye. A bluish, cloudy appearance of the eye leads to impaired vision and ultimately to blindness in the affected eye (see chapter 2).

Choke: food lodged in the oesophagus will lead to choke. The donkey will be unable to swallow, food may be regurgitated through the nose and, depending on the site of obstruction, there may be arching of the neck. The donkey is usually fairly distressed. Urgent veterinary attention should be sought. Treatment using a stomach tube passed through the nose to dislodge the obstruction is usually required and muscle relaxants may also be administered (see chapter 6).

Colic: the term applied to symptoms of abdominal pain. Donkeys are more stoic than the horse and the symptoms are usually less violent. Therefore signs of colic in donkeys should be taken very seriously and urgent veterinary attention sought. Signs to look for are:- acute loss of appetite, extreme dullness with low head carriage, restlessness, recumbency, rapid pulse and respiration, either constipation or diarrhoea. Rolling, looking at the belly, kicking at the flank are usually terminal signs. There are a number of different types of colic which require different forms of treatment, some of which are potentially surgical. The main types of colic are:

1. Spasmodic - This is usually seen in nervous donkeys possibly

after a change in environment. This type is the least serious and is usually very effectively treated with anti-spasmodic drugs.

2. Thrombo-embolic - This is caused by the occlusion of blood vessels to part of the gut and the most common cause of this is thought to be thrombi resulting from damage by migrating strongyle larvae. Regular worming is required to prevent this occurring.

3. Flatulent - This is due to a build-up of gas in the stomach or intestines particularly if a fermentable diet is being fed.

4. Impaction - This is caused by the build-up of hard, dry faeces, particularly in the caecum or colon, usually where the diameter of the intestine narrows at the pelvic flexure. Donkeys do normally need a diet that is high in fibre, but an impaction can occur if food is improperly digested or insufficient breakdown has occurred by chewing, or there has been inadequate intake of water. Pain can be quite severe and affected donkeys will sometimes lie on their backs to relieve pain caused by the pull of the heavy intestine on the sensitive connective tissue in which it is suspended. This type of colic can usually be relieved by medical treatment alone, although recovery may take several days. Surgery may be necessary in some extreme cases that do not respond to more conservative treatment.

5. Obstruction - occurs as a result of twisting of the intestine, strangulation of part of the gut, or a variety of other reasons. This type of colic nearly always requires surgical treatment but, if surgical facilities are not available, then euthanasia may be recommended by the attending vet, on humane grounds.

6. Grass sickness - This is a disease of equines, though not commonly seen in donkeys. The signs are those of severe colic with profuse sweating, muscle tremors over the body and also, normally, a green discharge from the nose (regurgitated food). The cause is unknown but it affects the nervous control of the gut. There is no effective treatment and euthanasia is usually advised.

Donkeys suffering from other conditions which give rise to abdominal pain such as hepatitis, cystitis, pancreatitis or imminent foaling may also show signs of colic (see chapters 2, 4, 6, 12, 14 & 18).

Colostrum: a thick secretion emitted from the mares mammary gland prior to the normal flow of milk. Colostrum contains the antibodies necessary for the foal to fight infection prior to full development of its own immune system. After twenty-four hours of age, the foal cannot absorb these antibodies from the gut, so it is vital that colostrum is obtained within this time (see chapter 15).

Congenital deformities: these are deformities that are present when the foal is born and can include undershot or overshot jaw, limb or spinal column deformities (see chapter 6).

Conjunctivitis: an inflammation of the conjunctival membranes (membrane which covers the surface of the eye and inner eyelids). There is redness of the eye and excessive discharge of tears which may later become thick and yellowish and the donkey may blink vigorously. In very severe cases the eye may be partially closed. The cause is usually a minor irritation, e.g. from dust in the hay or straw but is sometimes due to an infection or a foreign body in the eye (e.g. a piece of straw or hay seed). A persistently weeping eye will require veterinary treatment (see chapter 2).

COPD: chronic obstructive pulmonary disease, also known as broken wind, heaves, dust allergy or emphysema. This disease is similar to asthma in humans and is usually caused by an allergy, usually to fungal spores in the dust in hay or straw. The temperature of affected donkeys is usually normal although an episode may occur following any respiratory infection. Breathing is very laboured and wheezing can often be heard even without the aid of a stethoscope. Coughing is not common in donkeys, unlike horses. Affected donkeys are usually stabled and the condition is improved by turning them out and reducing the exposure to dust. If they need to be housed, then bedding should be changed from straw to either peat, wood shavings or paper, which are less dusty. Hay should be fed after soaking overnight to keep the dust down or a dust-free feed such as haylage can be given instead. The condition can usually be controlled by management alone but drugs to alleviate the bronchospasm can be useful in many cases. If the condition is truly allergic, the donkey will always be prone to it, so management changes will need to be maintained for the rest of the donkey's life (see chapter 6).

Cough: donkeys are not often heard to cough even when severe lung lesions are present. It does occur, however, when there is irritation of the upper respiratory tract and in certain types of infection. A persistent cough should always be investigated by a veterinary surgeon (see also COPD, Lungworm, Pneumonia and chapters 2, 4 & 12).

Cystitis: not very common, but can occur in donkeys. It is an inflammation of the bladder and is characterised by frequent voiding of small amounts of urine, often with difficulty, and straining. There is also usually fever and a loss of appetite. The cause is usually an infection and requires treatment with antibiotics. Similar signs are also seen with calculi (stones) in the bladder or urethra and this condition may require surgery to correct.

Dermatophilus: this infection results in a chronic dermatitis, in which the hairs stand erect and matted in tufts (see Rain scald and Mud fever and chapter 2).

Diarrhoea: causes of diarrhoea in donkeys can be:-

1. Nervous - donkeys which are easily upset will pass loose faeces from time to time but these become normal later when the donkey is allowed to settle down.
2. Dietary - sudden dietary changes can precipitate diarrhoea. Often seen when the donkeys are turned out to grass or if they are fed a high-protein feed. Foals can develop a nutritional diarrhoea due to intolerance to milk. It can also occur when the mare has her 'foal heat' approximately 1 week after foaling. A reduction in milk intake and replacement with glucose/electrolyte solutions is usually beneficial.
3. Parasitic - Intestinal parasitism can give rise to chronic diarrhoea. Most commonly this is due to the strongyle worm infections which regular worming should prevent. Infection with other species of worms or protozoan intestinal parasites may also cause diarrhoea.
4. Infections - with certain bacteria (including salmonella) and viruses can cause both acute and chronic diarrhoea. The donkey is usually ill and may require intensive therapy with replacement fluids and probably antibiotics.
5. Inability to digest food properly - may be caused by failure to chew properly (e.g. bad teeth), inappropriate food (e.g. adult diet in

young foal) or disease of the gut wall preventing ingress of dietary compounds.

If diarrhoea continues this can be serious as the digestive processes and the absorption of nutrients are impaired, but also the loss of fluid can give rise to dehydration. If diarrhoea persists for 48 hours or more, veterinary advice should be sought.

(See also Colic, Parascaris Infection, Salmonella, Strongyle Worm Infection, Strongyloides Infection, Tapeworms and chapters 4, 6, 12 & 18.)

Dysphagia: or difficulty in swallowing may be the result of a variety of causes. An inability to swallow will result in food being regurgitated down the nose and this will be seen as a greenish nasal discharge. This can also occur in choke, grass sickness, certain types of colic and certain conditions which affect the nervous system such as botulism, lead poisoning and rabies (see also Botulism, Choke, Colic, Teeth, Weight Loss).

Ectoparasites: external parasites (see chapter 4).

Ectropion: a congenital condition of the eye where the mucous membrane lining of the eyelid is everted giving a droopy eye appearance. It can also follow injury or swelling of the eyelid. If there is persistent inflammation or infection of the affected eye, surgery may be required to correct the condition.

Endoparasites: internal parasites (see chapter 4).

Entropion: a congenital condition of the eyelid (upper or lower) which turns inwards so that the eyelashes are rubbing on the surface of the eye. This causes intense irritation and damage to the eye and requires surgical correction under general anaesthetic. Usually a strip of skin is removed in order to return the eyelid to its normal position.

Equine herpes virus (*rhinopneumonitis*): this virus (EHV 1), of which there are two sub-types, is responsible for four different syndromes in equines. These are:-

1. A respiratory form which is contagious and easily spread by nasal

discharges. There is fever, dullness, nasal discharge and sometimes a cough.

2. Abortion usually in the latter part of gestation. Some infected mares will produce a live foal but this is usually weak and suffering from the third form of the disease.

3. Congenital *rhinopneumonitis*. Affected foals are weak at, or soon after, birth and refuse to suck. Treatment is usually unrewarding and most die within a few days.

4. Neurological disease. This may be preceded by respiratory signs. The hindquarters become unco-ordinated and there is sometimes urinary incontinence. In severe cases, the donkey may become recumbent.

The form most likely to be seen in donkeys is the respiratory disease and recovery from this is usually good although this may be complicated by infections by other organisms. There is a vaccine available which is mainly effective against abortion but the immunity it produces is not very strong and is rather short-lived.

Equine influenza: equine flu is caused by a group of viruses known as the myxoviruses, of which there are at least four sub-types. It is a highly contagious disease which is characterised by fever and nasal discharge with varying degrees of dullness and inappetence. The virus will also cause some inflammation of the heart and liver, so any strenuous exercise or stress should be avoided during the illness and for about a month afterwards. Recovery is usually good although secondary infections can be a problem. If the donkey is unwilling to eat, then this can lead to hyperlipaemia. It is possible (and recommended) to vaccinate against the commonly occurring strains of this virus. Two doses of vaccine are initially given, four to six weeks apart followed by boosters at least every year. It may be necessary to vaccinate at six-monthly intervals if the donkey is to mix with other equines, e.g. at shows, etc. Your veterinary surgeon will advise on the best regime for a particular individual. Following vaccination, exercise should be avoided for one week after a primary vaccine and three days after a booster vaccine. Flu like symptoms are often seen in donkeys that are fully vaccinated, since other strains of the virus may not be covered by the vaccine or a different type of virus (including equine herpesvirus) may be the cause. Occasionally, an animal may not respond adequately to the vaccine (see chapters 2, 12 & 14).

Eye problems: see Cataract, Conjunctivitis, Ectropion, Entropion and chapters 2, 3, 4, 7 & 14).

Fatty liver: see Hyperlipaemia (see chapters 2, 4 & 6).

Feet: donkeys' feet are often neglected and can soon become overgrown and twisted. In areas where the donkeys work on hard, rocky ground (e.g. Mediterranean countries) the rate of wear of the hoof is approximately equal to its rate of growth so that their feet maintain a good shape and length. However, in this country, most donkeys lead a fairly sedentary life on the soft ground and the hooves can grow unchecked. They become very long and will start to curl up into 'Arabian slippers', particularly the front feet. If left uncorrected, they will become twisted. These deformities can be painful for the donkey and it may take many months of trimming before a normal shaped hoof can be regained. Occasionally the deformity is so severe that it is impossible to obtain a normal foot. Regular trimming of hooves is required every six to eight weeks. Donkeys are not normally shod but this may be necessary if the donkey is to do a lot of roadwork. Most lameness in donkeys is in the foot, the commonest causes being abscesses, thrush, laminitis, seedy toe and of course, deformed feet (see chapters 3, 5, 10, 12 & 14).

Flies: a nuisance throughout the summer. Not only do they cause annoyance and irritation but they are capable of spreading and causing disease. They are found around the eyes and wounds, feeding off any secretions or discharge. The irritation delays the healing of wounds, and eggs, which develop into maggots, are often laid in the wound. This is called fly strike. Wounds should always be kept clean and, during the fly season, it is useful to apply an antibiotic powder which also contains an insecticide. Other flies (stable flies) can give painful bites which cause annoyance at the time and later give rise to swellings, sometimes with scabs, on the skin. Various measures can be taken to reduce the numbers of flies around the donkey, such as pour-on insect repellent and washes. Some people use a fringed browband or a fine-meshed mask over the face to keep flies away from the donkeys' eyes (see chapters 2, 3, 4, 10, 12, 13 & 14).

Grass sickness: see Colic.

Hinny: the offspring of a stallion horse and a jenny donkey.

Heart disease: clinical manifestations of heart disease are not commonly seen in donkeys, because they are not often asked to work hard (in the UK). Fairly severe heart murmurs can be heard in donkeys that appear to be normal as long as they are not subjected to strenuous exercise or a particularly stressful situation. When clinically affected, signs may include poor exercise tolerance, weakness, breathlessness and oedema, usually noticeable as a build-up of fluid under the skin of the belly but it may also be present as fluid in the lungs or abdominal cavity. Rarely, a foal may be born with a congenital heart defect. In some cases, the foal may be weak and stunted, breathless and may have a blue tinge to the gums.

Hydatid cysts: these are parasitic cysts which can be found usually in the liver but occasionally also in the lungs. They are the intermediate stage of the tapeworm, *Echinococcus granulosus*. A donkey is infected by eating pasture contaminated by infected dog/fox faeces. Although clinical signs are not often seen in infected donkeys, if there are a large number of cysts present much of the liver tissue is destroyed. In these cases there may be signs of liver insufficiency (see chapters 4 & 12).

Hyperlipaemia: this is a particularly distressing condition which can be fatal if not treated at an early stage. It occurs, particularly in fat donkeys, when food intake has been drastically reduced over a period of time (which can be as short as three to four days). It may also be a complication of another illness where appetite is reduced, e.g. colic, flu, laminitis, pneumonia, or the donkey may simply stop eating in response to a change in its environment (see chapters 2, 4 & 6).

Jack: a male donkey.

Jenny: a female donkey.

Kidney disease: this is not commonly diagnosed in donkeys, particularly in the early stages. The cause of kidney disease in donkeys is fatty kidneys (associated with hyperlipaemia); kidney infections; kidney damage following chronic infections elsewhere in the body and cystic enlargement which may be either congenital or due to an obstruction further down the urinary tract. The clinical signs are due to infection, if present, and to the build-up of the toxic waste products which are usually filtered out by the kidneys. These accumulate in the blood causing uraemia which can be detected by blood tests. Symptoms include chronic weight loss, excessive drinking and urination, inappetence, dullness and fever if infection is present. Treatment which may be prescribed includes antibiotics, fluids and anabolic steroids. However, in old animals with long-standing kidney disease, the prognosis is poor and euthanasia is often recommended (see chapters 2 & 3).

Lameness: is a common problem in donkeys. Most lamenesses are to be found in the foot (see Abscess, Laminitis, Seedy toe, Thrush, Mud fever) but a variety of other musculo-skeletal conditions can be the cause. A lot of the traumatic and stress injuries that are common in horses are not often seen in donkeys because they are not usually required to perform the same type of work. Strained tendons do sometimes occur in donkeys and injuries to joints can result in bruising and swelling, the knees and fetlocks being most frequently affected.

Arthritis is not uncommon in old donkeys, often with new bone growth around the joints. A specific example of this is bone spavin which occurs in the hocks, usually in both legs and can be very painful initially. See also Arthritis, Spavin.

Fractures and dislocations can occur following traumatic injury. Certain types of limb fractures are not easily treated and it is kindest to relieve the donkey of suffering by euthanasia. Dislocation of the hip can occur in donkeys. Some individuals appear to have a shallow socket in the hip joint and this allows the leg to be dislocated more easily. It usually occurs after an awkward fall (the donkey may do the splits) and there is a sudden onset of severe lameness in the affected hind limb, which is reluctant to bear weight.

Examination using X-rays is often required to establish the cause of lameness. Another aid to diagnosis is the use of temporary nerve blocks with local anaesthetic which can help to determine the site of lameness (see also Radial paralysis, Stifle lock, Stringhalt and chapters 2, 3 & 5).

Laminitis: an extremely painful condition of the feet and is due to congestion of the sensitive structures (laminae) within the foot. All four feet can be affected although the front feet are almost invariably affected first. The feet are warm to the touch and the soles of the feet are extremely tender.

Laminitis is usually precipitated by the over-zealous introduction of high quality feed (especially with a high-protein content) into the diet, or can occur following liver damage or illness accompanied by fever. Introduction of a new high-protein food should take place very gradually to avoid the likelihood of laminitis (see chapter 5).

Lice: donkeys are affected by both biting (*Damalinia equi*) and sucking lice (*Haematopinus asini*). Lice infestation causes intense irritation which results in hair loss from rubbing and biting (see Alopecia). Less severe infestation will give the coat a dull, scaly, unkempt appearance. In extreme cases the donkey may show a loss of condition and anaemia (see chapter 14 for treatment; see chapters 4 & 12).

Liver disease: liver lesions are quite common in donkeys but clinical signs are not seen until a large percentage of the organ is affected as the remaining healthy tissue can usually cope adequately. The most common causes of liver disease are:-
Fatty liver and hyperlipaemia.
Ragwort poisoning.
Hydatid cysts.
Hepatitis caused by bacterial or viral infection.
Bile duct obstruction. (See Hyperlipaemia, Hydatid Cysts, Ragwort Poisoning and chapters 2, 3, 4 & 18.)

Liver fluke (*Fasciola spp.*): See chapter 4.

Lungworm: found in equines and called *Dictyocaulus arnfieldi.* The donkey is the natural host for this parasite and can harbour large numbers of lungworm without showing any clinical signs (see chapters 2 & 4).

Mange: list as per chapter 4. There is extreme irritation and hair loss with thick, scabby lesions over the body. It is uncommon in donkeys (see chapters 4 & 12).

Mastitis: an inflammation of the udder. It is usually only seen in lactating mares but occasionally it can occur in the non lactating udder. Some offspring, if not properly weaned, will continue to suckle a little for many years and these mares are also prone to mastitis. One or both sides of the udder are hot, swollen and painful and there may be oedema along the belly in front of the udder. The milk will change its appearance usually becoming thicker and pus like or it may become grey and watery. Sometimes the milk is stained with blood. There may also be an accompanying fever with dullness and inappetence and the mare may vigorously resent handling of the udder. It is necessary to treat mastitis with antibiotics. Bathing the udder with warm water and stripping out the milk regularly will help to relieve pain.

Mud fever: seen in donkeys that are kept in wet and muddy conditions underfoot. There is a moist inflammation of the skin from the fetlock down and this allows entry of bacteria especially the dermatophilus organism which is also responsible for rain scald. The lower legs may become swollen and tender and the donkey is often lame. Some donkeys also show signs of systemic illness and become dull and inappetent. It is essential to keep affected animals inside on dry bedding to allow the legs to dry out and keep them clean using an antiseptic and possibly also anti inflammatory agents can be applied. It may also be necessary to administer antibiotics by injection (see Rain scald and chapter 12).

Mule: the sterile offspring of a jack donkey and a horse mare.

Nasal discharge: discharges from the nostrils can be unilateral or bilateral and the type of discharge can be classified as follows:-

1. Serous (watery) - which is usually very mild but which may progress to
2. Muco-purulent which can be thick and white or creamy in colour.
3. A green discharge, usually regurgutated food, as a result of vomiting or an inability to swallow (see Choke, Colic, Dysphagia, Grass sickness).
4. Blood - either from frank haemorrhage or in conjunction with a mucoid purulent discharge.

The most likely cause of serous or muco-purulent discharge is an upper respiratory tract infection such as flu or equine herpes virus infection and the discharge is usually bilateral. Other causes include sinusitis, strangles, guttural pouch infection, or the presence of a foreign body. These may cause a discharge from one or both nostrils. Blood from the nostrils may be due to ruptured blood vessels either in the back of the nose or possibly in the lungs. Occasionally there may be bleeding after a stomach tube has been passed through the nose. This may look rather dramatic but it is self-limiting and the bleeding usually stops quite quickly. Other possible causes of bloody nasal discharge are fungal infections or necrosis of the bones at the back of the nose, or rarely, a tumour may be involved (see chapter 2 & 12).

Obesity: a common problem in donkeys in this country but rarely encountered in countries where donkeys are required to work. The usual sites for deposition of fat in donkeys are on the neck, on either side of the chest wall giving a saddle bag appearance and around the buttocks. It is important not to try to lose weight too rapidly as this can also precipitate hyperlipaemia (see chapters 2, 3, 6, 13 & 14).

Oedema: an accumulation of exudate in one or more of the body cavities or under the skin. The subcutaneous site is the one most likely to be seen in the donkey, particularly in the region of the belly, where it is called ventral oedema or around the area of a wound where there is a lot of tissue reaction. Fluid tends to accumulate on the underside of the body due to the effects of gravity. When pressed with a finger, a depression is left in the affected area for a while (see chapters 2, 3, 4 & 12).

Parascaris infection: the large roundworm of equines and generally only a problem in foals as resistance is developed in older donkeys (see chapters 4 & 13).

Parasites: donkeys are commonly parasitised by endo- and ectoparasites. Ectoparasites are responsible for the majority of skin diseases which are characterised by itchiness. See Flies, Lice, Mange, Sweet itch. Endoparasites include ascarids, strongyle worms (large and small), pinworms, thread worms, tapeworms, bots, lungworms and liver fluke (see chapters 2, 4, 10, 12 & 13).

Photosensitisation: a type of sunburn and is seen in some white and broken coloured donkeys during the summer. Usually, only the pink, non pigmented skin around the muzzle and face is affected, though it can occur on any unprotected area of non pigmented skin. Some types of plants, e.g. St John's wort, contain substances which make the donkey prone to photosensitisation. Liver disease may have the same effect in some cases. The affected areas become inflamed and later raw and scabby. Barrier creams can be used to keep the skin supple and provide protection from the sun. Severe cases should be kept inside when the sun is shining. An anti bacterial, anti inflammatory ointment can be used to reduce the inflammation and prevent bacterial infection of the damaged skin (see chapters 2 & 18).

Pneumonia: inflammation of the lung tissue and is usually the result of infection. It may follow an upper respiratory tract infection or a period of general malaise where the donkey's resistance to pathogenic organisms in the environment is lowered. The affected donkey is usually dull and inappetent with a high temperature, rapid shallow breathing and raised pulse rate. There may be a cough and a nasal discharge and the lungs will sound harsh, often with the presence of fluid in the chest. Antibiotic therapy is required together with supportive nutritional therapy to prevent hyperlipaemia occurring. The environment should be kept as dust free as possible (see chapters 2, 12, 14 & 15).

Poisoning: most poisonings that occur in donkeys are the result of eating poisonous plants. Most common of these is ragwort poisoning but bracken and horsetail poisoning can also occur. Some plant poisons give rise to abdominal pain and diarrhoea, e.g. buttercups and acorns, and some will also produce nervous signs, e.g. nightshades, hemlock and laburnum. St John's wort is an example of a plant which causes photosensitisation and yew is extremely poisonous, affected animals usually being found dead. Poisoning by chemical agents can also occur but is not common. Lead poisoning may be induced by the donkey licking objects coated with a lead based paint. This will give rise to anaemia, weakness and neurological signs including inability to swallow. The feeding, to donkeys, of cattle feed containing the growth promoter, Monensin, can also lead to poisoning. Heart failure and death can occur if sufficient quantities are consumed.

Poisoning can occur from contaminated feed. The contamination may be the toxin of a fungus, e.g. aflatoxin, or the fungus itself, e.g. ergot of rye, which can cause poor circulation and, later, gangrene of the extremities (see chapter 18).

Quidding: the condition when a donkey will take food into the mouth, chew it and then expel it onto the floor. It is usually a result of improper chewing due to pain in the mouth or restricted movement of the jaws. Teeth abnormalities are usually to blame, either because they are loose, or they have worn down irregularly. Regular examination of the mouth is to be recommended and rasping of the cheek teeth at least once a year should be carried out in donkeys over five years of age (see Teeth and chapters 2 & 6).

Rabies: a viral infection of mammals transmitted in the saliva of a rabid animal. The most important hosts are carnivores and bats. In general, equine rabies is uncommon (see chapter 12).

Radial paralysis: occasionally seen in donkeys. The affected forelimb is paralysed and the donkey is unable to advance the leg or take weight on it. The nerve may be damaged following fracture of the first rib or by pressure on the nerve from a lesion such as an abscess or tumour in the axilla or elsewhere along the nerve's path. A similar type of paralysis is very occasionally seen following a period of recumbency where pressure on the underneath limb can cause a temporary paralysis of the nerve. It may be compounded by inflammation of the muscles of the forelimb.

Ragwort poisoning: ragwort is poisonous in both the fresh and dried states; however, when it is fresh it is bitter and so is avoided by donkeys unless there is little else to eat. When dried, in hay for example, it is tasteless and readily eaten therefore hay should never be made from fields where ragwort is present (see chapters 6, 14, 17 & 18).

Rain scald: a skin condition caused by *Dermatophilus congolensis*, this organism is also involved in mud fever. The condition can arise when the donkey has been standing in heavy, driving rain and excessive wetting of the skin has occurred. This allows penetration of the organism into the skin causing a dermatitis condition. The hair is usually lost in small patches over the body leaving pink skin exposed which may become moist and scabby. The hair is often in tufts, matted with dried crusts and giving a paint brush appearance. An affected donkey should be kept in the dry. Mild cases will improve by this treatment alone. Additionally, the skin can be washed with an antiseptic solution, but severe cases may require antibiotic treatment (see chapter 2).

Redworms: see Strongyle infection.

Rig: also known as a cryptorchid, is a male donkey in which one or both testicles remain undescended, at an age when it is expected that both testicles should have descended into the scrotum. A rig can often be aggressive and difficult to handle and surgery to remove the retained testicle is usually advisable. Sometimes following an injection with hormones or at a later date it may descend. The retained testicle is usually defective and may rarely become cancerous. If no testicles are present in the scrotum and it is suspected that a donkey is a rig, then a fairly simple blood test can be performed to confirm or deny this.

Ringworm: a highly contagious fungal infection of the skin which can be zoonotic. It can be spread by direct contact between affected and unaffected animals or indirectly by brushes, tack, stables, clothes, etc., which have been in contact with the fungus. There are several different types of fungus that can cause ringworm in donkeys and some types can be transmitted from other species of animal, notably cattle. The skin lesions are variable but usually start as raised patches of skin on which the hair breaks to give round or irregular areas of hair loss which are usually, but not always, itchy. The lesions are often found around the head and in the saddle or girth region (if tack is used on the donkey) but they can occur anywhere on the body. To confirm the diagnosis of ringworm, a skin scraping should be taken by the vet. Infected donkeys should be isolated from other animals to prevent further spread of the disease. Treatment then involves the administration of anti-fungal drugs as a wash, or in the feed, or both. Brushes, tack, rugs and stables should also be treated with anti-fungal preparation to prevent re-infection.

Saddle sores: these are seen in many Third World countries and are mainly caused by poorly fitting saddles and equipment used on donkeys in poor body condition. Either the equipment or the poor condition may result in excessive pressure and/or frictional rub. Signs are rubbed off hair and broken skin on the side of the withers or under the girth which often leaves raw bleeding sores that vary in size and are slow to heal. If the donkey is rested, the sores allowed to heal, and correctly fitting harness and padding is used and the donkey's body condition improved, the occurrence of saddle sores can be reduced.

Salmonella infection: not a common problem in donkeys. Salmonella may be suspected in cases of acute enteritis especially where there is blood present in the diarrhoea. Strict hygienic precautions must be taken when salmonella is suspected and affected donkeys should be kept in isolation. It should be remembered that humans can also be infected by salmonella, so cleanliness and disinfection is important after handling any infected donkeys.

Sandcrack: affects the hoof wall. It is a crack which can extend down from the coronary band to the base of the hoof. It is usually a consequence of an injury to the coronary band or caused by excessive dryness of the hoof wall. This over dryness is often due to over enthusiastic rasping. The donkey may become lame and rarely evidence of infection is found underneath the crack.

Sarcoids: skin tumours that are often seen in donkeys. It is thought that they may be caused by a viral infection, possibly spread by flying insects. The condition is not highly contagious although the incidence of the disease is probably higher where large numbers of donkeys are kept together (see chapters 2, 3 & 12).

Seedy toe: the characteristic lesion shows areas of grey crumbly horn which usually occurs at the toe but can extend to either side and result in triangular cavities within the hoof wall. Dirt and debris can also accumulate in this space further worsening the condition. An antibiotic is often applied to the cavity to prevent infection (see chapters 2 & 5).

Sinusitis: affects the paranasal sinuses of the donkey; these sinuses are cavities of the skull which are connected directly or indirectly with the nose. The roots of some of the cheek teeth extend into the maxillary sinus. Infection of the paranasal sinuses can occur after an upper respiratory tract infection such as flu, strangles or from an infected tooth root. The affected sinus will become filled with mucus and/or pus and will usually discharge this through the appropriate nostril. Treatment may require drilling a hole in the bone over the sinus and flushing out the cavity until the infection has been resolved. An infected tooth may need to be removed. Antibiotics are also used (see Nasal discharge, Teeth).

Skin diseases: a number of skin diseases are common in donkeys and the causes may be parasitic, allergic, bacterial, fungal, metabolic, neoplastic, or toxic (see Abscess, Alopecia, Flies, Lice, Mange, Mud Fever, Oedema, Photosensitisation, Rain Scald, Ringworm, Sarcoid, Sweet itch, Urticaria and chapters 2, 4 & 12).

Spavin: an osteoarthritis of the hock joint commonly seen in donkeys. It is an osteoarthritis of the hock joint (when new bone tissue is deposited around the small bones of this joint). Its occurrence is not restricted to old donkeys and the cause is not fully understood. It may follow a period of inflammation of the joint and some people think that there is an inherited predisposition to the condition. There will be a progressive stiffness and lameness in the affected hind legs. Usually both hind limbs are affected but one may become worse than the other. The donkey may be seen to hold each affected leg up, in turn, but resents the hock being fully flexed. Full flexion of the limb will result in a temporary increase in severity of the lameness. It may prove to be difficult to pick up the hind feet in order to trim the hooves and the donkey may have difficulty in lifting its hind legs over a raised obstacle. A bony enlargement is occasionally seen on the inner aspect of the hock. With rest and time, possibly up to a year, the joint will settle down and some of the small bones of the joint may fuse together. The lameness improves gradually and the donkey will eventually be nearly sound, although after recovery strenuous work is not advisable. As donkeys are not usually required to work, it is probably better to just rest them. Anti inflammatory pain killers can be used in the early, painful stages.

Stifle lock: affects the donkey's stifle (the equivalent of the human knee joint). The donkey is able to lock this joint in order to support the weight of its body when standing. By fixing the position of the patella (or knee cap) the donkey can support its weight with much less muscular exertion. Problems arise when the animal is unable to unlock the joint properly as it walks. Occasionally, the leg is completely locked and is dragged behind in an extended position. Veterinary attention is usually urgently required. More commonly, the condition in donkeys is seen as an abnormal hind leg gait. The affected leg (or both legs) will have a jerky action and the condition may be confused with stringhalt. Usually the condition is seen in young, unfit or thin donkeys and once the muscles of the hind leg become more developed by exercise and/or weight gain the gait returns to normal. In some persistent or very severe cases, surgery is necessary and this is carried out on the conscious animal under local anaesthetic.

Strangles: used to be very common but is now rarely seen. It is a highly contagious bacterial infection *Streptococcus equi* of the upper respiratory tract (see chapter 2 & 12).

Stringhalt: a condition in which the nervous control of the hind legs is affected. There is a sudden snatching up of one or both hind legs when the donkey is walking. This behaviour can be exacerbated by turning in circles (see chapter 2).

Strongyle worm infection: there are a number of species of strongyles that can infect donkeys. It is normally recommended that donkeys are wormed every four to eight weeks depending on the number of equines grazing together and the type of drug used. This may be modified if an effective system of pasture management is also employed. A worming and pasture management regime can be formulated for individual donkeys by your veterinary surgeon (see chapters 4, 12 & 13).

Strongyloides infection: *Strongyloides westeri* is the threadworm of equines (see chapters 4 & 13).

Sunburn: see Photosensitisation.

Sweet itch: an allergic skin reaction to the bite of *Culicoides* (midges). It will occur in affected animals, every year from about April until October in England. There is an intense itching and the donkey will usually rub the skin along its mane, back and base of the tail (see chapter 4).

Tapeworms: in donkeys and horses *Anoplocephala perfoliata* rarely causes clinical disease, but loss of condition, diarrhoea and colic have been attributed to severe infestations. Infection is caused by the eating of forage mites (the worm's intermediate stage of development). Treatment involves using a wormer which has an activity against tapeworms. The intermediate stage of the dog tapeworm gives rise to hydatid cysts in the liver (see Hydatid cysts and chapters 4 & 12).

Teeth problems: the majority of problems associated with teeth can be related to uneven wear of the cheek teeth as the donkey ages. Rough, sharp edges can form on the outer edges of the cheek teeth and can cause damage to the gums, making the mouth painful and chewing difficult. In extreme cases, the edges of the upper or lower teeth can overlap their opposite numbers to such an extent that sideways movement of the jaws is restricted. To prevent this, the donkey's mouth should be examined regularly and rasping of the outer edges of the cheek teeth should be carried out yearly from five years of age if necessary. The front cheek tooth in either the upper or lower jaw can overgrow the opposite one, thus forming a hook which will need to be clipped off (this procedure sometimes requires a general anaesthetic). Teeth may sometimes become loose in their sockets usually in old donkeys or as the result of infection, neoplasia or injury. Loose teeth should be removed as they can be painful. Infections of tooth roots can cause loosening of the tooth and if its root is located in a paranasal sinus then sinusitis can ensue. In young donkeys, there may be some pain associated with the loss of temporary teeth and the eruption of permanent teeth. The congenital conditions of over- or under-shot jaw, where the upper and lower rows of incisor teeth do not meet, may make the grazing of grass difficult, although other feeds are usually managed well. In an over-shot jaw the upper jaw projects too far forward and in an under-shot jaw the lower jaw is too long. In older donkeys the incisor teeth of the top jaw wear down, sometimes back to the gum. These donkeys may also have difficulty in grazing. Abnormalities of the teeth can lead to quidding, colic, dribbling, reluctance to eat, weight loss and in some cases sinusitis (see Colic, Dysphagia, Quidding, Sinusitis and Weight loss and chapters 2, 6, & 14).

Temperature: the normal temperature of a donkey is 98.8°F but can vary between 97.2°F-100°F in clinically normal donkeys. The temperature is usually raised as the result of an infection but can also be elevated if there is pain or following exercise. Healthy foals have a slightly higher temperature than adults (see chapters 2, 12, 15 & 19).

Tetanus: is a particularly distressing disease in donkeys which can easily be prevented by routine vaccination. The cause is a toxin produced by the bacterium *Clostridium tetani* which normally lives in the soil where it can survive for many years. The organism can gain entry to the body via wounds, particularly small puncture wounds which may not be immediately noticeable. It is simple to prevent the disease by following a routine vaccination programme. The vaccine (toxoid) will stimulate the donkey's immune system to produce its own antibodies to the disease and this may take several weeks to develop after an initial dose. The antiserum provides ready made antibodies which are effective immediately and this is often administered to donkeys with wounds, where their vaccinations are not up to date, or if the wound is particularly deep or contaminated. A booster toxoid can be given at the same time. Vaccination can begin in foals at three to five months of age and a second dose is required four to six weeks later. A booster is required one year later and after this, booster injections should be given at one or two year intervals. Pregnant mares should receive a booster dose a month before foaling so they can pass on a good level of antibodies to the foal in the colostrum. It may be advisable to give foals a dose of antiserum at birth and to treat the navel with an antibiotic or antiseptic as soon as possible after birth (see chapters 3, 5, 10, 12, 13, 14 & 15).

Thrush: an infection of the frog of the donkey's foot which, if very severe, may spread to adjacent areas. The horn of the frog becomes soft, black and very smelly. Lameness is not always present, but, if severe, the condition can be very painful. It is necessary to remove all the infected material and, if this is very extensive, a general anaesthetic is sometimes required. The foot should be kept clean and dry and an antibiotic is applied to the foot which may need to be kept bandaged initially. Spraying the feet with a gentian violet and antibiotic spray after trimming can help to keep the condition under control (see chapters 5 & 12).

Urticaria: an allergic reaction, usually to something that has been eaten or that has been in contact with the skin. The body and neck are covered with numerous small oedematous swellings which may merge to form larger plaques. The allergy may also affect other parts of the body, such as the lungs, and the donkey may become dull with laboured breathing and a rapid pulse rate. To treat the allergy corticosteroids and antihistamines are usually injected. If possible, the cause of the allergy should be identified and removed. Often the cause is a plant protein so donkeys at grass should be kept off the pasture until the condition is resolved (see chapters 2 & 12).

Vaccination: given against a specific disease, this stimulates the donkey's immune system to produce antibodies to protect it from that disease. It is absolutely essential that all donkeys are vaccinated for tetanus and it is highly recommended that vaccination against equine flu is carried out particularly if there are other donkeys or horses in the area (see Equine herpes virus, Equine influenza and Tetanus and chapters 2, 3, 12 & 15).

Venezuelan equine encephalomyelitis: a mosquito borne viral infection of horses, mules and donkeys in central America. Mosquitoes infect horses, donkeys and mules and, in addition, contact transmission may occur between sick and healthy animals. The affected equines become anorexic and depressed. Diarrhoea is common and weight loss is rapid. Encephalomyelitis is featured by drowsiness and hyper-excitability. As the disease progresses convulsions become increasingly frequent and are followed by collapse, prostration and death (see chapter 12).

Control: Equines at risk should be protected by vaccination and by applying movement restrictions on all horses, mules and donkeys. Inactivated virus vaccines are now available commercially. A modified, live vaccine (TC-83) is more effective in the prevention of VEE and is used annually.

Warts: some donkeys may be affected by multiple, small warts (which are not the same as sarcoids) but are caused by a virus. Usually the warts drop off without treatment but occasionally it may be necessary to remove them surgically. If the disease is allowed to take its course, a recovered animal is usually immune to re-infection.

Weight loss: can be a problem in some donkeys, particularly old ones. It can follow a period of debilitation or stress when the intake of food is reduced. In donkeys which have lost weight the diet should be checked to ensure that it is adequate. If the diet is correct then other common causes of weight loss include teeth abnormalities (which prevent food being properly chewed), heavy worm burdens and liver or kidney disease. Sometimes food intake is reduced in old donkeys that spend a lot of time standing around rather than eating. If this is the case more concentrates can be fed in the diet but these should always be introduced gradually to avoid diarrhoea and laminitis. Donkeys will often gain weight when turned out to grass but the quality of the grass is reduced later in the grazing season and good quality hay may be required to supplement the diet. Glucose licks are commercially available and are a useful additional source of energy as they are very palatable. If weight loss occurs too rapidly following an illness or an enforced diet then hyperlipaemia may be a complication (see Anorexia, Hyperlipaemia, Kidney Disease, Parascaris Infection, Parasites, Quidding, Strongyle worm infections, Teeth problems and chapters 2, 4, 6, 14 & 18).

Wounds: occur as the result of injury and may appear as bruising and swelling with intact skin or as open wounds. Minor skin wounds can usually be treated by keeping the wound clean and application of an antibiotic spray, powder or ointment. Extensive cuts in the skin may need to be stitched. Care should be taken with deep puncture wounds as they can heal quickly and seal in a deep infection. This leads to abscesses and infection of the underlying tissues. There is often a lot of reaction around wounds and there may be oedematous swelling and infection. Tetanus antiserum is usually administered to prevent the occurrence of tetanus and antibiotics are also often given (see Abscess, Castration, Lameness, Oedema, Tetanus and chapters 3, 4 & 12).

Appendices

Description

1 Physiological Parameters
2 Haematological Parameters
3 Biochemical Parameters
4 Modified Baerman Technique for Lungworm Larvae
5 Fluke Egg Count – Sedimentation Method
6 Modified McMaster Method
7 Modified Wisconsin Sugar Flotation Technique
8 Heart Girth Nomogram
9 Hand-rearing Donkey Foals
10 Training Courses
11 Fostering Donkeys

1 Physiological parameters

		average	**range**
temperature	°C donkey	37.1	36.2-37.8
	°F	98.8	97.2-100
	°C young donkey	37.6	36.6-38.9
	°F	99.6	97.8-102.1
pulse	donkey	44	36-68
beats/min	young donkey	60	44-80
respiration	donkey	20	12-44
inspiration/min	young donkey	28	16-48

2 Haematological parameters

		median	5 percentile	95 percentile
White blood cell count - $10^9/1$	donkey	10.2	6.1	16.1
	young donkey	13.5	7.8	21.9
Neutrophils - %	donkey	50.5	28	78
Neutrophil count - $10^9/1$	donkey	5.0	2.2	13.3
Lymphocytes - %	donkey	43	17	65
Lymphocyte count - $10^9/1$	donkey	4.2	1.8	7.8
	young donkey	6.2	2.5	14.0
Eosinophils - %	donkey	4	1	10
Eosinophil count - $10^9/1$	donkey	0.38	0.09	1.15
	young donkey	0.30	0	1.63
Basophils - %	donkey	0	0	0.08
Basophil count - $10^9/1$	donkey	0	0	0.5
Monocytes - %	donkey	1	0	5
Monocyte count - $10^9/1$	donkey	0.13	0	0.80
Total Red Blood Cell count - $10^{12}/1$	donkey	5.5	4	7.3
Packed Cell Volume - litre/litre	donkey	0.33	0.25	0.38
	young donkey	0.34	0.27	0.43
Haemoglobin - g/dl	donkey	11.6	9	15.3
Mean Corpuscular Volume - femtolitre	donkey	64	57	79
Mean Corpuscular Haem. - picograms	donkey	21.9	18.9	28.6
Mean Corpuscular Haem. Conc. - g/dl	donkey	34.8	31.4	39.1
	young donkey	35	25.3	54.0

3 Biochemical parameters

		median	5 percentile	95 percentile
Creatinine - µmol/l	donkey	75	53	141
	young donkey	83	61	107
Creatine Phosphokinase - IU/l	donkey	40	15	149
Total Bilirubin - µmol/l	donkey	2.7	1.4	7.7
Urea - µmol/l	donkey	3.9	1.9	7.6
Triglycerides - µmol/l	donkey	1	0.2	4.3
	young donkey	0.7	0.2	2.0
Total Protein - g/l	donkey	70	58	82
	young donkey	64	53	78
Albumin - g/l	donkey	28	20	34
Total globulins - g/l	donkey	40	29	53
	young donkey	34	23	50
γ-Glutamyl Transferase - IU/l	donkey	17	8	49
Glutamate Dehydrogenase - IU/l	donkey	1.6	0.4	8
	young donkey	1.2	0.4	3.9
Aspartate Aminotransferase IU/l	donkey	109	59	199
Alkaline Phosphatase - IU/l	donkey	265	150	563

young donkey =donkey less than 2 years old

4 Modified Baerman Technique for Lungworm Larvae

The Baerman apparatus consists of a large funnel supported upright by a stand. Rubber tubing is connected to the bottom of the funnel and a pipette tip inserted in this. A clip is fitted to the rubber tubing.

1. Fold a piece of filter paper into four and write the sample identity on it. Place the paper in the funnel, opening it out to line the funnel. Close the clip tightly. Add a small amount of water to wet the paper, check that there is no leakage from the pipette tip.

2. Place 50g of broken up faeces in the filter paper. (The amount of faeces, packed down, that reaches to the 60ml mark of the 100ml plastic beaker is approximately equal to 50g).

3. Pour on enough water to cover the faeces, mix it gently, taking care not to tear the paper.

4. Leave it to stand for at least 12 hours.

5. Open the clip and allow about 10ml to run into a centrifuge tube*.

6. Centrifuge for two minutes at 1,500 r.p.m. or leave to stand for 2 hours.

7. Using a pipette, take a small amount of fluid from the very bottom of the tube, where any larvae will have settled, and spread it out on a microscope slide. Examine using a low power and count all the lungworm larvae seen on that slide. The identity of the worms can be checked using a higher power. The number counted is the number of larvae per 50g of faeces.

* Qualitative results can be obtained without using a centrifuge. Gently open the clamp and allow a few drops of the sample to fall onto a microscope slide. These first few drops will contain larvae if they are pesent in the sample, but this method will not give a true quantitative count.

N.B. When fresh faeces are used, any larvae seen using this method are practically always lungworm larvae, because among the nematodes only lungworms are ovo-viviparous. If older faeces are used, strongyle larvae and free-living larvae may be seen.

5 Fluke Egg Count - Sedimentation Method

1. A faecal sample is taken directly from the rectum using a rubber-gloved hand, and placed in a clear plastic container with a screw top. The pot is labelled with the animal number using indelible pen.

2. A new glove is used for each sampling, or the original washed free of contaminating material.

3. Faecal samples must be kept cool, and should be processed as soon as possible after collection. If samples must be stored prior to examination, they must be kept in a refrigerator at +4°C and examined within seven days.

4. 10g of faeces sample (+ 0.05g) is weighed into a 100ml rigid polyethylene container (Fisons, Loughborough) with screw cap.

5. The lid is then secured and the sample shaken until a homogenous mixture is produced.

6. The faecal suspension is then poured through two sieves (a) and (b) into a 100ml distillation receiver (Gallenkamp, Loughborough).

Sieve (a) has a wide mesh - a metal tea strainer is ideal. (We use an 850µp or 1200µp sieve.)

Sieve (b) has a finer mesh (80 mesh). (We use a 150µp sieve.)

7. The container is rinsed with ~ 10ml tap water, and this is added to the sieve.

8. The surface of either/both sieves may be agitated with a blunt instrument to aid passage if necessary.

9. The debris in the sieves is discarded.

10. The suspension is allowed to sediment for 3 minutes.

11. The supernatant is drawn off to leave ~ 5ml sediment to which 3 drops of methylene blue (1% aq. solution) are added and shaken to mix.

12. Approximately 100ml tap water is added, and the receiver inverted to ensure thorough mixing.

13. The suspension is allowed to sediment for 3 minutes.

14. The supernatant is drawn off to leave ~ 5ml sediment. This is agitated and poured into a counting dish which is scored into squares to aid counting (Sterilin). The receiver is rinsed with a little tap water, and this is added to the dish.

15. Eggs are then counted using a binocular dissecting microscope at X10 to X15 magnification.

16. The number of eggs counted is then divided by ten to give the number of eggs per gram of faeces.

6 Modified McMaster Method

This method is less sensitive than the Wisconsin Sugar Flotation Method, but it is useful for screening a large group of animals positive for strongyles.

1. Weigh out 3g of faeces and place in a screw topped jar.

2. Add 42ml of water.

3. Shake the jar until all faecal matter is broken down.

4. Sieve the mixture through a 150µp sieve and pour some of the liquid into a centrifuge tube, filling it up to the line.

5. Centrifuge for 2 minutes at 1500 r.p.m.

6. Pour off the fluid and discard it.

7. Agitate the tube to loosen the sediment. Fill with saturated salt solution * to the line.

8. Mix the contents of the tube. Using a pipette, fill the cell of the counting chamber, taking care to cover the platform but not overfill the chamber. Put the ruled cover slip on etched side down.

9. Examine under the microscope, counting all the eggs inside the grid only.

10. Multiply the number of eggs counted by 100 to get the number of eggs per gram of faeces.

* Saturated salt solution = 400g salt, 1000ml water

7 Modified Wisconsin Sugar Flotation Technique

1. Pour 20ml saturated sugar solution* into a small beaker.

2. Add 5g faeces (the cap of a Universal container holds about 5g.

3. Mix carefully to break down the faeces, avoiding forming air bubbles.

4. Wet the sieve screen on both sides, place a funnel in a Universal container and strain the sample through the sieve into the container. Use forceps to squeeze most of the liquid out of the fibre.

5. Remove the sieve and funnel. Fill the Universal with saturated sugar solution until it forms a positive meniscus above the rim. Let the solution settle for a few minutes to allow any air bubbles to come up to the surface. Remove these by gently touching the surface with a coverslip, wipe the coverslip and place it on top of container. There should be no air between the sample and the coverslip, as air bubbles greatly reduce the surface of the coverslip that the eggs can adhere to.

6. Leave for at least 3 hours. Read as soon as possible after this as the eggs may distort or, particularly in a hot climate, hatch.

7. Lift off the coverslip and place it on a microscope slide. Examine it under the microscope using the low power objective and count all eggs seen. Divide this number by 5 to get the number of eggs per gram of faeces.

***Saturated sugar solution, specific gravity 1.27:**

450g sugar
400ml hot water

Keep refrigerated or add 6ml of 40% formaldehyde per litre of sugar solution to stop it fermenting, or make up as required.

N.B. If more than 50 eggs are seen in each field of vision, scan the whole coverslip to check that they are evenly distributed. If so, count all the eggs in one pass of the coverslip (either from side to side or top to bottom) and multiply this by the number of passes it takes to view the whole coverslip, then divide by 5 as before to get the number of eggs per gram. Check the whole coverslip for the presence of eggs of other species, e.g. tapeworm.

Appendix 8 Heart Girth Nomogram

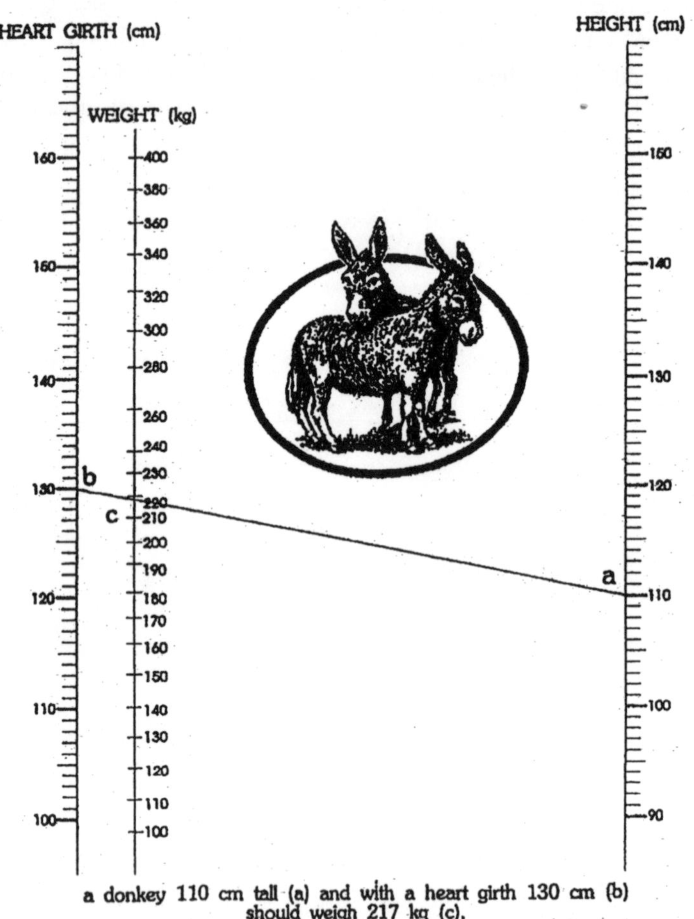

a donkey 110 cm tall (a) and with a heart girth 130 cm (b) should weigh 217 kg (c).

WEIGHT TABLE FOR DONKEYS UNDER 2 YEARS:

HEART GIRTH cm	75	76	77	78	79	80	81	82	83	84	85	86	87	88	89	90	91	92	93	94	95	96	97	98	99	100
WEIGHT kg	46	47	49	51	53	55	57	59	61	63	65	67	69	71	74	76	78	81	83	86	88	91	94	96	99	102

for adult donkey; $\text{WEIGHT} = 0.000252 \times \text{height}^{0.240} \times \text{heart girth}^{2.575}$

for donkey under 2 years; $\text{WEIGHT} = 0.000283 \times \text{heart girth}^{2.778}$

Appendix 9 Hand Rearing Donkey Foals

Orphan foals, or foals whose mothers have no milk, need to be bottle fed. It is important that the foal has some colostrum; if this is not possible your vet will be able to provide antibiotic cover and possibly a colostrum substitute. If the foal has no suck reflex your vet will have to stomach tube fluids into the foal until it is able to feed for itself.

Two types of mare's milk replacers on the market are Horsepower made by Championship Feeds and the one we have successfully used, Aintree Foal Milk made by Day, Son & Hewitt. For a new born foal $1\frac{1}{2}$ measures of Aintree Foal Milk should be added to $\frac{1}{2}$ pint of water and whisked with a fork. The measure and full instructions are included in the bag.

If no mare's milk replacer is available, 1 pint of feed can be made up using $\frac{3}{4}$ pint of cows milk, $\frac{1}{4}$ pint water and 1 tablespoon glucose. Alternatively goat's milk can be used. However a proprietary brand is the best solution. Bottles and teats meant for lambs are the best size for donkey foals and can be obtained at any agricultural supplier. Good hygiene should be practised, keeping all bottles, teats and mixing equipment clean. The milk should be fed at body temperature, but cooler rather than too hot.

Initially the foal should be fed to appetite every 2 hours. A good guide that the foal is getting enough is that it should lie down and sleep after feeding, but be up, active and hungry for its next feed. It is not a good sign if a foal stands looking dull. A rough guide to the quantity required is 80 - 100ml per kg bodyweight a day. This amount has to be divided out into the correct number of feeds. Some foals can become very greedy and get far too fat if fed to appetite after they are a few days old.

After one week the number of feeds can be reduced slightly; it is usually easiest to start reducing the night time feeds. The quantity given at the other feeds has to be increased. If the foal is not willing to take more at the other feeds then the frequency of feeds will have to be maintained.

When the foal is established in a routine and feeding keenly at every feed, it can be taught to drink from a bowl. This is quite a messy procedure to start with but can save a lot of time in the long run.

The foal can be offered a little hard food from about one week of age, and should always be left with access to drinking water.

Appendix 10 Training courses offered by The Donkey Sanctuary

Stage 1 - Basic Donkey Care Course: this covers all aspects of looking after a donkey.

It is aimed at the new donkey owner and includes theory and practical sessions on field and stable management. Attendance is compulsory for those about to foster donkeys from the Sanctuary.

Stage 2 - Basic Donkey Health Care Course

This follows on from the first course and covers first aid for donkeys, including how to recognise if your donkey is unwell, when to call the vet, how to treat minor wounds, foot care, body scoring and ageing by the teeth. Theory and practical sessions. We recommend that beginners attend Stage 1 before coming on the Stage 2 course.

Preparation for Riding Course

For people who would like young children to be able to ride their donkeys. We cover selection and fitting of a saddle and bridle, types of bit and their uses, preparing the donkey to be ridden, basic 'in hand' work, saddling up for the first time and introducing a rider to the donkey.

Stage 3 - Basic Donkey Harnessing and Preparation for Driving your Donkey Course: this covers assembly and fitting of the harness, long reining and the selection of a cart, followed by how to 'put to' and driving a novice donkey. This course is aimed at people with donkey handling knowledge but little or no experience of driving.

Courses are held regularly in Devon, Derbyshire, Essex and Mid Glamorgan. Special Donkey Days can be arranged locally.

There are no set charges for training courses but voluntary donations towards our costs are always gratefully received.

Donkey Care Courses stage 1 & 2 are complimentary for people who foster our donkeys.

If you would like more information or would like to book a place on one of these courses please contact:

Annie Chapman, Training Centre Co-ordinator, on 01395 597644

Appendix 11 Fostering scheme

Here at the Donkey Sanctuary we allow donkeys out in pairs to suitable homes. The donkeys remain under the ownership of the Sanctuary and are visited every four months by a Welfare Officer. If you would like further information please telephone the Welfare Department on 01395 578222.

Useful Addresses

United Kingdom
The Donkey Sanctuary, Sidmouth, Devon EX10 0NU, UK
(Reg Charity no 264818)

The Slade Centre, Sidmouth, Devon EX10 0NU, UK
(Reg Charity no 270551)

The Elisabeth Svendsen Trust for Children and Donkeys
Head Office: Sidmouth, Devon EX10 0NU, UK
(Reg Charity no 801070)

The International Donkey Protection Trust, Sidmouth, Devon EX10 0NU, UK
(Reg Charity no 271410)

Donkey Breed Society
Secretary: Mrs C Morse, The Hermitage, Pootings, Edenbridge, Kent TN8 6SD, UK

British Mule Society
Secretary: Mrs L Travis, Hope Mount Farm, Top of Hope Alston Field, Nr Ashbourne, Derbyshire, UK

Africa
South Africa Network on Animal Traction (SANAT)
Faculty of Agriculture, University of Fort Hare, Private Bag X1314
Alice 5700, South Africa

ATNESA (Animal Traction Network for Eastern and Southern Africa)
PO Box BW540, Borrowdale, Harare, Zimbabwe

Animal Power Network for Zimbabwe (APNEZ)
Agritex Institute of Agricultural Engineering, PO Box 330, Borrowdale, Harare, Zimbabwe

Kenya Network for Draught Animal Technology (KENDAT)
c/o Department of Agricultural Engineering, University of Nairobi, PO Box 30197, Nairobi, Kenya

America

The American Donkey and Mule Society Inc
Secretary, Registrar, Editor: Betsy Hutchins
Executive Director: Paul Hutchins
2901 North Elm St, Denton, Texas 76201, USA

International Society for the Protection of Mustangs and Burros
President: Karen A. Sussman, 6212 East Sweetwater Avenue, Scottsdale, Arizona 85254, USA

Australia

Good Samaritan Donkey Sanctuary
Hon Administrator: Christine Berry, Duns Creek, Maitland 2320, NSW, Australia

The Donkey Society of New South Wales Inc
Mrs Sue Mistler, 317 Pitt Town Road, Kenthurst, NSW 2156, Australia

The Donkey Society of Victoria Inc
Ms Leanne Davey, 725 North Road, Pearcedale, Vic 3912, Australia

The Donkey Society of Queensland Inc
Mrs Anne Jones, 18 Charles St, Kalbar, QLD 4309, Australia

The Donkey Society of Western Australia Inc
Jane Adams, 146 Bedford Street, Mount Helena, WA 6082, Australia

The Donkey Society of South Australia Inc
Ms Michelle Gladwin, 65 Clare Road, Kapunda, SA 5373, Australia

Belgium
Association of Donkey Owners
Mr P Lemal, Asinière de Sendrogne, Route de Sendrogne 63, B4141 Louveigne, Belgium

Belgian Donkey Association
Chairman: Schamp Celestin, Neerhofstraat 4, 9690 Kluisbergen, Belgium

Bonaire
Bonaire Donkey Help Foundation
Marina Melis, Punt Vierkant 5, Bonaire, Netherlands Antilles, Caribbean

Canada
The Donkey Sanctuary of Canada
Mrs Sandra J Pady, RR#6 Guelph, Ontario, Canada N1H 6J3

Canadian Donkey and Mule Association
Secretary: Jan and Rick Sterritt, Cedar Sands Farm, RR10 Brampton, Ont L6V 3N2, Canada

Cyprus
Friends of the Cyprus Donkey
Mr & Mrs Patrick Skinner, Vouni Village, Limassol District, Cyprus

Denmark
Donkey Society
Mr P Hoegh, Aeselforeningen Aagaardvej 38, Thyregod, DK - 7323 Give, Denmark

Danish Donkey Breed Society
Lars Gardan, Landsforeningen Dansk Aesel Avl, Praestebakkegaard, Baekkebrovej 15, Tibirke DK - 3220 Tisvildeleje, Denmark

France

Asinerie Picarde
Irene Van De Ponseele, 14 rue du Raguet, Cedex 35, 60800 Auger St Vincent, France

A.D.A.D.A. Association des Amis des Anes
Christine Peyramaure, Jacques Gounet, Pissevache 19450, Chamboulive, France

Federation Nationale Asine
32 rue Chalgrin, 75116 Paris, France

French Branch of Associario del Foment de la Raca
Asinina Catalana
Maryse Schild, Can Just, F-66320, Baillestavy, France

Association de l'Ane Normand
Secretary: Mairie de Cherisay, 72610 Cherisay, Normandy, France

Association de rehabilitation de l'âne Cotentin, Hameau de Fains, 14310 Villy-Bocage, Normandy, France

(The Pyrenean Donkey Breeders Association)
Association des Eleveurs D'Anes Pyreneens, Mazeves, F 65700, Castelnau R.B., France

Association Francaise de l'Ane Grand Noir du Berry
Maison de pays, Bp10, 18160 Lignières, France

Association de l'âne de Provence
Registered office: Haras National, 30701 Uzes, Cedex, France

Parc Naturel Regional du Marais Poitevin
M A Philippe, 17170 La Ronde, France

SABAUD
(Association pour la Sauvegarde du Baudet du Poitou)
Zoorama Européen de la Fôret de Chizé, 79360 Villiers en Bois, France

Holland
Donkey Rescue Foundation
Mrs A Boeree, Zuiderweg 43 8391 KG, Noordwolde, Holland

Stichting Ezelvreugd (Donkey Sanctuary)
Rudi en Vivian de Poorter, Horickheide 7, 6035 PN Ospel, Holland

Dutch Donkey Protection Trust
Mrs A C Bander, Buurting 161-2244 BJ, Wassenaar, Holland

Ireland
Irish Donkey Society
6 Glenart Avenue, Blackrock, Co Dublin, Eire

Italy
Associazione Italiana per la Valorizzazione dell'Asino e del Mulo
President: Aldo Vico, Borgata Piancera N17, 10094 Giaveno (To), Italy

Agro di Martina Franca & Crispiano
Ufficio Foreste Demaniali Regionali, 74015 Martina Franca, Italy

Sardinian Donkey Park
Comune di Ortueri, P.zza Marconi, 08036 Ortueri-Nu, Sardinia, Italy

New Zealand
Donkey Society of New Zealand
Librarian: Mrs S Harrewijn-Loffeld, Moana Farm Donkey Stud, RD4 Albany, New Zealand

Norway
Norway Donkey Breed Society
Ms E Stenseth, Norsk Eselforening Noklegard, N3180 Nykirke, Norway

Norwegian Donkey Association
Chairman: Lisen Ekre, Nedre Sorli Gaard, 2743 Harestua, Norway

Portugal
Associacao de Proteccao Animal do Algarve
President: Nan Richardson, Apartado 117, 8400 Lagoa, Algarve, Portugal

South America
RELATA (Red Latin-Americana de Tracción Animal)
c/o FOMENTA, Ap Postal 95 Telcor, Sucursal Douglas Mejía, Managua, Nicaragua

Spain
ADEBO (Associacion Para la Defensa del Borrico)
C/ Fresno 9, 14960 Rute, Cordoba, Spain

Horstmann Stiftung
C/ Corredera 42, E-04830 Velez-Blanco, Almeria, Spain

AFRAC (Associacio del Foment de la Raca Asinina Catalana)
Secretary: Dr Esteve Bosch, Rotes 48, 17820 Banyoles, Spain

ACRIPROASMA (Association Nationale d'éleveurs et de proprietaires d'ânes de Pure Race Mallorque)
Apartado 10, Esporlas 07190, Baleares

Sweden
Svenska Asneforeninggn, Foderbylund, Moinby, S-18694 Vallentuna, Sweden

Switzerland
IGM, Interessengemeinschaft Maultier, Postfach, CH-8370 Sirnach, Switzerland

Das Maultierforum, Stiftung zur Förderung und Erhaltung von Maultieren, Mauleseln und Eseln, Via dal Bagn 54, CH-7500, St Moritz, Switzerland

Schweizerische Interessengemeinschaft Eselfreunde (SIGEF)
Annamaria Matter, Mitteldorf 9, 3283 Kallnach, Switzerland

Index

The A-Z of Donkey Health is not included in the index since it is anyway arranged alphabetically; "ill" shows that a passage includes illustrations, and a page reference in bold indicates an illustration.